WORLD® AIR POWER
J O U R N A L

Aerospace Publishing Ltd
AIRtime Publishing Inc.

Published quarterly by
Aerospace Publishing Ltd
179 Dalling Road
London W6 0ES
UK

Copyright © Aerospace Publishing Ltd

Cutaway drawings copyright
© Mike Badrocke/Aviagraphica

ISSN 0959-7050

Aerospace ISBN 1 874023 49 2
                (softback)
                1 874023 50 6
                (hardback)
Airtime ISBN   1-880588-07-2
                (hardback)

Published under licence in USA and
Canada by AIRtime Publishing Inc.,
10 Bay Street, Westport,
CT 06880, USA

Editorial Offices:
WORLD AIR POWER JOURNAL
Aerospace Publishing Ltd
3A Brackenbury Road
London W6 0BE   UK

Publisher: Stan Morse
Managing Editor: David Donald
Editor: Jon Lake
Associate Editor: Robert Hewson
Production Editor: Karen Leverington
Editorial Assistant: Tim Senior

Origination and printing by
    Imago Publishing Ltd
Printed in Singapore

Europe Correspondent:
    Paul Jackson
Washington Correspondent:
    Robert F. Dorr
USA West Coast Correspondent:
    René J. Francillon
Asia Correspondent:
    Pushpindar Singh

The editors of WORLD AIR
POWER JOURNAL welcome
photographs for possible publication,
but cannot accept any responsibility for
loss or damage to unsolicited material.

The publishers gratefully acknowledge
the assistance given by the following
people:

Rostislav A. Belyakov, Nikolai Buntin,
Vladimir Godunov, Roman Taskaev
and Marat Alykov of the Mikoyan
Design Bureau, as well as Anatoly
Kanaschenkov and Vladimir Kucher of
Phazatron and Vladimir Perstnev of the
Ryazan Instruments Plant for their
enthusiastic help with the MiG-29M
briefing.

Mr Robert Pepper, 49th FW/PA, for
the F-117 Bandit listing.

Jahn Ahlgren, Åsa Holm and Pia Forés
of Saab Military Aircraft, Rolf
Sandström of Ericsson and Lieutenant
Colonel Anders Eisen of the Swedish
Air Staff for their invaluable and
enthusiastic assistance with the Gripen
feature.

Rene van Woezik, Tieme Festner,
Frank Rozendaal, Hans Nijhuis, Martin
Baumann, Werner Greppmeier, Kieron
Pilbeam, Chris Lofting, and Chris Ryan
for their generous help with the Soviet
Forces in East Germany article. All
shared the fruits of their many visits to
the former German Democratic
Republic with enthusiasm and
generosity. We would also like to thank
John Weal for his insights into
pre-Soviet use of many of the airfields
mentioned.

Dick Goddard, General Manager Flight
Systems Inc., and Jennie Hentges for
their time and trouble with the F-100
article.

**World Air Power Journal is a
registered trademark in the
United States of America of
AIRtime Publishing Inc.**

**World Air Power Journal is
published quarterly and is
available by subscription and
from many fine book and hobby
stores.**

**SUBSCRIPTION AND BACK
NUMBERS:**

**UK and World (except USA and
Canada) write to:
Aerospace Publishing Ltd
FREEPOST
PO Box 2822
London
W6 0BR
UK**

**(No stamp required if posted in
the UK)**

**USA and Canada, write to:
AIRtime Publishing Inc.
Subscription Dept
10 Bay Street
Westport
CT 06880, USA
(203) 266-3580
Toll-free order number in USA:
1 800 359-3003**

**Prevailing subscription rates are
as follows:
Softbound edition for 1 year:
    $58.00
Softbound edition for 2 years:
    $108.00
Softbound back numbers
(subject to availability) are
$17.95 each. All rates are for
delivery within mainland USA,
Alaska and Hawaii. Canadian
and overseas prices available
upon request. American Express,
Discover Card, MasterCard and
Visa accepted. When ordering
please include your card
number, expiration date and
signature.**

**Publisher, North America:
    Mel Williams
Subscription Director:
    Linda DeAngelis
Retail Sales Director:
    Jill Brooks
Charter Member Services
Managers:
    Janie Munroe**

WORLD AIR POWER®

JOURNAL

CONTENTS

Military Aviation Review

International

NATO AEWF E-3As have begun a systems upgrade at the hands of the Boeing Defence & Space Group. This Block 1 modification adds colour displays to the operators' stations, Have Quick secure radios and Link 16 – a new information distribution system. After the current engineering and installation phase, the programme will commence in 1996.

Eurofighter lay-up

Following a short programme of tests after their maiden flights, both Eurofighter 2000 prototypes were temporarily grounded in June for planned modifications. The cockpit changes and introduction of improved flight control software were expected to keep both on the ground until October, at the earliest, meaning that none was available for static display at Farnborough in September.

Shortly before its grounding, DA1/9829 was flown for the first time by a military test pilot (Lieutenant Colonel Harald Fehl), while DA2/ZH588 performed in the hands of three civilian pilots on the BAe staff. Total EFA time was a modest 15 hours, equally divided, although the UK aircraft have flown nine sorties, compared with eight by DA1. The new software will enable Eurofighter to operate at higher speeds than before and this will be the first area to be investigated when operations recommence. In 1995, the pair will be stood down again for replacement of their RB199 engines by Eurojet EJ200s. The first EJ200-powered aircraft is DA3, which will not now take to the air until early 1995. DA3 will also be the first with a full avionics fit.

New NATO command

Air Forces North-West Europe came into being on 1 July 1994 with its HQ at High Wycombe, UK. The command is an amalgamation of the former commands UK Air Forces and Norway-based Allied Forces Northern Europe. The C-in-C is automatically the RAF officer appointed as AOC-in-C Strike Command.

rennes to carry Oude Delft Orpheus camera pods. The systems have been loaned by the Netherlands and more are expected when the Dutch receive more advanced recce pods at the end of the 1990s.

Gendarmerie expands

The first two of three Cessna 182s were delivered to the Rijkswacht/Gendarmerie at Brussels/Melsbroek in June, wearing serials G01 and G03 – the identities of the two Pumas destroyed in 1993. The third Cessna is likely to become G04, as G05 is the unit's other aircraft, an Islander. Reports that the unit is to be civilianised appear to be in error, in view of the continued use of military numbers.

FRANCE:

Commands renamed

Reorganisation of the French air force's higher levels has resulted in changes of name for some well-known commands. Tactical Air Command (FATac), operating fighter and fighter-bomber aircraft, was redesignated Commandement de la Force Aérienne de Combat (CFAC) on 11 March 1994, while Transport Command (CoTAM) has become Commandement de la Force Aérienne de Projection (CFAP). On 1 June, Air Defence Command (CAFDA) and Telecommunications Command (CSTAA) – both mainly with ground assets – were disbanded. As replacements, Commandement de la Défense Aérienne et des Opérations Aériennes (CDAOA) was formed for airspace control (including the air defence interception zones) and Commandement Air des Systemes de Surveillance, d'Information et de Communications (CASSIC) took over ground radars, datalinks and the E-3F force. In the new structure, the seven air commands are CFAC, CFAP, CASSIC, CFCA, CDAOA and the

unchanged Strategic (FAS) and Training (CEAA) organisations.

Back to the 1960s

History was remade on 31 May when eight 1st FW F-15C Eagles from Langley AFB landed at Cambrai for a deployment in connection with NATO Exercise Central Enterprise. France withdrew from the military side of NATO in 1966, since which time no American fighter units have operated from French soil.

Recce Mirages move

Transfer of France's Mirage F1CR force from Strasbourg to Reims-Champagne was completed on 24 May when ER 1/33 'Belfort' flew to its new base, joining ER 2/33 'Savoie', which had made the move on 22 April. The 18 aircraft of each squadron have all been painted to reflect the addition of a third flight in August 1993, and the two badges on opposite sides of the fins are taken in rotation from the three allocated to each squadron. Although there is no longer an HQ of 33 Wing, traditions have been maintained at Reims by redesignating the resident EC 3/30 'Lorraine' as EC 3/33 'Lorraine', from 1 July.

Mirage III/5 withdrawn

The end of an era was marked at Colmar on 3 June when the Armée de l'Air bade farewell to the first-generation Mirage III/5. The last Mirage IIIE squadron, EC 3/3 'Ardennes' at Nancy, withdrew its aircraft during May to begin conversion to Mirage 2000Ds. Ceremony surrounded EC 2/13 'Alpes', which disbanded at Colmar on 3 June, having recently employed both the Mirage 5F and IIIBE trainer. For this event, the squadron painted its badge on the undersides of '13-PC'

Western Europe

AUSTRIA:

New fighters sought

Austria revealed in the spring that it is planning to withdraw its Saab J 35Ö Drakens in 1999 and obtain a more modern aircraft for its two interceptor squadrons – which nominally boast 24 aircraft. Types such as the F-16, F-18, Saab JAS 39 Gripen, Mirage 2000 and MiG-29 are being considered. Meanwhile, the Drakens have been fitted with Swedish-built AIM-9P3 Sidewinders (Austria's first AAMs) and No. 24 has received the trial installation of a radar warning receiver fitted by Danish personnel.

Intercepted over the Baltic, this Danish air force F-16A carries a hitherto unseen camera pod on its centreline pylon.

BELGIUM:

Surplus aircraft offered

By June, the storage airfield at Weelde had accumulated 32 F-16As, one F-16B and 32 assorted Mirage 5s towards a total of 96 of both types expected as a result of force reductions. Some of the Mirages were the first of 20 modernised aircraft fresh from rework, the sale of these to Chile having been agreed in July. Also on offer to potential buyers are 33 surplus F-16A/B Fighting Falcons. Unfortunately for Belgium, the USAF is also selling large numbers of these aircraft as spare parts at a price less than their value.

Following withdrawal of Belgium's Mirage 5BRs, a small reconnaissance capability has been maintained by converting two F-16As of 2 Wing at Flo-

4

and '13-PM', and flew a formation which included IIIBE '13-PZ'.

As if a formal retirement ceremony was not enough, examples of IIIE and 5F made another 'final flight' in the public setting of Châteaudun's open day on 19 June. After the surplus aircraft were ferried to the MU at Châteaudun, IIIE No. 554 and 5F No. 46 were decorated with a large fin badge of 70 Escadron de Convoyage and a light blue lightning flash along the fuselage for the last public flights of both variants.

On 1 June, Dassault held a ceremony in Paris to mark the Mirage III/5's 3,000,000th flying hour, the total accumulated by 457 French and 944 export aircraft.

GERMANY:

Overseas action approved

A historic decision by the Constitutional Court on 12 July (later ratified by a 424-44 vote in the Bundestag) has allowed German troops to take part in military operations outside the NATO area, with the proviso that they act under UN or similar international authority. German aircrew may now participate in the NATO E-3A operations watching Bosnian airspace and Bundesmarine ships in the Adriatic may fire warning shots at vessels suspected of embargo-breaking.

New structure for Luftwaffe

The new organisational plan for Germany's Luftwaffe came into effect on 1 April 1994, raising Berlin to the status of a major centre for the administration of combat aircraft units. Immediately following reunification, in October 1990, 5 Air Division was established at Berlin/Eggersdorf to control the air defence MiG-29s of 3 Wing. Forces have been spread more evenly since, with the result that the old 3 Division at Kalkar has disbanded and transferred its designation to Berlin. The air force remains divided into three major commands, but the previous Tactical Command has been expanded with the addition of the transport force (previously attached to Central Office) and renamed to reflect its changed status.

Luftwaffen Führungskommando (LwFuKdo) at Köln/Wahn is the new Lead Command, its components being:

EC 3/3 painted up this Mirage IIIE (No. 554) for the type's last flight in Armée de l'Air service.

LwKdo Sud (Southern Command) at Messstetten, comprising 1 Division at Karlsruhe (JBG 32, JBG 34 both with Tornados; the German NATO E-3A element; and FLGp at Furstenfeldbruck with Alpha Jets); and 2 Division at Birkenfeld (JBG 33 Tornado; JG 74 Phantom).

LwKdo Nord (Northern Command) at Kalkar, comprising 3 Division at Berlin/Gatow (JG 72 Phantom; JG 73 Phantom and MiG-29); and 4 Division at Aurich (JBG 31 and JBG 38, both Tornado; and JG 71 Phantom).

Lufttransportkommando (Air Transport Command) at Munster with LTGs 61, 62 and 63 operating C-160s and UH-1Ds; FlBschftStf (VIP Squadron) at Köln; and SAR detachments.

Lw Führungsdienstkommando (Service Command) at Köln/Wahn for ground radars and communications.

The two remaining major commands are essentially unchanged, apart from the loss of any flying units: Luftwaffenamt (Central Office) at Köln/Wahn is concerned with ground training and miscellaneous tasks, although it does administer the flying training organisation in the USA, and Luftwaffenunterstutzungskommando (Support Command) at Köln/Wahn is responsible for supplies and infrastructure.

(Note that in the listing above, JG 73 was not due to form until 1 October, when JG 35 at Pferdsfeld was redesignated and MiG-29s officially redeployed to Laage. The Pferdsfeld F-4E Phantoms are due to transfer to Laage in 1996, giving JG 73 one squadron each of the two types. These Phantoms are the only ones not undergoing conversion to F-4F/KWS standard with new AN/APG-65 radar and other avionics improvements. By mid-1994, JG 74 had re-equipped with KWS aircraft; JG 71 was nearly so; and JG 72 was expecting its last in 1996.)

Eurofighter under fire

A Federal Audit Office investigation leaked to the press during the summer alleged that the aircraft is far more costly than previously reported and that the Luftwaffe will be forced to reduce its procurement to only 85 (compared with the current 120-140 and original target of 250) unless more money is

This HARM-armed Tornado ECR of JBG 32 was present at the 1994 Tiger Meet at Cambrai.

found. It also recommended delaying the in-service date by four years to 2006.

Furthermore, the investigation questioned the need for Germany to have its own Eurofighter assembly line and went some way towards meeting partner nations' demands for Germany to reduce its claimed share of manufacturing work because of the cut in proposed orders.

Tigers return to full strength

Reversing its earlier decision to buy only 138 Eurocopter Tigers, the Heeresflieger (German army aviation) has reinstated the full programme of 212. Under current plans, however, these will all be of the UHU (Unterstutzungshubschrauber – support helicopter) variant, not the specific anti-tank PAH-2 (Panzerabwehrhubschrauber). PAH-2 was originally to be the only Tiger version in German service until the UHU was put forward as a more versatile aircraft with the ability to undertake close-support and escort missions. Three battalions of UHUs will be assigned to a new air-mobile brigade and a fourth to home defence, leaving other Tigers for the training unit (Heeresfliegerwaffenschule).

While causing some disruption to the programme, the decision to proceed with UHU appears to give Eurocopter a better chance of securing the British army's attack helicopter competition to be decided in May 1995. UHU is closer to the UK requirement than

other versions of Tiger, but will not be ready for at least two years after the Army Air Corps' planned 1997 IOC.

Base closure

Brandenburg/Briest aerodrome closed on 30 June with disbandment of the helicopter detachment of LTG 62, the Wunsdorf-based Transall C.160D and UH-1D wing. Operating Mi-2s and Mi-8s, the detachment originated with East German THG 34, which became the second squadron of LTG 65 after unification. When 65 Wing disbanded in 1993, LTG 62 took responsibility.

323 Squadron disbanded

Retirement of the last of seven HFB 320ECM Hansa Jets was effected on 30 June when 3 Staffel of JBG 32 disbanded at Lechfeld. The unit's An-26MS (5209) was also stood down and transferred to the Luftwaffenmuseum at Gatow. The unit originated when Flugvermessungstaffel 4/61 formed at Lechfeld on 30 May 1964 with a fleet of Pembrokes, Dakotas, Noratlases and Do 27s for calibration and radar/ECM training. The calibration element was civilianised when the Dakotas were withdrawn on 14 April 1976, but the first of the Hansa Jets arrived on 31 August after installation of jamming equipment. The squadron was administratively attached to (JBG 32) on 1 April 1980, becoming 3 Staffel.

The first of the Greek navy's five SH-60B/F hybrids (designated S-70B-6) have now been delivered to the newly established S-70 Mira, the navy's third helicopter unit.

Military Aviation Review

Portugal is now firmly established as an Alpha Jet operator with the delivery of 50 ex-German examples.

GREECE:

Orion requirements confirmed

The Greek requirement for Lockheed Orions was confirmed as four P-3Bs, which will be refurbished after storage at Davis-Monthan AFB and delivered by the end of 1995 for the current HU-16 Albatross unit, 353 Mira. Greece also proposes to acquire four P-3As which will be used for ground training and as a spares source.

ITALY:

Commando helicopter flight created

A new unit of naval aviation formed early in July as the Nucleo Elicotteristico per la Lotta Anfibia (Amphibious Forces' Helicopter Flight). NLA is part of the 4° Grupo Elicotteri at Grottaglie and is equipped with two Sea Kings and three AB 212s, all of which have had their anti-submarine warfare equipment removed to accommodate troops and equipment and received cockpit modifications for compatibility with night-vision goggles. Two of the AB 212s are also equipped with the army's HL 19/70 armament system of two rocket pods, each with 19 70-mm projectiles.

Last F-104G Starfighter retired

The Starfighter OCU, 20° Gruppo at Grosseto, withdrew Italy's last F-104G on 5 June. Five of the type were in use until recently, although the two-seat TF-104G remains the squadron's primary equipment. The AMI received 124 single-seat F-104Gs, the last fighter-bomber versions of which were withdrawn from 154° Gruppo early in 1983. The aircraft continued with 3° Stormo in the reconnaissance role until 28° Gruppo stood down in June 1993 for conversion to AMXs.

Harrier force expands

Italy's first Harrier II Plus, MM7199 '1-03', was handed over to the Marina Militare at McDonnell Douglas' St Louis plant on 20 April before being delivered to MCAS Cherry Point for crew training. Following transfer of another two aircraft, all three were formally accepted at Cherry Point on 10 June by Rear Admiral F. Pascali, chief of naval aviation. Delivery to Europe aboard the carrier *Giuseppe Garibaldi* was due in December to complete the direct US involvement in Italy's Harrier programme. The other 13 aircraft will be assembled in Italy by Alenia.

The service already has two TAV-8Bs trainers, received in June 1991. Based at Grottaglie, they had flown 1,600 hours by mid-1994.

NETHERLANDS:

Helicopter plans

The RNethAF requirement for attack helicopters apparently covers up to 40 Bell AH-1W Cobras or 33 McDonnell Douglas AH-64 Apaches. Associated weapons would include 500 Stinger AAMs and 950 Hellfire ATMs, as well as 25,000 2.75-in rockets. Like the UK, the Netherlands is also looking at the Eurocopter Tiger, Alenia A 129 and Atlas Rooivalk.

The last squadron to operate Alouette IIIs will be No. 302 at Soesterberg, which formed on 1 January 1993 with borrowed aircraft. In May 1995, the unit will receive Alouettes made surplus by the beginning of Chinook deliveries to 298 Squadron. The first seven CH-47Ds (all ex-Canadian CH-147s) are to be supplied between April and September 1995, following roll-out of the first on 31 March. No. 302 will build up to 24 Alouettes when No. 300 begins to receive Cougars late in 1995, and will remain as such until converted to new attack helicopters (with No. 301) in 1998.

PORTUGAL:

F-16s arrive

The first Portuguese Fighting Falcons arrived in Europe on 8 July when F-16As 15102 and 15103 and F-16Bs 15119 and 15120 landed at Monte Real after a direct ferry flight from Lockheed Fort Worth, flown by USAF pilots. The aircraft were formally accepted by the FAP on 18 July and joined Esq 201 'Falcones'. Portugal's first aircraft, 15101, and trainer 15118, were handed over in the USA on 18 February and held back for ground- and aircrew training.

SPAIN:

Elint 707 setback

Spain's 'Santiago' Elint Boeing 707 programme received a setback on 4 July when the aircraft was damaged landing at Ben Gurion Airport, Israel, with a hung-up starboard undercarriage leg. The 'Santiago' system is based on the Elta EL/L-8300 signals intelligence system, hence the aircraft's presence in Israel for test flying after the installation of equipment.

The 707-351C (c/n 19164, ex-SX-DBO) is to be operated by 408 Squadron, which has recently moved from Getafe to the larger aerodrome at Torrejón. No. 408 formed as a tactical ECM unit with two TR.12D Aviocars (since redesignated TM.12D) and has now added three TM.11s (Falcon 20s) from 452 Squadron at Torrejón.

SF-5 fleet reduced

By mid-1994, only about 29 CASA/Northrop SF-5 Freedom Fighters remained in Spanish service following the replacement of Ala 21's Morón-based single-seat aircraft by C.101 Aviojets. The SF-5s have been transferred to Talavera, joining the two-seat SF-5Bs used by the weapons school, Ala 23. Only three SF-5As and four SRF-5As (the latter lacking cameras) are airworthy as partners to 22 SF-5Bs. All of the SF-5Bs are currently undergoing a structural update for continued service. Those already modified can be distinguished by a new two-tone grey colour scheme.

US fighters still on target

Despite Spain's plans to buy surplus Mirage F1s from Qatar and France to maintain its fleet at a viable level until the next century, US officials have stated during that US fighters will still be bought. It had been supposed that the extra F1s would be the only aircraft required until Eurofighter 2000s are available to Spain from 2002 onwards. However, the need has been identified for 30-50 secondhand US F-16s or F/A-18s, a decision between the two to be made late in 1994.

The Mirage transfer was agreed during July with Qatar's acceptance of an offer for 12 F1EDAs and a single F1DDA which will be refurbished by Dassault, along with three F1Cs and two F1B trainers from French stocks. The Qatari aircraft are destined for Escuadron 111/Ala 11 at Valencia, which has been using F1CEs on loan from Ala 14 since its Mirage IIIEs were withdrawn in October 1992.

TURKEY:

Phantom deliveries resumed

Turkey will receive the full number of 46 RF-4E Phantoms from Germany. Deliveries were halted in April 1994 at

Portugal's Esquadrilha de Helicopteros de Marinha operates five Westland Super Lynx Mk 95s shipborne naval helicopters. The first two of these aircraft were converted from existing Royal Navy Lynx HAS.Mk 3s.

Right: Spain's force of five P-3Bs and two P-3As have moved to Morón after the closure of their former home at Jerez. There they operate alongside the Aviojets of Ala.21. Spanish Orions have flown over 700 hours for Operation Sharp Guard, on detachment from Sigonella.

the 30th aircraft after allegations that ex-East German BRT-60 armoured vehicles were used for suppression of the Kurdish minority in Turkey. Ankara was able to satisfy Germany that ex-Russian BRT-60s are involved, resulting in an immediate resumption of Phantom deliveries.

In addition to 'topping-up' 113 Filo of 1 Wing at Eskisehir, the RF-4Es are being issued to 173 Filo of 7 Wing at Erhac. The RF-4Es make 184 Filo's RF-5As surplus at Diyarbakir and the unit disbanded in July 1994, passing its aircraft to Merzifon, where 5 Wing is using them with cameras removed.

Starfighter withdrawal

Withdrawal of Turkey's last Starfighters was brought forward to September 1994, when 182 Filo at Diyarbakir relinquished its ex-Canadian CF-104s. Sister unit 181 Squadron was by then receiving F-16Cs, the equipping expected to be complete by the end of the year. The reformed 182 Squadron will follow early in 1995. F-16s are already in service with 141 and 142 Squadrons at Murted (or Akinci, as it is now known), 161 and 162 Squadrons at Bandirma, and 192 Squadron at Balikeshir (which took over the Deny Flight detachment at Ghedi in June 1994). Conversion of 191 Filo (previously the last user of the Italian-built F-104S) has proceeded more slowly than expected and the squadron is only due to receive its first F-16 in September 1994. A third squadron of 9 Wing, 193, stood down as an F-104G unit in February 1994 in expectation of receiving A-10A Thunderbolts, but has been left in limbo by the decision not to proceed with acceptance of 50 promised by the USAF.

Among the number of military and quasi-military air arms operating in Turkey is the Polis (police). Alongside a small number of S-70As and Pumas, the Polis flies several ex-Heer (German army) SA 318C Astazou Alouette IIs based at Eskisehir-Anadolk,with regular air force units.

Tanker request

Having originally rejected KC-135R tankers as too expensive, Turkey entered a request during the summer for 10 of the aircraft, to be converted from KC-135As in storage at Davis-Monthan. The KC-135s are needed to refuel the growing force of F-16Cs, but Turkey has also received a demonstration of an Israeli Boeing 707 fitted with an American-style 'flying boom'.

UNITED KINGDOM:

RAF suffers further cuts

As expected, the long-awaited 'Front Line First' defence review, published on 14 July, made large-scale reductions in all three armed services and will result in a further 18,700 job losses. Having been cut back to reflect the reduced defences required by the end of the Cold War, the Services have been further hit for no other reason than that the Treasury has demanded cost-savings of at least £750 million in FY 1996-97, and more thereafter.

Compounding the affront, the government sought to lessen the inevitable bad press by reannouncing equipment orders which were already common knowledge. The best that was offered to the RAF was approval for upgrading

142 Tornado GR.Mk 1s to GR.Mk 4s, although it was not mentioned that the Treasury had managed to delete the most important aspects from the planned update before it was agreed. The RAF is to gain a new type of laser-guidance system for bombs: Texas Instruments Paveway III, replacing Paveway II.

RAF strength will fall from 70,000 to 57,000 and three stations are to close. At Finningley, No. 6 FTS is to disband and have its aircrew training duties reassigned, while No. 45 (Reserve) Squadron will disband when multi-engined conversion is transferred to civilian schools. Laarbruch, currently home of Nos 3 and 4 Sqns with Harrier GR.Mk 7s, plus No. 18 Sqn flying Chinooks and Pumas, will close by 1999, with units withdrawn to the UK. Scampton, base of the CFS and 'Red Arrows', is to close in 1996-97. The CFS will have its activities 'reduced and rationalised', suggesting that more of its components may be lodged with flying schools.

The FAA will lose Portland and the Lynx force will relocate to Yeovilton by 1999. Closure of the naval HQ at Pitreavie in 1996 will result in the proposed unified Rescue Co-ordination Centre being established at Leuchars.

Training changes

Closure of Finningley is part of a training shake-up to save £330 million over 10 years. The RAF will employ more civilian flying instructors. Up to 40 per cent of the staff at basic flying schools will be civilians.

Shawbury and the AAC base at Middle Wallop are in competition to become home to the new Defence Helicopter Flying School, to be formed by 1997.

In an attempt to underline its commitment to the front line, the government offered a small number of enhancements in addition to the Tornado

Left: In Swedish service the Beech Super KingAir is the Tp 101, and aircraft are allotted to front-line units for liasion and light transport duties. This example is operated by Ronneby-based F17, a JA 37 wing.

GR.Mk 4 and Paveway III. Fast-jet pilots are to be assigned 8,000 more hours of training per year and Nos 3 and 4 Sqns will be increased in size from 12 to 18 Harrier GR.Mk 7s each.

The TIALD laser-designation pod, used for the first time by Tornados in the Gulf War, is to be bought in larger numbers and issued to selected Harrier and Jaguar units to give precision-bombing capability. It is also intended to obtain a conventional stand-off missile (CASOM) for the GR.Mk 4 force.

Tanker changes

Further savings in the RAF are understood to have been sought by phasing out the VC10 fleet of No. 10 Squadron at Brize Norton. No timetable has been revealed for transferring their duties to chartered civilian aircraft – which, of course, will be unable to undertake the tanker duties recently allocated to the VC10 C.Mk 1 (K) conversions. Royal and VVIP overseas flights, currently made in VC10s, may be switched to Tristars.

Also at Brize, No. 101 Squadron received its second VC10 K.Mk 4 (ZD240 'M') on 1 July 1994, following ZD242 'P' accepted on 28 April. 'Shake-down' flights were begun during July. Despite their smaller capacity, the K.Mk 4s are replacing K.Mk 2s, of which ZD140 'A' was withdrawn from use at St Athan in 1993, because of corrosion. The other Mk 2s are expected to follow for a similar reason. The promised repainting of 'tanker tens' began during the summer, with K.Mk 3 ZA149 'H' returning from Sogerma's overhaul plant in France in an overall grey scheme.

Helicopters delayed

The July defence announcements significantly failed to include a new order for support helicopters for the RAF. These are urgently required to assist – among other tasks – the new Joint Rapid Deployment Force foreshadowed in the 'Front Line First' White Paper. Comprising the Army's 5 Airborne Brigade and 24 Airmobile Brigade, and the RN's 3 Commando Brigade, this 20,000-man force will have access to RAF helicopters, attack aircraft, transports and satellite comms.

Approximately 25 EH.101s and 15 more Chinooks are needed by the RAF, but the long-awaited order is still held up in mid-1994 by negotiations over price. It appears to have been decided, however, that The Queen's Flight will not replace its two Wessex HC.Mk 4s with Sikorsky S-76s. Instead, No. 32 (The Royal) Squadron (as it will become in April 1995) will receive two surplus SAR Sea King HAR.Mk 3s. Also of note is the fact that two of No. 32's Andovers seem to have escaped retirement earlier in the year and will be kept in service for a further 12 months. Four of No 32's eight remaining BAe 125s will be operated by a civilian contractor and the four Gazelles replaced by helicopters chartered as required.

Various options have been studied to replace the remaining transport Wessex, principally with Nos 60 and 72 Squadrons. Although the RAF regards ex-Army Lynx as aircrew-intensive, it may have difficulty in rejecting the proposed transfer of 25 of these helicopters as a partial replacement. The remainder of the force would be substituted by 15 Pumas to be obtained secondhand.

Tornado update: restricted scope, limited number

Plans for the RAF's GR.Mk 1 to GR.Mk 4 mid-life update (MLU) reveal that the initial contract will cover only 80 aircraft to be modified between 1996 and 2000. An option will be taken out on a further 62 aircraft for rework in 2000-2002. Of the 228 production GR.Mk 1s delivered (including 30 GR.Mk 1As, 24 GR.Mk 1Bs under conversion and 50 with dual controls), 38 had been lost up to August 1994, leaving a force of 190. The implication is, therefore, that about 50 aircraft will not be modified.

The MLU has had to be drastically reduced in scope in order to gain Treasury approval. Deletions have included terrain-referenced navigation, covert radar altimeter, modified air intakes and gold-covered canopy, all of which would have reduced the aircraft's vulnerability to interception while penetrating enemy airspace.

Aspects allowed to proceed for the GR.Mk 4 include ability to carry the TIALD designator pod, a forward-looking infra-red scabbed on the lower front fuselage, global positioning system, and pilot's multi-function display. Upgrades will also be undertaken on the HUD, video recording system, armament controls and computer loading system.

SAR units reassigned

No. 22 Squadron became a Sea King HAR.Mk 3 operator on 1 July 1994 when 'A' Flight at Chivenor was re-equipped with the aircraft from disbanding 'B' Flight of No. 202 Squadron at Brawdy. Arrangements for SAR cover on the East Coast were changed on 18 July when 'B' Flight of

Above: The Royal Air Force's Institute of Aviation Medicine, still based at Farnborough, operates a Hawk and a Jaguar for research into the physiological effects of high-speed and high g-load flying.

Below: Another of the RAF's lesser known Hawk operators is the Boscombe Down-based Empire Test Pilots School. This aircraft is the unique ASTRA Hawk, with a modified fly-by-wire control system.

No. 22 formed at Wattisham, also using Sea Kings. In this case, the helicopters were provided by 'C' Flight of No. 202 Squadron at Manston, which was simultaneously disbanded, as was 'E' Flight of No. 22 at Coltishall.

The running-down of the rest of No. 22's Wessex fleet began shortly before, when five were earmarked for transfer to Akrotiri, Cyprus, some of them having been resprayed grey overall by the civilian contractor AIM at Hurn. They will be used by No. 84 Squadron, which currently operates five ex-navy Wessex HC.Mk 5Cs.

Main RAF SAR detachments are now A/22 at Chivenor, B/22 at Wattisham and C/22 still with Wessex (until 1996) at Valley; A/202 at Boulmer, D/202 at Lossiemouth and E/202 at Leconfield, all with Sea Kings.

Tornado damage estimates

Although some of the Tornado F.Mk 3s allegedly damaged by Airwork Ltd were returned to service during the spring, a recent estimate put at £30 million the cost of repairing the most seriously damaged of the batch of 18. The favoured solution in the most severe cases of weakened metal caused by careless drilling-out of fasteners is to cannibalise the Tornado F.Mk 2s held at St Athan and use their centre-sections in rebuilding the F.Mk 3s. At one time, the RAF had considered refurbishing the F.Mk 2s to near F.Mk 3 standard (apart from retaining their lower-powered engines) under the designation of Tornado F.Mk 2A.

PR consolidates at Marham

The RAF's regrouped photographic reconnaissance force was completing its consolidation at Marham during the summer, both Tornado GR.Mk 1A squadrons (Nos II and 13) being due to be in their hardened shelters by October and equipped entirely with a video reconnaissance system.

Development of video reconnaissance progressed slowly and with some problems until a major effort was made to rectify shortcomings just before the Gulf War. Ground analysis equipment has changed several times since the introduction of the Tornado GR.Mk 1A, but what it is hoped will be the definitive kit has now been installed, the last set as recently as April 1994. Known as the Enhanced Imagery Analysis Workstation, this is installed in each squadron's Reconnaissance Intelligence Centre (RIC): three sets each, plus one ready for immediate transfer overseas. The RICs at Marham are in 'soft' accommodation and not the hardened buildings used at Laarbruch (No. II) and Honington (No. 13).

No. 39 Squadron is also based at Marham with three plus two Canberra PR.Mk 9s (three on establishment, plus two in-use reserves) and one T.Mk 4. There are five two-man crews and 71 ground staff. On disbandment of No. 360 Squadron in October 1994, No. 39 expected to gain one plus one Canberra PR.Mk 7s and zero plus one T.Mk 4s, together with an extra crew and 20 ground personnel. PR.Mk 9s are currently engaged in aerial survey of the UK and

have completed 60 per cent of the task in three years. The precision flying required is assisted by GPS.

Harrier GR.Mk 7 afloat

Re-evaluating a capability first demonstrated a dozen years earlier during the Falklands War, and last practised in 1984, RAF Harriers returned to sea on 27 June 1994 when GR.Mk 7 ZG475 became the first UK-built Harrier II to land on an aircraft-carrier. The aircraft was one of three belonging to the Strike/Attack Operational Evaluation Unit (SAOEU) deployed to HMS *Illustrious* in the Southwestern Approaches.

The detachment established clearance limits, deck interface requirements and electromagnetic compatibility with ship's sensors, as well as assessing the integration of engineering support in the confined spaces of lower decks. A further priority was the investigation of pre-flight alignment of the Harrier's inertial navigation system while pitching on the ocean, this having proved to be a major problem during the Falklands War. Harrier GR.Mk 7s exceeded Sea Harrier take-off weights by up to 6,000 lb (2722 kg) during trials, flying close to the maximum 31,000 lb (14062 kg). By the time of the return to Boscombe Down on 8 July, 40 sorties and 44 hours had been generated.

As the navy has three ASW carriers and only two Sea Harrier air groups, it is suggested that mixed forces of Sea Harriers and Harrier GR.Mk 7s could be embarked at any time from 1996 onwards for specific operations, such as that off the coast of Bosnia.

Aircraft-less squadron

A change in RAF crew training procedures introduced during the spring of 1994 has resulted in No. 55(Reserve) Squadron being reduced to ground-based operations only. Previously known as No. 241 OCU, the training squadron borrowed aircraft from Brize Norton's resident VC10 and Tristar units when they were required for crew training. Following a revision of training, No. 55(R) has become the RAF's first numbered squadron to have no entitlement to aircraft. Aircrew receive only classroom training with No. 55(R) before transferring to Nos 10, 101 or 216 for on-the-job instruction. If successful, this procedure will be extended to the Hercules OCU, No. 57(R) Squadron at Lyneham.

Pumas leave Belize

The final RAF aircraft left the central American protectorate of Belize in August when No. 1563 Flight's three Puma HC.Mk 1s were dismantled for return to the UK. The unit stood down on 31 July, following Harrier-equipped No. 1417 Flight which completed its duty at the end of June 1993.

Eastern Europe

CZECH REPUBLIC:

'Fulcrum' phase-out

The Czech air force has disbanded its squadron of MiG-29s within the 11th Fighter Regiment at Ceske Budjovice on 1 July. All aircraft were offered for sale to India and Slovakia, and at least some have already transferred to the latter. By July, all MiG-23MF 'Flogger-Bs' had also been withdrawn, although the MiG-23ML 'Flogger-Gs' at Caslov are to remain in service for the foreseeable future, possibly with MATRA Magic 2s. Further withdrawals are the MiG-23BN 'Flogger-H' and MiG-21R 'Fishbed-H' before the end of 1994, when the air base at Ceske Budjovice will close.

MACEDONIA:

Embryo air arm

During July, deliveries began from Russia of an undisclosed number of Mi-17 'Hip-H' utility helicopters to the Macedonian armed forces at Skopje Airport, confirming that they are now under national control. Macedonia was recognised by the UN in April 1993, but its departure from Yugoslavia has not brought about the violent reaction seen in Bosnia-Herzegovina. National markings are a sun on a red background.

POLAND:

Air exercises

For the first since World War II, Polish air force aircraft flew operations against naval targets when Exercise Karat '94 was staged in conjunction with the navy during the final week of May. A expansion of operational horizons was due between 12 and 16 September 1994 when NATO and former Warsaw Pact countries conducted their first joint manoeuvres under Partnership For Peace, using Polish territory.

Orlik deliveries gather speed

By mid-1994, the 60th Air School Regiment at Radom had received nine PZL-130TB Orlik basic trainers, following arrival of the first on 4 March. Subsequent deliveries have been of the slightly modified PZL-130TC and it was planned that 31 Orliks should be in service by the end of 1994. Graduates from Radom fly the equally new PZL Iryda at 58 Regiment, Deblin.

Air Cavalry Division formed

Following the trend in Western Europe towards rapid intervention forces, Poland formed the 25 Dywizja Kawalerii Powietrznej (Air Cavalry Division) at Leznica Wielka on 15 June. The division will eventually comprise three Pulki Kawalerii Powietrznej (Air Cavalry Regiments), each with 50 helicopters. The 25th ACD is part of the newly-formed army aviation (Lotnictwo Wojsk Ladowych) and gained its first unit when the 251st ACR was formed at Leczyca out of the former 37th Transport Helicopter Regiment of the air force, equipped with 25 Mi-8T/P/S 'Hip-Cs' and three Mi-17 'Hip-Ks'. Late in 1995, the 47th Air School Regiment will be redesignated 253rd ACR at Nowe Miasto with PZL W-3 Sokols. The third component, the 252nd ACR, is to be established at Tomaszow Mazowiecki with undisclosed equipment.

RUSSIA:

Peace partnership with West

Confirming its earlier intention, Russia officially signed the NATO Partnership For Peace on 23 June, ending nearly 50 years of hostility. As the 21st signatory, Russia is entitled to have observers at NATO's Mons HQ and provide staff for peacekeeping operations and military exercises organised by the alliance. The deal was struck after NATO acceded to demands that Russia's special status as a major power should be recognised, but it stopped short of granting unique privileges.

SLOVENIA:

More equipment

Military aircraft were ordered for the Slovenian Territorial Forces on 1 June when Bell received a contract for five 412EPs to be used for border patrol and two 206B-3 JetRangers as helicopter trainers. Slovenia is also looking for 20-30 combat aircraft and may have reached an advanced stage of negotiations with Israel for secondhand Kfir C2s, although other reports suggest ex-USAF F-16s are the Slovenian choice. Neither can be delivered until the UN lifts arms restrictions on all states of former Yugoslavia.

(FORMER) YUGOSLAVIA:

Sarajevo airlift landmark

The USAF Provide Promise airlift into Sarajevo was largely turned over to C-141B StarLifters following the assignment of five aircraft from the 437th AW to Rhein Main on 2 May. The C-141s joined the 38th ALS (Provisional), alongside 10 C-130Es formerly known as Delta Squadron, although the number of the latter fell to five in June. Typical daily tasking of the 38th is one Hercules mission and three by StarLifters, with the C-141s taking three times the Hercules' load.

An RAF Hercules had the honour of flying the 10,000th UN supply flight into Sarajevo on 12 July 1994. The relief operation, which began on 3 July 1992 and by then comfortably exceeded the duration of the Berlin Airlift of 1948-49, had delivered nearly 121000 tonnes to the city's 380,000 inhabitants. Operating countries are now the UK, US, Canada, France and Germany, but 20 nations and five organisations have contributed aircraft over the past two years.

Along with 31 RAF personnel, ZG475 became the first Harrier GR.Mk 7 to go to sea, with a June 1994 deployment aboard HMS Illustrious.

At the peak, 23 aircraft per day were flying into Sarajevo's airport, but the introduction of summer rations, as well as the larger C-141B StarLifter, has reduced the tasking and limited operations to a five-day week. The average day sees 14 flights carrying 163 tonnes of food, medicine and other aid.

The RAF's Hercules detachment (Operation Cheshire) moved from Zagreb to Ancona, Italy, on 14 February 1993, having been in-theatre from the outset. Up to 21 July 1994, when the airlift was temporarily suspended because of small-arms attacks on three aircraft, including a C-141B, by Bosnian Serbs, the RAF had flown 1,398 sorties (over 2,800 hours) to deliver more than 16920 tonnes of supplies. Operations resumed on 9 August.

Reconnaissance over Bosnia

The CIA is again planning to operate reconnaissance drones over Bosnia from a base in Croatia, having abandoned its Albania-based venture early in 1994 when only 12 out of 30 planned missions by Gnat 750s could be launched. The agency hopes to buy at least three of the four Gnats ordered by Turkey but not accepted because of budgetary problems, although introduction of the new Tier 1 RPV is another alternative. An additional three Gnats have already been delivered to Turkey. Not previously reported is the fact that both Gnat and Tier systems use a Schweizer RG-8 powered

A Sea King AEW.Mk 2A of No. 849 Sqn wears D-Day invasion stripes harking back to the days when the squadron was an Avenger unit.

As part of the RAF's ongoing CASOM requirement, this SAOEU Tornado GR.Mk 1 carried out AGM-130 powered stand-off bomb trials at Eglin AFB.

Above: The W-3W Huzar will be an important element of the Polish air force's new Air Cavalry Divisions. The Huzar is armed with South African weapons, including a Denel 20-mm undernose cannon.

Below: Poland's An-28B1R Bryza maritime reconnaissance/SAR aircraft are fitted with ventral radomes for SRN-441XA search radars, plus GPS Doppler nav, flares and dinghies.

sailplane as a relay aircraft for video signals transmitted by the RPVs. The CIA hopes to be able to convert Gnat 750s to air relay configuration to eliminate the risk of a manned sailplane being shot down.

The USAF has admitted that the presence of SA-5, SA-10 and SA-12 long-range SAMs has forced even the U-2R to fly only stand-off missions using powerful side-looking cameras. It may be presumed that RAF Canberra PR.Mk 9s on Operation Hampden are, likewise, skirting the operational area and relying on System 3 – the long-focus camera borrowed from the U-2 – to gather information.

A-10s in action

AFRes A-10As of the 303rd FS/442nd FW, 47th FS/917th Wg and 45th FS/930th OG/434th Wg, were joined by six from 104th FS/175th FG Maryland ANG in an 18-aircraft deployment to Aviano in mid-July to relieve the 52nd FW's detachment there for a two-month period. It fell to two A-10s to make a retaliatory attack on a Serbian 76-mm anti-tank gun on 5 August, a few hours after an impounded T-55 tank and several pieces of artillery had been forcibly removed from a UN compound at Ilidza. A French Puma attempted to track the weapons as they were taken to Serbian lines, but withdrew when hit by small arms fire. An air strike was ordered.

The A-10s were the only element of a larger force which mostly failed to find its targets because of poor weather. The weapon they destroyed was a predetermined target 12 km (7.5 miles) south-west of Sarajevo and not one of those taken earlier in the day. Four RAF Jaguars from Gioia, four French

Mirage F1CTs from Istrana and four Netherlands F-16As from Villafranca could not locate their assigned objectives in the area of Sarajevo.

Two RNethAF F-16A(R)s later overflew the scene for damage assessment. Serbian troops promptly returned the stolen weapons after the attack, but on 10 August a Royal Navy Sea King HC.Mk 4 was hit by small-arms fire as it lifted off from Sarajevo airport on a routine flight to Gorazde.

Deny Flight rotations

An RAF landmark in Bosnia was recorded on 23 July when the 5,000th Tornado F.Mk 3 hour was flown. Flight Lieutenant Gordon MacLeod and Flying Officer Shaun Vickers of No. 111 Squadron landed back at Gioia del Colle at 0300 hours after a five-hour patrol supporting Operation Deny Flight.

The aircraft used was a Leeming Wing (ex-No. 23 Squadron) Tornado, many of No. 111 Squadron's aircraft being passed on to the Yorkshire base for the duration of the Leuchars Wing's term in southern Europe. Changes in other fighter elements of Deny Flight included the arrival at Ghedi in June of 192 Filo to assume the Turkish F-16C tasking. Arrival date at Istrana for French Jaguars is now known to have been 22 January, followed by the Mirage F1CTs on 6 February. Spain has pledged a squadron of F-18A+ Hornets to Deny Flight as replacements for other NATO aircraft as they are rotated home for resting. Until now, the EdA commitment has comprised a single Aviocar based at Vicenza, Italy. However, this aircraft was damaged by a Serbian SAM while overflying Croatia in March

Middle East

ABU DHABI:

More Pumas

Having just taken delivery of the last of a batch of 10 Romanian-built Aérospatiale Pumas to augment the survivors of 10 from French production, the UAEAF was considering in July the possibility of ordering 10 more. Abu Dhabi turned to the Super Puma when manufacture of the original version was terminated, but the IAR330 is most likely to have a considerable price advantage.

Tornado interest

A possible UAEAF lease of 12 RAF Tornado GR.Mk 1s was discussed in London during May. The aircraft, which are surplus to current requirements, would complement Mirage 2000s in the attack role.

ISRAEL:

More F-16s

Delivery of a promised batch of 50 ex-USAF F-16A/Bs began on 1 August when the initial six arrived on Israeli soil. These are the first used Fighting Falcons delivered to the IDF/AF, which has already received 67 F-16As, eight F-16Bs, 81 F-16Cs and 54 F-16Ds. The latest aircraft are Block 10 machines, half direct from the ANG and AFRes, the remainder taken from store at Davis-Monthan. The 50 require modification in Israel to achieve the same standard as other IDF/AF F-16s, and none will enter squadron service before late 1995. Deliveries are therefore proceeding at a measured pace, with only 35 due by the end of 1994.

IDF/AF F-16s are to be fitted with Rafael Litening IR targeting and navigation pods to replace the similar Martin-Marietta Sharpshooter (a down-rated version of AN/AAQ-14, forming the targeting half of the LANTIRN system). Sharpshooters will be transferred to the 21 F-15I Eagles which Israel is receiving from 1997. The F-15I contract was signed on 12 May after a price readjustment which allowed one extra aircraft to be bought beyond the 20 originally planned. An option is retained on four more.

Lebanon air raids

Helicopter gunships were in action against Arab guerrillas who attacked four observation posts in the Israeli-occupied border strip in south Lebanon on 20 May.

The largest Israeli air attack on southern Lebanon for several years was made on 2 June when the Ain Dardara terrorist training camp was hit by fighter-bombers and strafed for 15 minutes by helicopter gunships.

IDF/AF aircraft made three strikes on Lebanese terrorist targets on 4 August in retaliation for bomb attacks on Jewish targets in Argentina and the UK. Four fighter-bombers raided Ein Bouswar, followed by two an hour later, while three jets struck Deir Zahrani in the final attack.

JORDAN:

F-16 request

Having taken part in a public reconciliation with Israel during July (including King Hussain's symbolic transit of Israeli airspace in his personal TriStar, escorted by Israeli F-15 Eagles), Jordan lost no time in seeking its 'reward' from the USA in the form of up to 42 F-16A/B Fighting Falcons, as well as the cancellation of $650 million of debts to America. The F-16s are required to boost fighter strength, which seems to have suffered of late. No. 25 Squadron, the Mirage F1CJ interceptor unit at Azraq, appears to have disbanded and passed its aircraft to co-located No. 1 Squadron, the operator of multi-role Mirage F1EJs.

All-jet historic flight

The world's first all-jet, air force-operated historic flight came into being during the spring when the RJAF Historic Flight was established in the UK with an ex-British civilian Hunter T.Mk 7 and former Swiss Vampire T.Mk 55. Both have been repainted in the UK in RJAF colours and are due to be joined in 1995 by a single-seat Hunter. There is also a taxiable F-104A Starfighter in Jordan, while a Mirage F1 and an F-5E Tiger II will be obtained when the types withdraw from the front line.

QATAR:

Mirage swap

An agreement signed on 31 July between Dassault and Qatar commits the latter to sell back 12 Mirage F1EDAs and a single F1DDA trainer in part exchange for at least 12 Mirage 2000-5s. Delivery will take place from 1997, together with supplies of MATRA Mica and Magic 2 AAMs, as well as the MATRA Apache stand-off weapons dispenser.

YEMEN:

Civil war

Newly-received MiG-29 'Fulcrums' were reported in combat for the first time on 30 June when they joined with MiG-21 'Fishbeds' in a raid on Marib oilfield. The aircraft were part of a batch of two MiG-29s, 16 MiG-21s and 12 Su-22 'Fitters' bought by South Yemen with funds from a neighbouring country to bolster its campaign against

navy is acquiring six Type 21s, so more helicopters may be needed.

SRI LANKA:

New squadrons

Two new squadrons formed to operate recently-delivered equipment are No. 6 with Mil Mi-17 'Hips' (three, plus three on order) at Vavuniya and No. 7 with four IA-58 Pucarás. The latter were based at Anuradhapura early in 1994 but should transfer to Vavuniya.

advance of the visit to Russia of Prime Minister Benazir Bhutto in September. Items were believed to include MiG-29 'Fulcrums' and Su-27 'Flankers' for interception and Su-25 'Frogfoots' for ground attack.

Lynx from UK

An order signed in June covered the transfer to Pakistan's navy of three ex-RN Lynx HAS.Mk 3 anti-submarine helicopters for operation from Type 21 frigates, also bought from the UK. The

the (legitimate) North Yemen armed forces. Also received were at least three Mi-17 'Hips' (allegedly funded by Kuwait) which defected to the North during the two-month conflict. The MiG-29s, at least, were shipped to Mukalla and assembled at al-Rayan Airport, where they were captured by the North on 5 July, two days before the ceasefire. Bulgarian and Syrian mercenaries are reported to have flown the MiG-21s and Su-22s, although none was seen at al-Rayan when journalists arrived on 6 July.

Fighting between the two Yemens (which had notionally become a single state on 22 May 1990) erupted on 27 April after the South refused to participate in joint government. All-out war followed on 5 May when reciprocal air attacks began. With about two-thirds of the 110 MiG-17 'Frescos', MiG-21s and Su-20/22s on the strength of Yemen's still-divided air force, the South appeared to have the advantage and was able to mount bombing raids almost daily. Air superiority was confirmed after the first week in May, when Northern air operations were

Although the Czech Republic has abandoned the MiG-29, its smaller Slovakian neighbour still values the type. This tiger-striped MiG-29UB attended the 1994 IAT.

reduced due to maintenance problems.

By the end of May, 30 aircraft from both sides reportedly had been shot down. Both sides used a limited number of SS-1 'Scud' SSMs, the attacks beginning with the killing of 25 civilians in Sana'a, in the North, on 11 May. Aden, in the South, was next to be hit, on 21 May, while it was the turn of Sana'a again on 24 May. Foreign nationals were evacuated, including 180 Britons by a BA DC-10 on 9 May and a further 100 in two RAF Hercules operating out of Cyprus on 12 May. The South's declaration of independence on 21 May and the influx of additional air power was to no avail, and the North completed its advance two and a half weeks later. Shortly before the fall of Aden and its airport on 7 July, three transport aircraft were used to spirit away 85 fighter pilots to the UAE.

Far East

JAPAN:

Beechjet in service

Japan's initial three Beechjet T400 crew trainers have entered service with 403 Hikotai (a Kawasaki C-1A transport squadron) at Miho. Ordered in FY 1992, the trio will be joined by an additional three funded the following year, plus two from 1994.

NORTH KOREA:

Stand-off with USA

North Korea's refusal to open its suspected nuclear weapons programme to international inspection was the cause of increased friction with the US during the spring. On 25 May, an RC-135 of the 55th Wing was reported to have undertaken an electronic surveillance operation off North Korea, while an E-3 Sentry was noted arriving in the South. At the same time, two RV-1D Mohawks of Coy 'A'/3d MIB from Camp Humphries/Pyongtaek allegedly flew a coastal and border reconnaissance. A Lockheed U-2R was active on 2 June, according to the North Koreans. Subsequently, the death of Kim Il Sung defused the situation when his son and successor, Kim Il Jong, adopted a less belligerent attitude to world opinion.

There were 'Bears' in abundance at the 1994 IAT, at RAF Fairford. Escorted by a No. 25 Sqn Tornado F.Mk 3, this is the visiting Tu-95MS 'Bear-H' of the Mozdok-based 182nd Bomber Regiment, which participated in the flying display. A Tu-142M 'Bear-F' of the Northern Fleet Training Regiment at Pskov was on static display.

SOUTH KOREA:

Orion roll-out

The first of eight P-3C-III Orions for South Korea (USN 165098) was rolled out at Marietta on 28 June, being also the first Orion built in Georgia. The batch will be delivered in 1995 to replace S-2A Trackers in 613 Squadron at Pohang, following which there will be a hiatus in P-3 production until another customer is found.

PC-9 abandoned

Switzerland's offer to South Korea of 20 Pilatus PC-9 turboprop trainers expired at the end of June without a contract signature. A parallel interest in Shorts-built Tucanos is also understood not to have been developed, leaving the indigenous Daewoo KTX-1 as the most likely contender for an RoKAF order. Two KTX-1s have been produced, but the air force is unhappy with their flying characteristics and a third, modified prototype is expected in July 1995.

MALAYSIA:

New orders

Having announced its intention of ordering three CN.235 transports, the RMAF increased its total to six when placing a firm order with IPTN on 16 May. The aircraft are to replace the Caribous of 8 Sekuadron at Labuan in 1995-96. Also ordered is a single NAS 332 Super Puma which will, presumably, replace the one lost in December 1993 and return the complement to two. The previously-announced $600

Southern Asia

AFGHANISTAN:

Private air force in action

The private air force of warlord General Rashid Dostum was in action against ground targets in Kabul on 27 June, killing six civilians. The air arm, using equipment captured from the legitimate air force, was retaliating for government operations which ejected the general's troops from the capital on 25-26 June.

PAKISTAN:

F-16 transfer abandoned

Islamabad's refusal to halt its nuclear arms programme has ended all possibilities for the PAF's receipt of 71 F-16A/Bs under construction in the US. The US government had offered an interim deal involving 38 of the

embargoed aircraft built up to mid-1994 and in storage at Davis-Monthan AFB, if Pakistan agreed to produce no more weapons-grade material. Instead, Pakistan demanded return of the $658 million already paid for the F-16s.

Following this impasse, Pakistani officials were understood to be preparing a large 'shopping list' of weapons in

Painted as an 'N-22C', A18-317 is one of several recent additions to the Australian army's GAF Nomad fleet.

million MiG-29 sale was finalised on 7 June as 16 single-seat and two trainer aircraft to be delivered from April 1995.

SINGAPORE:

F-16s reinstated

Singapore's defence minister announced in July that the RSAF would, after all, proceed with its second purchase of Fighting Falcons. Having bought four each of the F-16A/B and leased nine aircraft from the USAF for training at Luke AFB, Singapore announced plans to buy 11 F-16C/Ds, then hastily retracted when neighbouring Malaysia secured eight F/A-18 Hornets. After assessment of the Hornet, it has been decided to remain with the Fighting Falcon and increase the contract to 18 aircraft (eight F-16Cs and 10 F-16Ds), including nine to replace the present Luke-based machines. Powerplant has yet to be decided, although the avionics standard is likely to be the latest Block 50D/52D. Current F-16As of the RSAF have AIM-9J/P Sidewinder missiles, but the F-16C package will include the AIM-9S and AIM-7M Sparrow as well as a downrated version of the LANTIRN pod system and AGM-84 Harpoon anti-ship missiles.

TAIWAN:

First Hawkeye

The first Northrop Grumman E-2C Hawkeye AEW aircraft was handed over to Taiwan in the USA for training early in June and was due to be followed by the remaining three before the end of November. Taiwan had originally intended to receive E-2T versions, being upgrades of E-2B airframes with AN/APS-138 radar, but changed to the current 'Group II' standard of E-2C with AN/APS-145 in 1993. The fourth Taiwanese E-2 will be the last built at Calverton before manufacture switches to St Augustine.

Australasia

AUSTRALIA:

Unit news

The days of the CA.25 Winjeel as a FAC trainer appear to be drawing to a close following delivery to No. 76 Sqn at Williamtown early in 1994 of its first two PC-9s. With army aviation, the Bell UH-1H fleet has been rationalised with the allocation of at least nine to 171 Sqn at Oakey. The UH-1Hs with 5 Avn Reg at Townsville have been grouped within C Company, leaving A and B Companies to fly the S.70A.

No. 92 Wing at Edinburgh is to receive three ex-USN P-3Bs converted to TAP-3B aircrew trainers/transports, to reduce flying hours on the P-3C fleet. Users will be 292 Sqn (the OCU) and Nos 10 and 11 Sqns. A fourth P-3B has been obtained for spares.

Aircraft upgrades

The navy's Sea King squadron, HS-827, has had its future assured to 2008 by the award to Westland and BAe Australia on 12 July of a contract to upgrade the seven remaining Mk 50/50A helicopters, the work to be undertaken at Nowra. At the same time, E-Systems of the USA has been selected to upgrade the 19 P-3Cs for continued service. Finalisation of the $A500 million deal was expected in December 1994, with the first aircraft redelivered late in 1997.

C-130J prospects

By July, the RAAF had decided in principle to replace No. 37 Squadron's 12 ageing C-130E Hercules with the latest Lockheed C-130J model. Deliveries are scheduled to take place between 1997 and 1999. No. 36 Squadron's C-130Hs are next on the agenda for replacements, from 2003, about which time the RNZAF will be looking for a follow-on to its five aircraft, perhaps in a joint purchase. Deliveries of Australia's C-130Es began in 1966 replacing C-130As which entered service in 1958.

Thirty years of the Caribou

On 22 April 1994 an important milestone in RAAF DHC-4 Caribou operations was realised, as that day marked the occasion of the type's 30th anniversary with the RAAF. It was on that day in 1964 that the first three machines flew into RAAFB Richmond to complete the last leg of the long ferry flight from Canada. A total of 29 machines was eventually procured for the RAAF, 12 of which saw service in South Vietnam with No. 35 Squadron. Present planning is for 16 of the type to remain in service until the year 2004, when they will be replaced by an as-yet unidentified successor. In recognition of those 30 years of continuous service, a Caribou (A4-236) from No. 38 Squadron was decorated with commemorative tail markings to celebrate the occasion.

New Nomads for Army Aviation

The Australian Army Aviation Corp (AAAvn) Nomad fleet has received an injection of 'new blood' with the delivery of five additional N-22s and five examples of the stretched N-24, the latter variant being new to AAAvn operations. Taken on strength to replace the Pilatus PC-6 Turbo-Porters which were retired in October 1992, this new mix of Nomads will join the 10 remaining N-22s, the first of which entered service in 1975. As a point of interest, only one of the N-24s has had the disruptive camouflage livery applied, as the intention is for the remainder to be used in the coastal surveillance role, hence the retention of the overall white livery. To reflect this broadening of operational responsibilities, the Oakey-based Nomad operational squadron has been renamed 173 Surveillance Squadron (formerly 173 General Support Squadron). This squadron still retains the red-backed spider as its emblem, this venomous

Wearing rather violent camouflage which extends to the fuselage titles, this No. 35 Squadron RAAF Caribou also displays a cartoon version of the squadron badge on its fin.

arachnid now adorning the unit's white-tailed aircraft.

Displaying a unique mix of civil and military markings, A18-317 was used as a demonstrator for the N-22C variant before entering AAAvn service recently. The 'Charlie' variant featured a strengthened undercarriage and additional modifications to provide a modest increase in uplift capacity. In reality, '317' is not an N-22C, but was simply painted up to represent the C model after the real demonstrator (A18-321) became unserviceable. The disguise is effective, as there are no obvious external differences.

Africa

RWANDA:

International aid airlift

When government Falcon 50 9XR-NN was shot down on the Kigali approach on 6 April by the Rwandan Patriotic Front, killing President Habyarimana of Rwanda and President Ntaryamina of Burundi, it proved to be the overture to a civil war of unimaginable brutality. A mass exodus of refugees, notably to Zaïre, resulted in further deaths due to disease and starvation, prompting emergency action by the world community.

American food supplies were promised by President Clinton on 22 July and operations began to Entebbe, in neighbouring Uganda, on 24 July, the intention being to deliver eight or nine C-141 loads and four or five C-5 loads per day. Additionally, a C-5A made the first flight into the refugee camp at Goma (just over the border in Zaïre) at night on an unlit runway as the precursor of 22 aircraft movements on 25 July, the first full day of operations. Three MC-130H Hercules of the 7th SOS/352nd SOG from Alconbury, operating out of Entebbe, also air-dropped 30,000 lb (13608 kg) of MRE rations over the Katale camp, 15 miles (24 km) north-east of Goma, on 24 July, but the airlift was scaled down the following day after aid workers criticised its effectiveness. Many of the USAF flights to Entebbe were being made directly from America with inflight refuelling provided by KC-135s based in Europe.

The RAF became involved in the relief operation (codenamed Gabriel) on 1 August when the first Hercules left Lyneham en route to Rwanda with the advanced party of 615 engineers and medical personnel.

SOUTH AFRICA:

'Black' programmes emerge

Arrival of democratic rule in South Africa has been the signal for additional information to be revealed on the undercover programmes by which the SAAF obtained aircraft in spite of the UN arms embargo. First reported in *World Air Power*, Volume 16, the conversion of ex-Israeli Kfirs into Cheetahs is now known to be more extensive than imagined, apparently involving 45 Kfir and 23 Mirage airframes and kits of Israeli avionics. These have been converted in South Africa to produce 16 Cheetah Es, 36 Cheetah Cs, 15 Cheetah D trainers and one Cheetah R.

Cheetah C – the most advanced version, with a sophisticated nav/attack suite – has not previously been revealed, all apparently being rebuilt Kfirs. Allocated serials beginning 341 (reusing numbers formerly allocated to NA Mustangs and F-86 Sabres), at least 24 had been completed up to early 1994. Of these, 341, 342, 343, 345, 346 and 347 have been evaluated at Louis Trichardt AB in anticipation of a release-to-service late in 1994. The Cheetah C has Atar 09K-50 engines reportedly taken from the SAAF's Mirage F1s. These must be presumed to be the 15 F1CZs which have been withdrawn, perhaps with the addition of a few spare motors and some obtained on the open market via Israel. There is therefore a possibility that some completed Cheetah Cs are awaiting an engine. In the longer term, however, more Atars might become available if the SAAF proceeds with plans to re-engine its Mirage F1AZs with Russian RD-33 powerplants.

Regarding the previously known Cheetah D/E, at least four Ds and five Es have been produced from Kfirs, as

their serial numbers (858-861 and 862-866) are above the last legitimate Mirage III, 857. Eleven more Cheetah Ds are confirmed to have been produced from Mirage IIIDZ/IIID2Zs (840-847, 849, 852 and 853). The number of Cheetah Es rebuilt from Mirages is also 11 (822, 824, 825, 827-834), excluding the unique Cheetah R (855 ex-Mirage IIIR2Z). Reports suggest that only the Cheetah D is in service, the C still being in production and the Es withdrawn at Pietersburg AB because of funding shortages.

As one of South Africa's very few potential trading partners prior to the lifting of the UN arms embargo, Israel appears to have done well out of the Cheetah programme. Discussing cost, one senior SAAF officer said, "They saw us coming a mile off. They had us over a barrel." The agreement was signed with IAI in 1988 at a price of $1.7 billion, and the last Cheetah C is due for completion early in 1995. The type has an Elta radar, Elbit mission computer and Elisra EW suite, but many of the systems are South African. Efforts are being made to sell the Cheetah Cs and Es.

The SAAF's No. 41 Sqn has been operating nominally civil-registered Cessna 208 Caravans on light transport and communications duties. These have been adopting regular military identities, beginning with serial number 3001. About 12 are involved.

Celebrating 30 years of operations with the DHC Caribou, No. 36 Sqn painted up one of its DHC-7s in this commemorative scheme. The sound of their 14-cylinder R-2000 piston engines will be heard until 2004.

South America

CHILE:

Belgium sells Mirages

As expected, Belgium sold its surplus Mirages to Chile in a contract signed on 19 July. The FAC was to receive its first aircraft in October 1994, and will receive the remainder of the 20 modernised aircraft (including five trainers) during the course of their update by SABCA. Another five unmodified aircraft are included. In FAC service, the Mirage 5 will be known as Elkan (Guardian) and serve with Grupo 8 of Ala 1, replacing Hawker Hunters.

More RAF Canberras

Ex-DRA Canberra T.Mk 4 WJ992 was in storage at Hurn during summer 1994, for export to Chile later in the year, along with another undisclosed

pair. It is reported that the FAC has lost a second PR.Mk 9, leaving only one in service from 1982 deliveries.

Naval aviation changes

A new naval air squadron, HU-1, appears to have been formed for the trials of a Bell 230 completed early in 1994. HS-1, the operator of Alouette IIIs and JetRangers, has been confirmed as receiving the navy's four AS 532SC Cougars, while the two P-3A Orions are with VP-1.

PERU:

Naval Antonovs

Delivery took pace to Naval Aviation in May of two Antonov An-32 transports, presumably to replace ageing C-47s. A third may follow. The air force already operates at least 16.

No. 82 Wing's component units celebrated another 1994 anniversary after 20 years of F-111C operations. The F-111 in the foreground is obviously a No. 6 Sqn example; the other carries the yellow markings of No. 1 Sqn.

North America

UNITED STATES

JPATS developments

Seven aircraft competing for the JPATS (Joint Primary Aircraft Training System) began a flight evaluation at Wright-Patterson AFB, Ohio, in July 1994. Not described as a fly-off competition, the three-month event is the final test before a choice is made among two turboprop-, four turbofan- and one turbojet-powered candidates. The future of the entire JPATS programme is far from clear, but the result may be the largest US order for military aircraft for the rest of the century.

The third Rockwell/Deutsche Aerospace Fan Ranger 2000 made its first flight at Manching on 20 June 1994, flown by Eugene Arnold and Horst Hickl. The Northrop Grumman/Agusta S.211A by chance drew the first slot in the sequential flight evaluation, and all of the contenders were scheduled to be finished by early October 1994. The fly-off schedule is as follows: Northrop Grumman/Agusta S.211A (Pratt & Whitney JT15D-5C turbofan), 24 July-6 August; Vought/FMA (Fabrica Militar de Aviones) IA-63 Pampa 2000 (Garrett TFE731-2-2B turbofan), 31 July-13 August; Rockwell/Deutsche Aerospace Fan Ranger 2000 (Pratt & Whitney JT15D-4 turbofan), 14-27 August; Cessna JPATS Citation Jet (Williams F129 turbofan), 21 August-3 September; Northrop Grumman/EMBRAER EMB-312H Super Tucano 2 (Pratt & Whitney PT6A-68 turboprop), 4-17 September; Lockheed/Aermacchi M.B.339 T-Bird II (Rolls-Royce RB582-01 turbojet), 11-24 September; and Beech/Pilatus PC-9 Mk II (Pratt & Whitney PT6A-62 turboprop), 25 September-8 October.

Each candidate was scheduled to conduct 14 flights, duplicating mission profiles flown by US Air Force and Navy students during primary training. A selection and contract award are scheduled for February 1995.

Current plans call for delivery of JPATS aircraft to begin in 1998 and run through 2010. Pentagon officials have been studying a 'stretch-out' which would delay production, and reduce expenses in the short term but raise the unit cost per aircraft. The future of JPATS is clouded further by a Congressional Budget Officer report which says that the programme could be delayed at least a decade if the US Air Force and Navy would establish common core training in the Beech T-34C Turbo Mentor, which is likely to be available in large numbers well into the new century.

Long Shot contest

A Ninth Air Force team was named winner at the Long Shot competition, Nellis AFB, Nevada, in June 1994. The team was a composite strike force of A-10s and F-16s from Shaw AFB,

South Carolina, F-16s from Moody AFB, Georgia, F-15s from Eglin AFB, Florida, and B-52s from Griffiss AFB, New York. A Twelfth Air Force team took second place, and an Eighth Air Force team third.

Long Shot is a short-notice, long-range conventional bombing competition designed to consolidate Air Combat Command (ACC) assets into a conventional combat strike force. Each numbered air force in ACC fielded two teams with 18 aircraft apiece. Competing aircraft included A-10, B-1B, B-52, F-111F, F-16, F-15A/C and F-15E. Combat support was provided for each team by KC-135A/R, KC-10, and E-3B/C AWACS (airborne warning and control system) aircraft. Marine F/A-18s served as adversaries.

Proud Shield competition

The 27th Fighter Wing, Cannon AFB, New Mexico, flying the F-111F, won Proud Shield '94, ACC's bombing competition, which traces its heritage to the now-defunct Strategic Air Command. Best crew awards for participating aircraft types included those flying a McDonnell Douglas F-15E Eagle from the 4th Wing, Seymour Johnson AFB, North Carolina, an F-111F from Cannon, a Rockwell B-1B Lancer of the 7th Wing, Dyess AFB, Texas, and a Boeing B-52H Stratofortress of the 5th Bombardment Wing from Minot AFB, North Dakota.

V-22 developments

The Bell-Boeing V-22 Osprey tiltrotor aircraft is to have forebody strakes added ahead of its wingroots to solve empennage buffeting problems encountered during flight tests.

The manufacturing team is also addressing cost and weight issues. The Osprey has typically been about 2,000 lb (907 kg) above its target weight. The airframes now being flown, which represent the full-scale development configuration, weigh just under 35,000 lb (15875 kg), while the manufacturers' target is 33,140 lb (15031 kg).

Two V-22s have been continuing flight tests at NAS Patuxent River, Maryland. Initial operational flight tests by US Air Force and Marine Corps crews took place in July 1994. The No. 2 Osprey (BuNo. 161912), in modified full-scale configuration, logged 20.2 flight hours during the 27-day test phase which included pilot training, simulated night refuelling, and night- and high-altitude operations. This aircraft was scheduled to go into flight-ready storage in October 1994. Aircraft No. 3 (BuNo. 161913) was to continue test flying through 1997.

The current requirement is for 523 Ospreys, including 425 for the Marines, 48 for the Navy, and 50 for Air Force special operations users. The Marine Corps MV-22, much-wanted

by the service to replace its Vertol CH-46 Sea Knight helicopter fleet, would carry 24 troops on a land assault mission to a radius of 200 nm (230 miles; 370 km), or the same number of troops 50 nm (57 miles; 92 km) from ship to shore twice in an amphibious assault without refuelling. The aircraft can hover out of ground effect at 3,000 ft (915 m) at 91.5° F (33° C) with its mission payload.

In July 1994, the USN awarded Sikorsky a two-year contract to study the feasibility of upgrading the CH-53E/MH-53E fleet. This is a measure aimed at finding ways to make greater use of the H-53 series as a 'fill-in' for the long-delayed V-22 Osprey.

H-2 Seasprite developments

On 26 July 1994, the proposed sale of 10 SH-2G LAMPS (Light Airborne Multi-Purpose System) Mk III anti-submarine warfare helicopters to Egypt was announced. Turkey was expected to receive 14 surplus SH-2F LAMPS Mk I ASW helicopters under an FMS (foreign military sales) agreement proposed on 9 August 1994. Two of the helicopters were to be dismantled and used for parts, and the remaining 12 were to be overhauled and used aboard Turkey's 'Knox'-class (FF-1052) frigates leased from the US Navy.

C-17 developments

The 10th production Douglas C-17 Globemaster III transport made its first flight at Long Beach, California, on 10 February 1994. A C-17 at Edwards AFB, California, made the first aerial delivery using LAPES (low-altitude parachute extraction system) in May. Also in May, a C-17 made the type's first transatlantic flight to Europe to test overwater navigation software. This aircraft took part in Air Fete '94 at RAF Mildenhall, England.

The seventh production C-17 was modified at Tulsa, Oklahoma, with the installation of an interim airlift defensive system and is now being tested at Eglin AFB, Florida. The Douglas-designed system consists of four missile-warning sensors, two at the front and two at the back of the aircraft, flare dispensers on each side of the aircraft and under the nose, and controllers to operate the system.

An independent US Air Force review panel has recommended rejection of Rolls-Royce's unsolicited proposal to qualify the RB211-535

The Japanese Maritime Safety Agency has taken delivery of its first Sikorsky S-76C equipped with a hoist, Nitesun light and specialised avionics for SAR and coast guard duties. The JMSA will acquire at least one more.

three-shaft high-bypass turbofan as a second powerplant for the C-17. Rolls-Royce argued that buying RB211s for 88 four-engined airlifters would save $1.5 billion in direct and support costs. The proposal has been made before but has never met with encouragement. The USAF is not currently committed to purchase more than 40 C-17s, with an eventual goal of 120 aircraft.

F-15/F-16 developments

McDonnell Douglas is continuing efforts to persuade the US Air Force to buy additional F-15E Eagles. The company has delivered its 209th and last F-15E, but next year will resume building the almost identical F-15S and F-15I for Saudi Arabia and Israel, respectively. There has long been some interest on the Air Force's part in obtaining a small number of additional F-15Es, but the service is unlikely to seek these soon, given current budget constraints. The manufacturer is using the deteriorating aerospace industrial base as an argument: only three production lines in the United States are currently producing fighters. In an unsolicited May 1994 proposal to the F-15E System Program Office at Wright-Patterson AFB, Ohio, the company offered four options – from three to 36 aircraft – at around $50 million apiece.

On 12 May 1994, the US and Israel signed letters of offer and acceptance for 21 F-15Is with delivery from 1997, with an option for four more. This adds to 72 F-15s for Saudi Arabia.

A further fighter competition is likely as a result of a plan by the United Arab Emirates (UAE) to underwrite development of its own version of either the F-15 or F-16.

McDonnell Douglas and Lockheed are seeking US government approval for direct commercial sales of their respective fighters outside the scope of the Pentagon's foreign military sales (FMS) programme. The US government has already informed the UAE that it would not be willing to sell non-standard aircraft through FMS.

McDonnell Douglas plans to offer the F-15U+ to counter Lockheed's proposed F-16U, which is not a new

Another recent addition to South Korea's naval forces has been 12 Sea Skua-armed Mk 99 Super Lynx, now in the hands of 627 Sqn.

version of the Fighting Falcon but rather a wholly new aircraft. The F-16U is described as an 'all-wing' aircraft with a larger delta wing developed from the company's F-16XL. The F-16U would introduce a new FLIR and extra fuel.

Doubts exist as to whether Washington would agree to the number wanted by the UAE (80) or to any aircraft with longer range or greater ordnance-carrying capability than the Israeli F-15I.

F/A-18 developments

More US Marine Corps squadrons are expected to deploy on US Navy carriers and for longer periods to compensate for what both services see as a shortage of McDonnell Douglas F/A-18 Hornets. On 1 September 1994, the chief of naval operations and Marine Corps commandant agreed on a plan to equip the Navy's 10 carrier air wings and one reserve air wing, as well as one to two marine expeditionary forces, using the 42 F/A-18 squadrons now available. The F/A-18 shortage is the result of the Navy's decision to retire the A-6 by 1997.

McDonnell Douglas and Israel's Rafael Armament Development Authority are studying a joint venture to equip the F/A-18 Hornet fighter with the Israeli Python-4 infra-red air-to-air missile. If approved, the Israeli Python could be integrated with the F/A-18 and be available for international sales by early 1996. Rafael, owned and operated by Israel's Ministry of Defence, would need US government approval for the release of technology and software to integrate and test the missile on the F/A-18.

Rwanda refugee relief

The US role in the humanitarian airlift for Rwanda refugees began 11 May 1994 when four Lockheed C-141B StarLifters began flying regular missions. Some C-141Bs brought relief supplies to Mwanza, Tanzania, where numerous refugees had gathered. Subsequently, three C-17 Globemaster IIIs of the 17th Airlift Squadron, 437th Airlift Wing, Charleston AFB, South Carolina, were alerted to begin operations between Germany and Zaïre shuttling medicine, food and water for Rwandan refugees. The C-17s were expected to operate from a 5,200-ft (1610-m) runway at Bukavu, Zaïre, on the Rwandan border, which is deemed too short to accommodate a C-141 with a full load.

USAF accepts final E-3

Nineteen years after performing its first flight, the final E-3B Sentry (73-1674) was delivered to the 552nd Air Control Wing at Tinker AFB, Oklahoma, on 28 April 1994. The aircraft was retained by Boeing as a development airframe to perform various flight tests and rarely ventured away from the Renton, Washington, area. The E-3 was originally rolled out during mid-1975 and performed its maiden flight on 21 July 1975. Among the modifications carried out to 31674 was the fitment of additional computers and surveillance equipment to enable the earlier versions to perform a maritime capability. One of the most recent modifications was the installation of Quick Look electronic support measures system to detect signals emitted from both friendly and hostile targets. The equipment is housed in an elongated fairing mounted

on the forward fuselage. To date, this is the only USAF example to receive the modification, although others will be updated in due course. The entry into service of this airframe enables it to claim the distinction of being the final 707 to be delivered by Boeing.

P-3 developments

The first of eight Lockheed P-3C Orion Update III aircraft for South Korea was rolled out at Marietta, Georgia, on 28 June 1994. Orions will replace Grumman S-2E Trackers with the Republic of Korea navy's 613 Squadron at Pohang.

Skyhawks forever?

The last US Marine Corps Douglas Skyhawk, an A-4M (BuNo. 160024) belonging to reserve squadron VMA-131 'Diamondbacks' at NAS Willow Grove, Pennsylvania, was retired from service in August 1994.

US Navy/Marine Corps squadrons

The US Navy and Marine Corps continue to disestablish and consolidate flying squadrons as the size of the forces are reduced. The number of hulls is also being reduced.

USS *Saratoga* (CV-60) was decommissioned on 20 August 1994 and is expected to become a floating museum in Jacksonville, Florida, leaving the Japan-based USS *Independence* (CV-62) as the oldest aircraft-carrier in the fleet. The amphibious assault ship *Guadalcanal* (LPH-7) was decommissioned on 31 August 1994 and reportedly will be used as a civil heliport in New York harbour.

HC-1 'Fleet Angels' at NAS North

Island, California ('UP' tailcode), was disestablished on 29 April 1994. The squadron operated a mix of Sikorsky SH-3G and SH-3H Sea King and CH-53E Super Stallion helicopters in utility and transport duties. HC-16 'Bullfrogs' ('BF') at NAS Pensacola, Florida, an operator of Sikorsky SH-3D Sea Kings and Bell HH-1N Hueys in support of the Atlantic Fleet, was disestablished on 1 April 1994.

HSL-32 'Tridents' ('HV') at NAS Norfolk, Virginia, which flew Kaman SH-2F Seasprite LAMPS Mk Is, was disestablished 31 January 1994. HSL-33 'Sea Snakes' ('TF') at North Island, another operator of the fast-disappearing SH-2F, was disestablished on 29 April 1994. The date was changed from an originally planned 31 March 1994 because the squadron still had a detachment at sea. HSL-74 'Demon Elves' ('NW') at NAS South Weymouth, Massachusetts, a Naval Air Reserve operator of the SH-2F which had been scheduled to convert to the SH-2G LAMPS Mk III, was disestablished on 1 April 1994.

VA-36 'Roadrunners' at NAS Oceana, Virginia, which flew Grumman A-6E and KA-6D Intruders, was disestablished on 1 April 1994. VA-42 'Green Pawns' at Oceana, the East Coast fleet replenishment squadron for the KA-6D and A-6E Intruder, which also operated four Grumman TC-4C Academe trainers and three Beech T-34C Turbo Mentors, was scheduled to be disestablished on 30 September 1994. The move will leave VA-128 'Golden Intruders' at NAS Whidbey Island, Washington, as the sole Intruder training outfit, reflecting the Navy's plans to eliminate the Intruder from inventory by the end of 1997. VA-85 'Buckeyes' at Oceana, another Intruder squadron, was scheduled to be disestablished on 30 September 1994.

VAQ-137 'Rooks' at Whidbey Island, which flew the Grumman EA-6B Prowler, was scheduled to be disestablished on 1 October 1994.

VAW-110 'Firebirds' at NAS Miramar, California, the West Coast FRS squadron for the Grumman E-2C Hawkeye and C-2A Greyhound was to be disestablished on 30 September 1994.

VF-43 'Challengers' at Oceana,

Left: South Korea accepted its first P-3C-III Orion on 28 June 1994, at Lockheed's Marietta, Georgia, plant. These aircraft, which will enter service with 613 Squadron, are currently the last Orions scheduled for construction.

Right: The AMRAAM-equipped F-16Cs of the 512th Fighter Squadron (the 'Dragons') are now firmly established at Aviano, having previously operated from Ramstein with the 86th Fighter Wing.

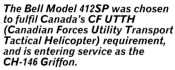

The Bell Model 412SP was chosen to fulfil Canada's CF UTTH (Canadian Forces Utility Transport Tactical Helicopter) requirement, and is entering service as the CH-146 Griffon.

which operated various aircraft types including A-4F/TA-4J Skyhawks, F-5E/F-5F Tigers, F-16N and TF-16N Fighting Falcons, and used North American T-2C Buckeyes for training, was scheduled to be disestablished on 1 July 1994 after earlier plans for May 1994 disestablishment were revised. VF-74 'Bedevilers' at Oceana, which flew the Grumman F-14A Tomcat, was disestablished on 30 April 1994, not on 28 April 1994 as reported in some sources. VF-124 'Gunfighters' at Miramar, which flew the Grumman F-14A Tomcat, was disestablished on 30 September 1994. The squadron had been the West Coast FRS for the F-14 and leaves VF-101 'Grim Reapers' at Oceana as the only Tomcat training squadron. VF-126 'Fighting Seahawks' at Miramar, with Douglas A-4E/F/TA-4J Skyhawks and Lockheed F-16N and TF-16N Fighting Falcons, was disestablished on 1 April 1994.

VP-22 'Blue Geese' ('QA' tailcode) at NAS Barbers Point, Hawaii, which flew the Lockheed P-3C Orion Update II.5, was disestablished on 31 March 1994. VP-49 'Woodpeckers' ('LP') at NAS Jacksonville, Florida, which flew the Lockheed P-3C Orion Update III Retrofit, was disestablished on 1 March 1994. VP-60 'Cobras' ('LS') at NAS Glenview, Illinois, a Naval Air Reserve user of the Lockheed P-3B Orion, was to be disestablished 1 September 1994. NAS Glenview was to be closed. VP-67 'Golden Hawks' ('PL') at NAS Memphis, Tennessee, a Reserve user of the Lockheed P-3B Orion, was to be disestablished on 1 September 1994. VP-90 'Lions' ('LX') at Glenview, a Reserve user of the P-3B, was scheduled to be disestablished on 30 September 1994. VP-93 'Executioners' ('LH') at NAF Detroit, Michigan, a Reserve P-3B user, was scheduled to be disestablished

30 September 1994.

VS-27 'Seawolves' at NAS Cecil Field, Florida, the East Coast FRS for the Lockheed S-3B Viking, was scheduled to be disestablished on 30 September 1994. The move leaves VS-41 'Shamrocks' at North Island as the only replenishment squadron for the Viking.

VX-5 'Vampires', an operational test and evaluation squadron at NWTC China Lake, California, was disestablished on 29 April 1994 and its people and equipment became a detachment of newly-formed VX-9. Plans to make the same change on the same date with VX-4 'Evaluators' ('XE') at NAS Point Mugu, California, were postponed; the date for disestablishment of that squadron became 30 September 1994. VX-9 is headquartered at China Lake.

The Marine Corps is also moving squadrons to Miramar from MCAS El Toro, California, the first two being VMFA(AW)-121 'Green Knights' ('UK') with F/A-18D Hornets and the Reserves' VMFA-134 'Hawks' ('MF') with F/A-18s.

Revision of dedicated CAS?

After a long period of indecision, the Air Force has revived its plan for a dedicated close air support (CAS) aircraft. The role is seen as crucial to support the Army on the battlefield and is the result of studies of recent conflicts involving CAS, as well as the increasing need to be effective during UN-backed peacekeeping roles. The Air Force performed an evaluation of the role at Nellis AFB, Nevada, during the 1980s with a number of A-10s and F-16s. The Air Force appeared to have shelved the proposal, with Congress witholding funds accordingly.

The new plan calls for the modification of 200 A-10As for a 'low-intensi-

ty' close air support mission, while 200 Block 30 F-16C/Ds will be employed for higher-intensity day CAS. An additional 200 F-16C/Ds from Block 40 will have enhanced capability for night CAS patrols. Modifications to the A-10 will be fairly simple, consisting of the cockpit lighting being changed to enable the pilot to wear night-vision goggles. The A-10 was designed to perform a limited CAS role to kill tanks and heavy armour on the battlefield with a variety of weapons including bombs, guided missiles and its 30-mm GAU-8A cannon.

The daylight dedicated F-16s will receive more extensive modifications, including the fitment of an improved data computer, a laser spot tracker, and possibly a missile approach warning system. Night CAS aircraft will feature the Martin-Marietta LANTIRN system upgraded to incorporate a laser spot tracker to enhance identification of ground targets. The Block 40 F-16s will perform the CAS role in addition to their conventional ground attack mission. The F-16 has an internal 20-mm multi-barrelled cannon, although it is the AGM-65 Maverick missile that will be the primary weapons system for close air support.

Most of the LANTIRN-equipped Block 40 F-16C/D aircraft are at present in service with Air Combat Command, including the 23rd Wing at Pope AFB, North Carolina, 56th FW at Luke AFB, Arizona, 347th Wing at Moody AFB, Georgia, and 388th FW at Hill AFB, Utah. It seems likely that most of the units operating the appropriate aircraft will be assigned the CAS role, thereby enabling ACC to deploy a variety of its forces to perform this mission. Over 450 F-16Cs and Ds were constructed to Blocks 40 and 42 standard with funding from FY 1987 to 1990, although this number has been reduced slightly through attrition.

Funding for the programme was first identified in the FY 1994 budget, with work due to start in 1997/1998. However, Congress requested the DoD to review the CAS requirement prior to releasing the finances.

Senator stops airlift reduction

Since the Cold War ended, the US government has guided the military towards a massive cut in the quantity of air assets. The recent announcement that the Reserves were to see a reduction in the number of aircraft assigned to each squadron was opposed by Senator Wendell H. Ford of Kentucky, who considered the effectiveness of the

USAF was becoming dangerously impaired. Single-handedly, Senator Ford held up the confirmation of six promotions to the rank of general.

His main concern was the reduction of the complement of C-130Hs of the 165th AS at Standiford Airport, Louisville, in the senator's home state of Kentucky. Ford also expressed reservations at the proposed reduction of airlift capabilities in nearby states including Ohio, Pennsylvania, Tennessee and West Virginia, and went as far as to request the Pentagon to consider the possibility of transferring all US-based C-130 transport operations to the ANG and Air Force Reserve.

The threat to block the promotions appears to have been successful, as the 105th AS, 118th AW at Nashville Metro Airport, Tennessee, 167th AS, 167th AG at Shepherd Field, Martinsburg, West Virginia, as well as the 165th AS at Louisville will remain at 12 aircraft. In addition, the 327th AS, 913th AG at NAS Willow Grove, Pennsylvania, will also retain this number of C-130Es, while the 757th AS, 910th AG at Youngstown MAP, Ohio, will actually double its complement from eight to 16 C-130Hs.

ACC's long-distance missions

On the first day of Operation Desert Storm, seven B-52Gs of the 2nd BW flew from Barksdale AFB, Louisiana, to launch a salvo of AGM-86C cruise missiles at heavily defended high-value targets in Iraq. Aided by inflight refuelling, the bombers made the round trip – lasting more than 35 hours – non-stop. Apart from inflicting damage to heavily defended Iraqi military complexes, the mission, which was called Secret Squirrel, proved that bomber crews could strike at any target worldwide from the USA without the need to land away from home base. The mission was carried out shortly before Strategic Air Command was dissolved, although its effectiveness was not lost on the senior planners when Air Combat Command assumed the strategic bomber role in June 1992. Gradually, the nuclear strike mission by manned bombers has assumed less importance, with crews regularly training to deliver conventional weapons. The advent of the cruise missile, which can be released at great distances from its intended target, has also added to the capabilities of bomber crews

During 1993, B-1Bs and B-52Hs of ACC began practising the role of global power projection with intercontinental, non-stop sorties to ranges in Europe and the Pacific. The duration of these sorties was approximately 25 hours, which placed a strain on the stamina of the crews in their cramped cockpits. While both the B-52H and the B-1B were designed for long-range missions, neither was constructed for total crew comfort, with restrooms confined to floor space between the operator stations.

During Exercise Bright Star 4 in November 1993, the Air Force organised

NASA proposes using four of the once highly secret Lockheed D-21 reconnaissance drones for high-speed ramjet flight research. Four examples have been delivered to the Dryden facility at Edwards AFB.

a bomber bridge across the Atlantic and the Mediterranean to Egypt for almost five days. B-52Hs from the 2nd BW at Barksdale AFB, 5th BW at Minot AFB, North Dakota, 410th BW at K. I. Sawyer AFB, Michigan, and 416th BW at Griffiss AFB, New York, were participants, alongside B-1Bs of the 7th Wing at Dyess AFB, Texas, and 384th BW at McConnell AFB, Kansas. The 93rd BW at Castle AFB, California, also flew two non-stop sorties with their B-52s, although the aircraft were permitted a brief refuelling stop at Lajes Field in the Azores. Bright Star was the last major exercise for the B-52G before the version was retired from service. The two B-52Gs flew the longest distance, although their J57 powerplants produce less thrust than the TF33 turbofans of the B-52Hs.

The success of these intercontinental sorties led ACC to mount additional training missions earlier in 1994. During the four-week period between mid-February and mid-March 1994, eight B-52H and B-1B squadrons performed non-stop flights of 20- to 25-hour duration. Some B-1B sorties were to a practice range in the Netherlands to deliver ordnance prior to returning home. SAC had for many years performed training sorties of 12 hours or more, although these recent flights necessitated much additional planning and effective co-ordination with tanker aircraft stationed at European and Pacific bases.

During June, a pair of 28th BW B-1Bs flew a 21-hour non-stop mission from Ellsworth AFB to a bombing range at Captieux (north-east of Biarritz, France) at the start of a six-month Congressionally authorised evaluation. The sorties were the wing's first overseas flights as part of the bomber operational readiness assessment.

More funding for FY 1995

At its meeting on 10 June, the Senate Armed Services Committee approved much needed additional funding for a variety of projects for Fiscal Year 1995. The SASC also approved sufficient money for the full allocation of six C-17s to be acquired, instead of four. The option to purchase additional Northrop B-2s, past the 20 already authorised, was retained, with the allocation of $150 million to keep the production line open pending a decision. The outer wing sections for the 21st and final B-2 were completed by subcontractor Boeing Defense & Space Group during May.

An additional $100 million was set aside for the purchase of more second-hand commercial Boeing 707s to be converted at a later date into E-8 J-STARS airframes. The committee also set aside $100 million as a contingency for the limited return to service of three SR-71As, should the need arise. The Department of Defense has a short-term gap in its surveillance capabilities, particularly to monitor the production of nuclear weapons by the North Koreans. The funding was not requested by the Air Force, although the SASC made the money available as an option should the Pentagon decide to return the SR-71s to service. The three SR-71As involved are 64-17962, 17967 and 17968, which were placed in flyable storage at Palmdale, California, shortly after being withdrawn from service early in 1990.

The air-refuelling support KC-135Q tankers have continued to be active throughout the intervening period. At present they are being upgraded and receiving new powerplants to become KC-135Ts, but have retained the special radio fit necessary to communicate with the SR-71.

493rd FS ends re-equipment

The 493rd FS at Lakenheath completed its re-equipment programme on 11 April when the last of 21 F-15C/Ds were delivered from the USA. The final example to arrive landed in the company of two additional F-15Es. All three Eagles flew directly from the McDonnell Douglas facility at St Louis, Missouri, although the F-15C had actually commenced its journey at Robins AFB, Georgia, following overhaul with the Warner Robins Air Logistics Center. The 492nd and 494th Fighter Squadrons have received six of the nine additional F-15Es which were funded during FY 1991 and 1992. Two of the other three joined the 57th Wing at Nellis AFB, Nevada, during 1994.

The complement of the 493rd FS is currently 20 F-15Cs and one F-15D. The aircraft frequently fly with the AIM-120A AMRAAM attached to the fuselage hardpoint. In addition, the squadron has made much use of the BAe Air Combat Manoeuvring Range above the North Sea, with aircraft carrying an airborne instrumentation pod fitted beneath the wing to record mission data for subsequent analysis.

Lakenheath was connected to the ACMI range by land-line earlier this year, enabling resident and visiting aircrew to review their performance at the completion of their sortie. Other NATO air arms have made frequent visits to Lakenheath for range training. Among these have been the Royal Norwegian air force, which usually deployed a pair of F-16A/Bs for three or four days each month. The RNoAF added the F-5A/B during early May when F-16s were joined by F-5s from 336 Skv, all from Rygge. The German Luftwaffe has also sent aircraft to Lakenheath for sorties over the ACMI range, including F-4Fs from JG 74 at Neuburg.

Germany-based USAFE aircraft commenced deploying for ACMI

training during March, with the 53rd FS from Spangdahlem initiating the process. The 52nd FW returned to Lakenheath on 5 July with a complement of six F-16s of the 22nd FS for a two-week stay. With a much reduced complement in USAFE, it is not expected that usage of the range will be as intense as that at Decimomannu, Sardinia. During August, the 53rd FS deployed for a second visit to Lakenheath alongside the F-16C/Ds of the 510th FS, 31st FW from Aviano AB, Italy.

Southern Watch reductions

The complement of the 4404th Composite Wing at Dhahran was reduced earlier in the year, with the number of F-15C/Es being cut by three aircraft each. The 33rd FW from Eglin AFB, Florida, and the 4th Wing at Seymour Johnson AFB, North Carolina, each dispatched three aircraft to the USA during March 1994. Both units each had operated a dozen aircraft prior to the reduction. The aircraft were part of the ongoing Operation Southern Watch, monitoring the United Nations' 'No-Fly Zone' over southern Iraq. Earlier in January 1994, the six 49th FW F-117As stationed at Khamis Mushait in southern Saudi Arabia were flown home, and were not replaced. With the situation inside Iraq becoming less tense than during the period following the Gulf War, the Pentagon decided the time was right to scale back slightly the number of aircraft in Saudi Arabia.

Despite this reduction, Stateside squadrons have continued to rotate at regular intervals, with F-4Gs, F-15C/Ds, F-15Es, F-16C/Ds, EF-111As and E-3B/Cs from the majority of US-based front-line squadrons being involved.

The US has sought to amend its relationship with Jordan, which was strained during the Gulf War when that country was seen to side with Iraq. To this end, some NATO squadrons have begun deploying to Jordan for exercises with the host nation. RAF Jaguar GR.Mk 1As operated with their Jordanian allies during March, followed by eight F-15Cs of the 94th FS, 1st FW from Langley AFB, Virginia, during early May 1994. The eight Eagles flew to King Faisal Air Base at Al Jafr, Jordan, for an exercise.

Bede is offering its BD-10 supersonic 'homebuilt' as an affordable military trainer.

BRIEFING

SOKO G-4 Super Galeb
Serbian target tug

At a time when Serbian warplanes are more likely to be in the headlines for violating the UN-imposed 'No-Fly Zone' over Bosnia, or even bombing targets in Bosnia, it is interesting to see aircraft operating in second-line roles.

The SOKO G-4 Super Galeb photographed here (actually the fifth of six prototype/pre-production G-4PPP aircraft) is one of those modified for target-towing duties. It features what appears to be a locally designed target-towing winch under the starboard rear fuselage.

The Super Galeb was designed to replace the G-2 Galeb and T-33 Shooting Star in the advanced training role. The prototype made its maiden flight on 17 July 1978 and production continued until the break-up of the former Yugoslavia, when the SOKO factory was aban-

The target is streamed from this fitting, mounted on the side of the starboard rear fuselage. A simple fabric target drogue is attached by a short cable to a dart, which appears to have an IR flare and perhaps a radar reflector fitted. The towing cable then goes from the dart holder to the winch.

doned and tooling was moved to the Utva factory at Pancevo. Production has not resumed. Some 150 G-4s were delivered to the Yugoslav air force, and 12 have been delivered to Myanmar. Today, the G-4 serves with the 249th Fighter-Bomber Squadron at Kovin, the 239th Fighter-Bomber Squadron at Golubovci and the 252nd Fighter-Bomber Squadron at Batajnica, as well as the flying schools at Udbina and Titograd.

It is to be hoped that the tragic situation in the Balkans will soon be resolved, and that the flimsy fabric banner targets towed by aircraft like this one will be the only targets fired upon by Serbian anti-aircraft gunners and fighter pilots.

Below: Trailing a target drogue, '605' taxis out for a target-towing sortie. The aircraft wears the old-style 'red star and roundel' insignia of the Federal Republic of Yugoslavia air force, replaced on many aircraft by a simple disc with horizontal stripes of blue, white and red.

Right: A rear view of a target-towing Super Galeb, carrying underwing fuel tanks, shows to advantage the pylon-mounted target winch with its distinctive eight-bladed turbine. The pylon is mounted to the right of the aircraft centreline, forward of the ventral airbrake.

HMS *Invincible*
Sharp Guard shakedown

After a well-earned period of leave, HMS *Invincible* has returned to the Adriatic for a term of service supporting Operations Deny Flight and Sharp Guard. HMS *Invincible* first deployed to the Adriatic in July 1993, taking over the responsibility from *Ark Royal* on 1 August, and flying its first Sea Harrier sorties over Bosnia-Herzegovina the following day. *Invincible* was relieved by *Ark Royal* and returned home to Portsmouth in February.

Another deployment

With no end to the conflict raging in the former Yugoslavia, and with Britain continuing to support UN Security Council resolutions, it rapidly became clear that *Invincible* would have to relieve *Ark Royal* again, and preparations began for another operational deployment. The ship was dry-docked at Portsmouth for a four-month assisted maintenance period, returning to sea in June to begin a work-up to full operational readiness. Exercises in the South West Approaches included live firings of the ship's Sea Dart missiles, before the Air Group re-embarked at the end of June, together with officers from the staffs of both Flag Officer Naval Aviation and Flag Officer Sea Training.

A two-week 'aviation shakedown' cruise began when the ship sailed from Portsmouth on the morning of 27 June. The Air Group consisted of No. 800 Squadron (800 NAS) with BAe Sea Harrier FRS.Mk 1s, No. 814 Squadron (814 NAS) with Westland Sea King HAS.Mk 6s, and A Flight of No. 849 Squadron (849 NAS) with Westland Sea King AEW.Mk 2As. The aircraft of the carrier air group embarked during the afternoon of 27 June, in the Portland Exercise Area, together with two Sea Harrier FRS.Mk 2s from the Sea Harrier FRS.Mk 2 Operational Evaluation Unit.

The Sea Harriers flew with AIM-9M Sidewinders and inert 1,000-lb bombs, and were fitted with AN/ALE-40 chaff/flare dispensers. The Sea Kings flew with

This pair of Sea Harrier FRS.Mk 1s is from 800 NAS. The aircraft on the deck carries AIM-9 acquisition rounds, while the aircraft waiting to land carries live AIM-9M Sidewinders. Both aircraft are fitted with bolt-on inflight-refuelling probes. Squadron insignia and even the Royal Navy titles are removed from RN aircraft deploying to the war zone.

Mk 11 depth charges and Stingray ASW torpedoes.

After a final three days of intensive pre-deployment training befitting an aircraft-carrier about to deploy to a war zone, *Invincible* returned to Portsmouth on 8 July. Despite a large turnover of personnel since the end of the first Adriatic deployment, *Invincible*'s complement – and particularly the Air Department – showed themselves to be ready to return to the hazards of an operational deployment. Such hazards were dramatically demonstrated on 16 April 1994, when No. 801 Squadron aboard HMS *Ark Royal* lost one of its Sea Harriers (XZ498) to a Bosnian Serb SA-7 SAM west of Gorazde.

HMS *Invincible* will be replaced by HMS *Illustrious* in January 1995, when *Ark Royal* will be placed in storage. This is necessary because funds have yet to be made available for *Ark Royal* to undergo the necessary refit and modernisation.

Sea Harrier F/A.Mk 2

When HMS *Illustrious* deploys to the Adriatic, it will deploy with the first operational Sea Harrier FRS.Mk 2s, which are reportedly to be redesignated as Sea Harrier F/A.Mk 2s in an inexplicable, unpopular and unnecessary departure from MoD practice in allocat-

Above: The Invincible *will almost certainly deploy to the Adriatic with a reduced complement of Sea Harriers, since many aircraft are currently going through the FRS.Mk 2 conversion programme.*

Below: Two Sea Harrier FRS.Mk 2s from the OEU were deployed aboard the Invincible *for its aviation shakedown. The deck crew took the opportunity to familiarise themselves with the new type.*

BRIEFING

Two of No. 814 Squadron's Sea King HAS.Mk 6s are seen on the deck of the Invincible. The squadron's aircraft practised the use of Mk 11 depth charges and Stingray ASW torpedoes. Helicopter inflight refuelling, search and rescue, Hi-line transfers and external load carrying were also undertaken during the shakedown.

ing designations. The S in the designation is apparently being dropped because the Sea Harrier has lost its nuclear strike role. The designations FG.Mk 2, FGR.Mk 2 or FR.Mk 2 would have been more appropriate. The carrier has also recently undertaken trials with the Harrier GR.Mk 7, perhaps paving the way for the deployment of these RAF aircraft for operations over Bosnia. The GR.Mk 7 carrier trials were generally successful, but the type's extended wingspan made clearance very tight on the deck hoist.

Below: 814 NAS (a member of the NATO Tiger Association) embarks six Sea King HAS.Mk 6s and operates primarily in the anti-submarine warfare role.

Right: A Flight of 849 NAS consists of three Westland Sea King AEW.Mk 2A early warning platforms. Tenders have been requested for a new radar to equip the type.

Pilatus PC-7 Mk II
Turbo trainer for South Africa

Despite the successful development of the Denel Ace (formerly known as the Ovid), an indigenous tandem-seat turboprop trainer and advanced composites technology demonstrator, the South African Air Force has actually selected the Swiss Pilatus PC-7 Mk II as its new pilot training aircraft. It replaces the long-serving North American T-6 Harvard, many examples of which date back to World War II. The abandonment of the indigenous aircraft was necessitated by the perceived need to replace the Harvards earlier than had been originally planned, while purchase of a foreign aircraft was made possible by the political changes which have swept South Africa.

The SAAF was mindful of the

desirability of keeping an indigenous design and manufacturing capability, but other local programmes were underway and the low unit price of foreign-built trainers (which are obviously built in much larger numbers) proved too seductive. Thus, some 60 PC-7 Mk IIs are on order at a reported price of SFr 200 million. Despite its PC-7 designation, the new trainer clearly owes a great deal to

The PC-7 Mk II being supplied to South Africa differs in many respects to the basic PC-7. Externally, it more closely resembles the PC-9. Here, a demonstrator flies over the Swiss Alps. Production aircraft will incorporate indigenously manufactured components.

the more advanced PC-9, sharing the same slightly reduced-span wing, stepped cockpits, four-bladed propeller, ventral airbrake and Martin-Baker ejection seats (the PC-7 Mk II uses CH 11As). The engine is a 700-shp (522-kW) Pratt & Whitney PT6A-25C; the basic PC-7 uses a 650-shp (485-kW) PT6A-25A flat rated to 550 shp (410 kW) and the PC-9 uses a 950-shp (708-kW) PT6A-62. The PC-7 Mk II has some features in common with the PC-9 Mk II that is being offered as a contender to meet the joint USAF/USN JPATS requirement, featuring a similar increased-area fin fillet and square-ended horizontal tailplanes.

Despite the blow of not having had its own trainer design selected for production, Denel/Atlas Aviation will benefit from the PC-7 Mk II order, having been contracted to produce sub-components for the Swiss aircraft as part of the off-set arrangements. Four technicians from the Atlas sheet metal shop were sent to Switzerland to prepare for the manufacture of 65 sets of components, which will include flaps, horizontal stabilisers, elevators, rudders and engine cowlings. Deliveries of the first machined and welded fabrications for the nose and main landing gear began in June 1994, with the remainder of the locally produced components due to follow at the rate of four sets per month.

Such is the extent of the differences between the PC-7 and the

Wearing a South African Air Force insignia over its civilian colour scheme, this PC-7 Mk II demonstrator pulls up to the vertical. The five-pointed blue shape is a representation of the old fort at Cape Town, and has a springbok superimposed. A change of national insignia is likely, now that apartheid has been swept away and a democratic government has been installed.

PC-7 Mk II that the three PC-7s taken over from Bophuthatswana after the reintegration of the 'homeland' states are unlikely to be retained, except, perhaps, for trials and test purposes.

Interestingly, South Africa is aware of the value of its Harvards to warbird collectors, and is making efforts to avoid releasing all of the Harvards onto the market simultaneously, preferring instead to trickle the aircraft onto the market to avoid undue deflation of the aircraft's unit price. Thus, when South Africa sent a display team of Harvards to the FIDAE show in Chile, they were left behind for local sale, while other aircraft continue in service with the Central Flying School at Dunnotar. The unsuccessful Ace (Ovid) is still being marketed by Atlas, and has made a significant impact at a number of overseas air shows, including Dubai, Malaysia and Farnborough. Despite its lack of a domestic order, the aircraft may yet find a customer, and will be featured in a forthcoming edition of *World Air Power Journal.*

Bell 230
A new low-cost naval helicopter

Developed from the Bell 222, which it has replaced in Bell's current model line-up, the Bell 230 has been delivered primarily to civilian customers in utility, executive and EMS (emergency medical service) variants. Two prototypes were produced by conversion of Bell 222 airframes at Bell Helicopter Textron Canada's Mirabel facility during 1990-1991, the first of these making its maiden flight on 12 August 1991.

Essentially a re-engined Bell 222, with 700-shp (522-kW) Allison 250-C30G/2 turboshafts replacing the earlier aircraft's 600-shp (447-kW) Lycoming LTS 101s, the Bell 230 retains a similar rotor system and has very similar equipment options. Utility versions introduced a skid landing gear, but most aircraft have been delivered with a conventional retractable tricycle undercarriage. Bell has marketed the aircraft

as combining reliability with very low bottom-line operating costs, and is eager to expand its customer base. One strategy has been to pursue military applications for the new helicopter.

A single Bell 230 (actually the eighth Bell 230 off the Canadian production line) was converted to serve as a special mission demonstrator, following 1992 meetings between Bell and the Chilean navy. Following the suspension of the US arms embargo on Chile, Bell was keen to re-establish its links with that country and to reverse the navy's enforced purchase of Aérospatiale helicopters. Bell and the Chilean navy together formulated a loose requirement, but aimed to fulfil as much of the requirement as was possible with an existing helicopter, and not build a new aircraft specifically to meet 100 per cent of the requirement.

The Chilean navy wanted a helicopter which could fulfil three roles: troop transport, SAR and over-the-horizon reconnaissance and targeting. Bell realised that the best solution to the requirement would be to provide the equipment required for each role in easily replaceable modular packages, and used two man-hours/60 elapsed minutes as the goal. This was achieved easily, and the 275-lb (125-kg) mission systems operator's console for the FLIR, radar, communications and navigation equip-

This Bell 230 Special Mission Demonstrator has had its Chilean national markings removed.

ment can be removed in less than 10 minutes. The Chilean navy's need for a three-hour endurance at 50 nm (57 miles/92 km) from the ship, with three crew, helped Bell and Chile to decide that the Bell 230 was the ideal basis for a demonstrator aircraft, which was developed at the expense of Bell and its vendors. This aircraft was handed over to Chile for a six-month evaluation in October 1993.

Basically an off-the-shelf 230 with retractable landing gear, emergency flotation gear, a 2,800-lb (1270-kg) cargo hook and a 48-US gal (180-litre) auxiliary fuel tank, the new demonstrator was customised by Heli-Dyne with a number of specifically maritime features. For the search and rescue role, the 230 has provision for a 1,224-lb (555-kg) Breeze Eastern BL 16600 Personnel Rescue Hoist above the main door, and for a Spectrolab SX-5 Starburst search light on the tailboom. The starboard cabin door was redesigned to slide fully back, with the lower portion folding up to clear the undercarriage sponson, and is cleared for use at speeds of up to 70 kt (81 mph; 130 km/h). All mission equipment was commercially certificated to add credibility.

The aircraft was painted light grey overall and featured an extended nose. This contains the 360° antenna for an X-band AlliedSignal (Bendix King) RDR 1500B search radar (specified by the Chilean navy), and an Agena Infrared Systems (or EOS 2602) FLIR in a two-axis gimballed turret, with FLIR imagery presented on either of the pilot's radar screens. A commercial weather radar originally specified was rejected because it was felt not to offer sufficient range and bearing accuracy for the targeting of ship-launched weapons. Using the radar to gather very accurate targeting data and then datalinking this back to the parent ship was thought to be an extremely important part of the aircraft's role. The helicopter (the first commercial helicopter to receive full IFR certification using a HUD) has a Flight Visions FV-2000/H overhead head-up display, and an SPZ 7000 digital AFCS and an EDZ 705 digital EFIS.

The much enhanced avionics suite includes a Magnavox AN/RC-164 UHF radio, a Rockwell International AN/ARC-186 VHF/AM/FM radio, a six-channel GPS receiver giving accuracy down to 50 ft (15 m), a DAC/Trimble TNL-7880 GPS/Omega/VLF navigation system and a Teledyne AN/APX-101 transponder. Search patterns generated by the TNL-7880 are supplied to the AFCS to allow them to be flown automatically, and are displayed in the HUD and EFIS screens, and on full-colour HDDs.

For the Chilean navy evaluation, the aircraft was fitted with an Indal Technologies of Canada ASIST retractable deck harpoon, the system used aboard the navy's 'Leander'-class frigates and 'County'-class destroyers. This locks into a securing device on the deck which can then align the helicopter and traverse it in and out of the hangar. The system allows safe operations at ship roll rates of up to 31°. The wide track landing gear, low centre of gravity and effective brakes give

A port side view of the Bell 230 demonstrator clearly shows the undernose FLIR turret and the searchlight under the tailboom, as well as the unusual shape of the undernose radar antenna.

excellent deck handling characteristics, and the Chilean navy imposed a 12° roll limit, compared with the 6° limit imposed on the BO 105 and Super Puma. Chief evaluation pilot Captain Mariano Barros Orrego also flew from various ships in cross-deck winds of up to 25 kt (29 mph; 46 km/h) and even in a 45-kt (52-mph; 83-km/h) wind from the bow, which created severe turbulence around the superstructure. The aircraft was flown from land bases as well as from ships, operating at high altitudes and under arctic conditions.

Although the Chilean navy usually operated the helicopter with a crew of three, with the pilot flying the aircraft, the co-pilot operating the radar and the mission systems operator using the FLIR, the aircraft may be recertificated for single-pilot operation, with the co-pilot's position being converted into a mission systems operator's station.

Bell has reportedly prepared proposals for the sale of four to six Bell 230s, which would augment the air arm's Super Pumas and which would finally meet the requirement for a small helicopter left open since the 1992 cancellation of an order for four AS 365 Dauphins. Following an intensive demonstration tour in South America, the Bell 230 Special Mission Demonstrator made a low-key appearance at Farnborough, and then flew on to Morocco and the Middle East for further demonstrations. Plans reportedly exist for the development of a derivative with fixed landing gear, door jettison, fuel dumping, cockpit displays with superimposed radar and FLIR displays, and a removable modular radar nose.

PZL Mielec I-22 Iryda
Polish trainer progress

The 1994 Farnborough air show saw the public debut of the latest version of the PZL I-22 Iryda, the Rolls-Royce Viper-engined M93V, following its 26 April first flight. Since the maiden flight of the first I-22 prototype on 3 March 1985, the Cold War has ended, leading to much closer links with Western aerospace companies. The new-found availability of Western systems and components has allowed the development of an astonishing range of sub-variants.

The I-22 programme was launched in 1977, and a Ministry of National Defence requirement for the 'Iskra 22' was issued in 1980, calling for a combat-capable jet trainer to replace the TS-11 and the Lim-6 in the advanced and tactical training roles. The anticipated requirement was for some 50 aircraft to equip the Aviation Academy at Deblin and 45 LPSz-B at Babimost, with others serving as hacks with different units for IR training, standardisation, spin training and

communications. The I-22 was designed by a joint team from PZL, the Instytut Lotnictwa (Aviation Institute) and other companies, initially led (until 1987) by Dr Ing Alfred Baron.

Five flying prototypes were constructed, all powered by non-afterburning 10.79-kN (2,425-lb st) SO-3W22 turbojets. The fourth aircraft (SP-PWD) was re-engined with 14.71-kN (3,307-lb st) Instytut Lotnictwa K-15 turbojets (first flying with these, as the M-92 demonstrator, on 22 December 1992), while the fifth (SP-PWE) was re-engined with 3,340-lb st (14.86-kN) Rolls-Royce Viper 535s (first flying as the M-93V on 26 April 1994).

The five initial aircraft delivered to Deblin (commencing with 103 and 105 on 24 October 1992) were designated I-22 and are powered by the PZL-5, as the SO-3W22 has been redesignated. Subsequent aircraft (delivered from 1994) are K-15 powered and are designated I-22M92 or M-92. The combat

Above: The fifth I-22 is seen wearing tactical camouflage, and carries a centreline gun pod containing a 23-mm twin-barrelled cannon. Four underwing pylons are available, each stressed for the carriage of loads of up to 500 kg (1,102 lb); the inboard pair also is plumbed for the carriage of 380-litre (83.6-Imp gal) external fuel tanks.

Below: 105 was the second production I-22 Iryda delivered to the Polish air force at Deblin. Five basic I-22s were delivered to the air force, before production switched to the re-engined M-92. The aircraft's similarity to the Alpha Jet's basic configuration is pronounced.

The fourth prototype I-22 served as the M-93S SAGEM avionics prototype. The aircraft previously had been re-engined with the K-15 engine.

The fifth I-22 prototype (illustrated on the previous page) was repainted in red and white and now serves as a demonstrator for both the Viper engine and the SAGEM avionics suite.

trainer version, with strengthened wings, extra hardpoints and upgraded avionics, is known as the M-93. The latter version also introduces Martin-Baker Mk 10L ejection seats and can be offered with various engine options, including the Viper 535 (M-93V), the 14.12-kN (3,175-lb st) SNECMA Larzac 04-C20, the 14.19-kN (3,190-lb st) Pratt & Whitney Canada JT15D-5C and the indigenous 17.65-kN (3,968-lb st) D-18A.

On 24 May 1994, an Iryda (SP-PWD, the fourth prototype) flew with a SAGEM-integrated avionics suite, with HOTAS, a Uliss INS, wide field-of-view HUD and full-colour EFIS, gaining the new designation M-93S. There are a number of specialised ground attack versions of the I-22 Iryda on the drawing board, including the two-seat M-95 and the single-seat M-97S and M-97MS. All three versions feature a new supercritical wing of increased sweep, the M-93 engine options, an internal 30-mm cannon, six underwing hardpoints and wingtip missile launch rails. The proposed M-99 Orkan has an even larger wing, and would be powered by the 25.8-kN (5,800-lb st) DV-2 or the slightly lower rated Rolls-Royce Turboméca Adour.

Kamov Ka-50 'Hokum'
New 'Hokum' variants and colours

The Kamov Ka-50 'Hokum' (described in detail in *World Air Power Journal*, Volume 19) is continuing development, with reports emerging of various new derivatives, including a two-seater, the V80Sh2. This has apparently been drawn up as a combat aircraft at the request of the Russian army, and is not a dual-control trainer, with pilot and weapons system operator/gunner, which may reflect Kamov's difficulty in selling the single-seat concept to Russian army aviation and to a cynical world. There are reports that the army wants a 60/40 mix of single- and two-seaters. An alternative explanation could be that Kamov has had trouble integrating the advanced automated systems which would be necessary for single-crew operation. The Kamov marketing effort seems to have slowed down, with the OKB failing to send examples of the Ka-50 to major trade shows at Singapore and Farnborough in 1994. At Dubai in late 1993, however, one of the Ka-50 prototypes (018) was present, flying and appearing in the aircraft static display in the new camouflage scheme illustrated here. The overall black colour scheme has given way to a simple disruptive camouflage pattern with grey-edged black areas over a basic sand/stone background.

The Mil OKB seems to be growing increasingly confident and has become more active in promoting its Mil Mi-28 'Havoc', designed as the Ka-50's competitor. The Mi-28 will be featured in a future edition of *World Air Power Journal*.

Above: While the agility of the Ka-50 cannot be questioned, Kamov has been unable to convince potential customers that the single-seat configuration is viable in a modern attack/anti-armour helicopter. Some analysts question the wisdom of having such limited movement on the cannon.

This unusual photograph reveals a late Ka-50 prototype in an advanced stage of construction. The rugged airframe is designed to soak up heavy punishment, but many believe that the fundamental concept behind the aircraft is flawed.

Below: Previously painted black overall, this Ka-50 was repainted in desert camouflage for its participation at Dubai. This was not enough to secure any export orders for the aircraft in the region, where the AH-64 Apache is currently enjoying great success.

Tupolev Tu-142 'Bear-F Mod 3'

Inside the mighty 'Bear'

The International Air Tattoo at Fairford, which took place on 30/31 July 1994, afforded aircraft enthusiasts the opportunity to view two examples of Tupolev's 'Bear'. In 1993, Fairford marked the Western air show debut of the type and welcomed a single Tu-95MS 'Bear-H', an example of which returned in 1994, accompanied on this occasion by a naval aviation Tu-142M-2 'Bear-F Mod 3'.

While the Tu-142M-2 is not the latest maritime version of the 'Bear', it does remain in widespread service with the AV-MF and with the Indian navy. Identifiable by its fin-mounted MAD spike and smooth undernose contours, the Tu-142M-2 is the third sub-variant of the ASW 'Bear-F' noted by NATO.

The Tu-142 series are dedicated anti-submarine warfare aircraft and differ from the land-based Tu-95 series in having a redesigned fuselage, with the main weapons bay divided into tandem halves and with a new sonobuoy bay replacing the old ventral gun turret. The wing has been redesigned, with increased strength for operation at higher all-up weights, and with new double-slotted flaps. The higher operating weights of the Tu-142 also dictated the provision of a new undercarriage, with larger tyres, 12-wheel main gear bogies and more powerful brakes. These were accommodated by providing bulged nose-wheel doors and (initially) enlarged inboard nacelle/landing gear fair-

ings. The fuselage itself was lengthened, a 70-in (178-cm) section allowing the provision of new sensor operators' positions immediately aft of the flight deck. To compensate for the increased forward fuselage length, rudder chord was increased. The Tu-142's primary sensor is a massive J-band (21-gHz) search radar, and the antenna for this is housed in a ventral radome, similar to that fitted to the 'Bear-D' but smaller and located further forward.

The original Tu-142 had a second, smaller radar antenna under the nose, and had fairings on each tailplane tip, each probably housing a galvanometer for the magnetic anomaly detector. The similar Tu-142A (ASCC reporting name 'Bear-F Mod 2') had the undernose radome removed, and reverted to standard four-wheel undercarriage bogies, with the original small nacelle tails.

The Tu-142M introduced major airframe changes, with an additional 9-in (23-cm) forward fuselage extension and a raised cockpit roof. The inflight-refuelling probe is drooped by about 4° to further improve the view forward over the nose. The observation blisters on each side of the rear fuselage were finally deleted, reflecting the deletion of all but the tail turret. The Tu-142M-2 introduced the new fin-mounted MAD described earlier, and had an increased-length sonobuoy bay, while the Tu-142M-3

Above: Most of the crew of the Tu-142M-2 which visited Fairford wore distinctive striped blue and white naval T-shirts under their standard issue flying kit.

Below: The navigator's station in the nose of the Tu-142M-2 has a swivelling chair, allowing the occupant to face forward to look through the glazed nose or to face to starboard to scan his instruments.

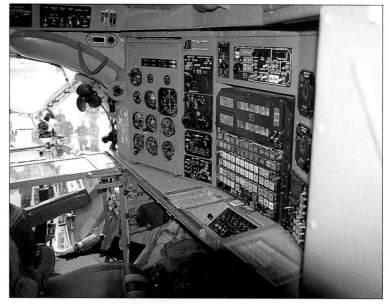

Left and below: The pilot's instrument panel of the Tu-142M-2 is painted in the same shade of blue-green as are many Soviet tactical aircraft, a colour shown by Soviet psychologists to be particularly restful. The top of the instrument panel coaming is a forest of warning and caution lights. Not seen here is the unusual floor-mounted powered conveyor that runs aft from the pilot's position to the escape hatch and is used in emergencies. The autopilot controller pulls out from the centre of the panel and can be swung left or right for use by the captain or co-pilot.

('Bear-F Mod 4') has a new under-nose sensor pod, a thimble nose radome and new antenna pods under the rear gun turret. This turret was changed to that of the land-based Tu-95MS, with a single twin-barrelled GSh-23 23-mm cannon replacing the usual pair of NR-23 23-mm cannon.

Despite an archaic appearance, with its 1950s-style silver finish, power-operated gun turrets and four massive airscrews, the 'Bear' remains an extremely viable stand-off missile carrier and ASW/maritime reconnaissance platform, and the latest versions (like those at Fairford) are packed with sophisticated equipment, sensors and weapons systems. Furthermore, the 'Bear's' combination of swept wing and powerful turboprops give it a competitive performance, and many Western fighters find it hard to keep up at certain altitudes without plugging in afterburner.

Although the end of the Cold War has led to an unforeseeable level of openness by the Russians, they remain secretive about some of their latest in-service weapons and systems. This was demonstrated at Fairford, where access to the cockpit of the 'Bear-F' was limited and photography of the sensor operators' and EWO's stations was strictly prohibited, although the flight deck itself was not off-limits.

The 'Bear-F' at Fairford wore the

The Tu-142M-2 arrives at Fairford, shadowed by an RAF BAe Hawk. The bulged nosewheel doors and double-slotted flaps of the 'Bear-F' are readily apparent.

same silver finish as the 'Bear-H' it accompanied, with white nacelle undersurfaces and underwing panels. Some 'Bear-F Mod 3s', including those delivered to India, wear an overall light grey colour scheme, which reportedly affords better protection against corrosion.

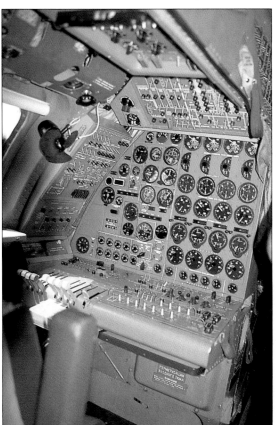

Left: The flight engineer faces aft, on the starboard side of the aircraft, behind the co-pilot. The array of conventional analog dials, throttles and rpm levers allows him to fine-tune the running of the powerful 11033-kW (14,975-ehp) KKBM Kuznetsov NK-12M turboprops, each of which drives a contra-rotating reversible-pitch AV-60N propeller. Noise levels within the cabin are said to be extremely high, resulting in crew fatigue problems. In the 'Bear-F' there is a crew rest area behind the wingspar. In an emergency, the flight engineer simply swivels his chair to face inwards, and falls onto the moving conveyor.

Right: More 'restful' turquoise paint. The radio operator's station is opposite that of the flight engineer, facing aft on the port side. It is believed that various items of equipment were removed from this station on this aircraft to sanitise it for its trip to Fairford, while some non-standard radio and navigation gear may also have been fitted temporarily. Aft of the entry hatch are EWO and sensor operators' positions, but it was not possible to photograph these. A tail gunner is housed in the rear fuselage, but the precise number of sensor operators carried is unknown. The Tu-142's interior is surprisingly bright, and seems roomier than its cramped dimensions would suggest.

BRIEFING

Mikoyan MiG-33
New designation for export super-'Fulcrum'

Further to our article on modernised versions of the MiG-29 in *World Air Power Journal*, Volume 17, we can reveal that the MiG-33 designation sometimes erroneously applied to the MiG-29M (and used by deputy general designer Anatoly Belosvet until publicly contradicted by Rostislav Belyakov) has now been applied by the bureau to proposed export versions of the super-'Fulcrum'. Interestingly, this appears to be a reuse of the designation, which is believed to have originally been reserved for an early 1980s study for a lightweight fighter. This aircraft was of broadly similar configuration to the F-16 (albeit somewhat smaller), with a single engine, single tailfin and chin inlet. This aircraft was not selected for further development, the then-Soviet air force preferring to go with the multi-role MiG-29M. The Izdelye 33 was then transformed into the Izdelye 821-33, a proposed trainer which eventually lost out to the SNECMA-engined, T-tailed Mikoyan AT.

The 1994 Farnborough SBAC show saw the Western debut of the fifth MiG-29M prototype, masquerading as a new MiG-33 and carrying an extensive load of air-to-air and air-to-ground weapons to reflect the new sub-variant's impressive multi-role capability. The sales effort for the MiG-29 seems to be gathering momentum, and Mikoyan kept the aircraft in the static display for much of the week, where it was most accessible to potential purchasers. The Mikoyan effort was supported by radar designers Phazatron, and by the engine designers, the Klimov corporation.

Below and below right: Simple test screens demonstrate the brightness of the MiG-29M's CRT displays, but are much simpler than the screens usually used by the pilot. These are simple pitch angle displays, with a direction indicator above and a rate bar below. Some combat displays might use this as a basis.

Mikoyan was eager to show off the aircraft, and even had it towed aside for *World Air Power Journal*, where it was specially connected to an APU to allow the cockpit displays to be demonstrated and photographed 'live'. This marks an unusual degree of openness, and contrasts sharply with some manufacturers, who refuse photographic access to modern cockpits even without the displays being 'powered-up'.

The MiG-29M's displays are monochrome (green) (probably raster scanned) CRTs of extraordinary brightness, with simple, bold graphics. Several Russian test pilots confirmed that Mikoyan is about to fly high-brightness, full-colour LCD displays, but several expressed a preference for simple monochrome displays, especially under combat conditions. "I feel that colour displays are an unnecessary distraction, and simple single-colour symbols are easier to interpret, especially as you begin to grey out. It's too easy for designers to use colour instead of thinking hard about making symbology clear and unmistakable," said one pilot.

The most revolutionary feature of the MiG-29M displays is the method of calling up information, using HOTAS controllers to directly reference particular modes without moving a cursor through menus, or using input buttons on the screens themselves. Instead, a sequence of directional moves of the three-axis input button (eg. left-up-right) will directly access a particular display, these movements being indicated by keyed arrows arrayed around the edges of the screens, where one would usually expect to see input buttons. The ease and speed of use of these displays may explain why the aircraft has only two screens, instead of four like the Su-35. On aircraft 155 the displays have been

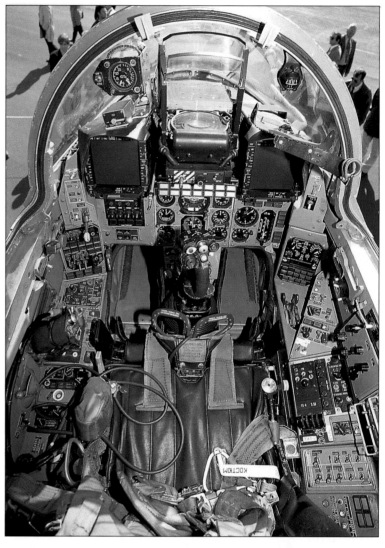

Just as Lockheed has raised the position of the pilot's MFDs in illustrations of a planned F-16 'Future Cockpit', Mikoyan has raised the position of displays in aircraft 155 closer to the pilot's eyeline. This is, however, only a test configuration, and does not represent a production MiG-29M panel.

moved upwards to positions on each side of the base of the HUD, closer to the pilot's eyeline. It is uncertain as to whether this represents a final position.

While it has now become clear that Malaysia will receive a version of the basic MiG-29, probably based on the big-spined 9-13 Gorbatov 'Fulcrum-C', there remain a

More test screens, this time on the right-hand screen, show a simple compass rose (below left) and a more complex systems status test (below). The screens were extremely flicker-free, and all symbology was shown on our photos, even when using high shutter speeds, which indicates a high refresh rate even when full tonal raster imagery is shown. (Such images were seen, but too briefly to record.)

The fifth prototype MiG-29M carries Kh-31P radar-homing ASMs inboard and Kh-29T TV-guided ASMs outboard. Mikoyan groundcrew unloaded AAM-AE air-to-air missiles from the outboard pairs of pylons to provide this unobstructed view of the ASMs.

number of possible purchasers for versions of the multi-role MiG-29M, including India and the Federal Republic of Germany.

It remains unclear as to exactly which variant of the MiG-29 the Malaysians will receive; informed sources quote both the MiG-29SD and MiG-29SE. The MiG-29SE differs from the SD in having a KCA-3 accessory gear box, with reduced maintenance demands and changes to the electrical system, improved air conditioning, and a new active jammer linked to the radar warning receiver.

By comparison with the basic MiG-29, both the SE and the SD have provision for underwing fuel tanks, a new IFF system and tandem underwing bomb racks allowing carriage of up to 4 tonnes of bombs, as well as a new flight control system with an improved roll limiter and greater rudder deflection angles that also allowed higher angles of attack to be attained.

The MiG-29M has now completed its initial flight development programme, and has received its state acceptance certificate but has, as yet, received no Russian air force orders. Such an order may still materialise, since the aircraft has some powerful friends within the air force hierarchy, which may help counterbalance the political advantage enjoyed by the rival Sukhoi Su-35.

Whatever happens to the Russian MiG-29M order, there may be some chance of an export order being placed. India has a pressing requirement for additional fighters, and has reportedly evaluated the Sukhoi Su-30 and the Su-35, as well as considering the option of simply acquiring more MiG-29s to augment its existing fleet of 65 MiG-29s and five MiG-29UBs.

The possibility of obtaining the MiG-29M has also been under active consideration, as this type offers the advantage of ease of pilot conversion, plus spares and ground support equipment commonality with the existing MiG-29.

Another potential customer for the MiG-29M is the German Luftwaffe, an existing MiG-29 operator. Despite being nominally committed to the quadrinational Eurofighter, various factions within Germany continue to press the case for possible alternative or interim aircraft, while the Social Democrat opposition is formally committed to cancelling the aircraft if that party comes to power. Thus, the cost-cutting interventions by Mr Volke Rühe, the Christian Democrat/Liberal coalition Defence Minister, can be seen as being necessary if the project is to be saved. The latest organisation to add to the controversy surrounding the cost of Eurofighter is the Federal Audit Agency (Bundesrechung-

shof, or BRH), whose confidential report on Eurofighter has been widely leaked.

While recognising that too much money has now been spent on the development of Eurofighter to make cancellation a sensible option, the BRH continues to press for cuts in the number of aircraft procured and in the equipment fit of the aircraft delivered, and for a delay to the in-service date. The BRH (which has been accused of going far beyond its narrow financial remit) has assessed the MiG-29M and has concluded that it offers the same performance (or better) than the reduced-capability Eurofighter that will result from Mr Rühe's savings (the German Eurofighter will lack the defensive aids sub-system, FLIR, integrated fire control system and multiple information distribution system).

They suggest that the F-4F ICE upgrade should be stopped at 70 aircraft, and that batches of 12

The fifth MiG-29M, in ferry configuration, departs from Farnborough after its 1994 SBAC show appearance. The MiG-29S that accompanied it carried a centreline tank, but the MiG-29M's huge internal fuel capacity made this unnecessary on the newer version.

MiG-29Ms should be acquired in 1997, 1998 and 1999, with procurement of the (full-standard) EFA reduced from 140 to 100, with deliveries delayed from 2002 to 2006. This would have the advantage of giving the Luftwaffe a more credible interim fighter (the MiG-29M) than the F-4F ICE during the turn of the century period. The BRH plan ignores the fact that some development of the MiG-29M remains unfinished and that, politically, acquisition of the aircraft might prove impossible.

An exploded view of the MiG-29M's NO-11 (Zhuk) radar. Phazotron has started development of a version of Zhuk with a fixed, phased-array antenna that could be applied to future MiG-29M sub-variants.

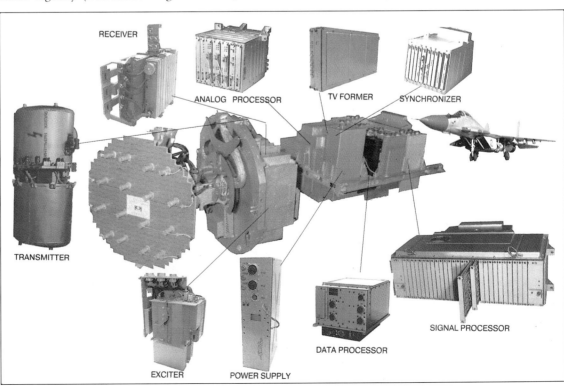

F-117 Bandit list

To supplement the main feature on the Lockheed F-117 in Volume 19, the following roll of honour lists all the F-117 pilots, together with their individual numbers and date of achieving 'Bandit' status. When a pilot has re-entered the F-117 programme, and undertaken refresher training, the second date is also given. Ranks given are as at the time of F-117 training.

Test pilots

117	Hal Farley	105	Dave Ferguson
84	Skip Anderson	106	Paul Watson
100	Roger Moseley	107	William Aten
	Don Cornell		Jim Thomas
	Bob Chedister	108	Craig Dunn
101	Tom Morgenfeld	109	Dale Irving
102	Jon Beesley	110	Pete Barnes
	Steven A. Green	111	Tom Abel
103	Bob Riedenauer		Ken Grubbs
	Tom Darner	112	Ken Linn
	David Imig	113	Jim Dunn
104	Skip Holm	114	Paul Tackabury
			Denny Mangum
		115	Chris Seat

Operational pilots

150	Major Alton C. Whitley	15 Oct 1982
151	Major Charlie Harr	16 Nov 1982
152	Lieutenant Colonel Jerry Fleming	2 Dec 1982
153	Lieutenant Colonel Sandy Sharpe	13 Jan 1983
154	Captain Denny Larson	10 Apr 1983
155	Captain Brian Wilson	6 May 1983
156	Captain Dennis Day	16 Jun 1983
157	Captain Garry Gee	14 Jul 1983
158	Colonel Jim Allen	8 Sep 1983
159	Captain Tommy Crawford	11 Aug 1983
160	Captain Jett Crouch	15 Sep 1983
161	Major Byron Nelson	19 Oct 1983
162	Major Robert Williams	16 Nov 1983
163	Captain Wayne Mudge	14 Dec 1983
164	Captain William Aten	10 Jan 1984
	(Lieutenant Colonel)	5 Mar 1993
165	Captain Stephen Paulsen	31 Jan 1984
166	Captain Dutch Riefler	15 Feb 1984
167	Colonel Michael Harris	7 Mar 1984
168	Captain Mark Dougherty	28 Mar 1984
169	Colonel Milan Zimer	4 Apr 1984
170	Captain Michael Gill	1 May 1984
171	Major Wally Moorhead	16 May 1984
172	Lieutenant Colonel Dave Jenny	30 May 1984
173	Lieutenant Colonel Medford C. Bowman	29 Jun 1984
174	Colonel Howell Estes	11 Sep 1984
175	Captain Glen Johnson	23 Oct 1984
176	Major Dick Hoey	15 Nov 1984
177	Captain Al Frierson	6 Dec 1984
178	Captain Robin E. Scott	15 Jan 1985
179	Captain Greg 'Curly' Nicholl	11 Feb 1985
	(Lieutenant Colonel)	8 Jul 1992
180	Captain Mike Merritt	26 Feb 1985
	(Lieutenant Colonel)	28 Aug 1991
181	Major Richard B. Wade	28 Mar 1985
182	Captain Harry E. Greer III	10 Apr 1985
183	Captain John Krese	3 May 1985
184	Lieutenant Colonel John Miller	30 May 1985
	(Brigadier General)	13 Sep 1993
185	Lieutenant Colonel Thomas Goslin	20 Jun 1985
186	Captain Teddy V. Hale	10 Jul 1985
187	Colonel Thomas Mahan	29 Jul 1985
188	Captain Wade McRoberts	13 Aug 1985
189	Captain Gary 'Gar' Frith	27 Aug 1985
	(Major)	14 Nov 1991
190	Major Lou Alekna	10 Sep 1985
191	Major Don Hansen	18 Sep 1985
192	Captain Tim Sims	9 Oct 1985
193	Captain Guy Bower	17 Oct 1985
194	Captain Brad L. Carlson	29 Oct 1985
195	Major Bob Ryals	14 Nov 1985
196	Major David Greenlee	21 Nov 1985
197	Major Michael D. Farmer	11 Dec 1985
198	Major Ross E. Mulhare	7 Jan 1986
199	Colonel Michael C. Short	14 Jan 1986
200	Major Darryl Leger	28 Jan 1986

201	Lieutenant Colonel David McCloud	5 Feb 1986
202	Captain David B. Wind	25 Feb 1986
203	Captain Robert A. Wesolowski	4 Mar 1986
204	Captain Ben G. Brockman Jr	19 Mar 1986
205	Lieutenant Colonel Rodger C. Locher	3 Apr 1986
206	Captain Michael R. Cook	17 Apr 1986
207	Captain Lawrence E. Lee	2 May 1986
208	Captain Roderick R. Kallman	14 May 1986
209	Captain Michael S. Sackley	4 Jun 1986
210	Captain Richard W. Glitz	17 Jun 1986
211	Major Blaine D. Maw	9 Jul 1986
212	Captain Paul J. Madson	29 Jul 1986
213	Captain John C. Peterson Jr	14 Aug 1986
214	Major John W. Zink	26 Aug 1986
215	Captain David L. Russell	5 Sep 1986
216	Captain John L. Hensley	8 Oct 1986
217	Captain Michael C. Setnor	21 Oct 1986
218	Colonel Herbert T. Pickering Jr	4 Nov 1986
219	Lieutenant Colonel David T. Holmes	5 Nov 1986
220	Major Bernard D. Stubbs	2 Dec 1986
221	Captain Karl R. Vonkessel	12 Dec 1986
222	Captain Bruce L. Teagraden	22 Jan 1987
223	Major Jack W. Shaw	29 Jan 1987
224	Captain Bryan R. Wright	4 Mar 1987
225	Major Lance V.L. Romer	17 Mar 1987
226	Captain Jonathan P. Staniforth	20 Mar 1987
227	Captain Daniel W. Jordan III	20 Mar 1987
228	Captain Gary H. Maupin	16 Apr 1987
229	Captain Craig N. Gourley	22 Apr 1987
230	Captain Edmund D. Walker	1 May 1987
231	Major Michael C. Stewart	1 May 1987
232	Lieutenant Colonel Arthur P. 'Art' Weyermuller	
		27 May 1987
	(Colonel)	3 Sep 1992
233	Major Paul E. Butalla	2 Jun 1987
234	Lieutenant Colonel James W. Teak	10 Jun 1987
235	Captain Leonard M. Ritchey	17 Jun 1987
236	Major Mark D. McConnell	7 Jul 1987
237	Captain John Q. 'JQ' Watton	9 Jul 1987
238	Lieutenant Colonel Richard C. Groesch	23 Jul 1987
239	Major Dale R. Hanner	11 Aug 1987
240	Captain George T. Doran	11 Aug 1987
241	Lieutenant Colonel James G. Ferguson	24 Aug 1987
242	Captain Robert Yates	26 Aug 1987
243	Lieutenant Colonel Keat Griggers	9 Sep 1987
244	Captain Samuel Hartmann	22 Sep 1987
245	Major Gary M. Sanders	8 Oct 1987
246	Captain Randall G. Peterson	20 Oct 1987
247	Captain Gary N. Flatt	11 Nov 1987
248	Captain Joel M. Horie	3 Dec 1987
249	Major David A. Ruddock	8 Dec 1987
250	Captain Daniel F. Haggerty	13 Jan 1988
251	Colonel Anthony J. Tolin	4 Feb 1988
252	Lieutenant Colonel William J. Lake	17 Feb 1988
253	Captain Joseph M. Ford	11 Mar 1988
254	Major Douglas S. Higgins	17 Mar 1988
255	Captain Thomas C. Seckman	17 Mar 1988
256	Lieutenant Colonel Donald C. Schramski	12 Apr 1988

On his way to becoming a fully-fledged 'Bandit', a trainee F-117 pilot takes his first few flights with a T-38 as company. Flying the Talon is an experienced instructor, who monitors the F-117's progress and calls out instructions.

257	Captain Jon W. Behymer	12 Apr 1988
258	Major Charles E. Hicks	10 May 1988
259	Captain Jerry Leatherman	10 May 1988
260	Major Samuel R. Hays III	10 May 1988
261	Captain Gregory A. Feest	26 May 1988
	(Lieutenant Colonel)	7 Jul 1994
262	Captain James J. Villers	1 Jun 1988
263	Major Steven R. Charles	2 Jun 1988
264	Captain Mark W. Renelt	8 Jun 1988
265	Captain Nicholas A. Santangelo	28 Jun 1988
266	Major Jerry A. Howalt	28 Jun 1988
267	Lieutenant Colonel Robert S. Temkow	29 Jun 1988
268	Captain James R. Mastny	2 Aug 1988
269	Captain Daniel R. Backus	5 Aug 1988
	(Major)	16 Nov 1993
270	Captain Scott R. Stimpert	8 Aug 1988
271	Colonel Gary A. Voellger	1 Sep 1988
272	Captain David R. Brown	14 Sep 1988
273	Major Frank A. Holmes	11 Oct 1988
274	Captain Robert G. Bledsoe	12 Oct 1988
275	Captain Kenneth B. Huff	12 Oct 1988
276	Captain Donald R. Chapman	14 Oct 1988
277	Major Walter E. Rhoads	22 Nov 1988
278	Major Robert D. Eskridge	22 Nov 1988
279	Major Steven L. Marquez	22 Nov 1988
280	Lieutenant Colonel Charles R. Greer Jr	13 Dec 1988
281	Major George L. Kelman	14 Dec 1988
282	Squadron Leader Graham Wardell (RAF)	14 Dec 1988
283	Colonel Klaus J. Klause	4 Jan 1989
284	Captain Marcel E. Kerdavid	19 Jan 1989
285	Lieutenant Colonel Gerald C. Carpenter	6 Feb 1989
286	Major Timothy D. Phillips	7 Feb 1989
287	Lieutenant Colonel Ralph W. Getchell	15 Feb 1989
288	Major Kimble N. Fieldstad	15 Feb 1989
289	Major Jon R. Boyd	14 Mar 1989
290	Major Lorin C. Long	14 Mar 1989
291	Captain Robert L. Warren	15 Mar 1989
292	Captain Jeffery A. Moore	11 Apr 1989
293	Captain Philip A. Mahon	13 Apr 1989
294	Major Jerry T. Sink	18 Apr 1989
295	Captain Joseph A. Salata	2 May 1989
296	Lieutenant Colonel Lewis S. Weiland	2 May 1989
297	Major Lee D. Gustin	3 May 1989
298	Captain Daniel J. 'Beaner' Decamp	4 May 1989
299	Captain Niel H. McCaskill	7 Jun 1989
300	Major Alan D. Minnich	7 Jun 1989
301	Major Walker B. Bourland	8 Jun 1989
302	Captain Dennis K. Baker	9 Jun 1989
303	Captain Brian R. Foley	6 Jul 1989
304	Major Michael T. Mahar	6 Jul 1989
305	Captain Charles D. Link	6 Jul 1989
306	Captain Philip W. McDaniel	17 Jul 1989
307	Captain Mark J. Lindstrom	28 Jul 1989
308	Lieutenant Colonel Robert J. Maher	1 Aug 1989
309	Captain Michael E. McKinney	1 Aug 1989
310	Captain Gregg K. Verser	1 Aug 1989
311	Major Miles S. Pound	24 Aug 1989
312	Major Rodney L. Shrader	29 Aug 1989
313	Major Leonard C. Broline	30 Aug 1989
314	Lieutenant Colonel Barry E. Horne	31 Aug 1989
315	Major Robert R. Sarnoski	3 Oct 1989
316	Captain Richard 'RC' Cline	5 Oct 1989
317	Captain David W. Francis	12 Oct 1989
318	Captain Wesley E. Cockman	25 Oct 1989
319	Captain Andrew Nichols	26 Oct 1989
320	Captain Michael D. Riehl	1 Nov 1989
321	Captain Robert B. Donaldson	27 Nov 1989
322	Captain John F. Savidge	28 Nov 1989

In a scene at Khamis Mushait during Desert Storm, the nearest aircraft carries the name of the first RAF exchange officer to fly the F-117. Subsequently, Squadron Leaders Chris Topham and Ian Wood have filled the RAF F-117 slot.

323	Captain Michael W. Mahan	29 Nov 1989	
324	Captain Russell W. Travis	4 Jan 1990	
325	Captain Paul T. 'Psycho' Dolson	25 Jan 1990	
326	Major Mark W. Leeson	13 Feb 1990	
327	Captain Terrence J. 'Flo' Foley	14 Feb 1990	
328	Major Steven C. Edgar	15 Feb 1990	
329	Lieutenant Colonel Gregory T. Gonyea	20 Mar 1990	
330	Major Wesley T. Wyrick	20 Mar 1990	
331	Major Joseph R. Bouley	22 Mar 1990	
332	Captain Louis McDonald	25 Apr 1990	
333	Major Clare G. Whitescarver	25 Apr 1990	
334	Captain Steven E. Troyer	1 May 1990	
335	Captain Kevin A. Tarrant	1 May 1990	
336	Major Charles G. Treadway	29 May 1990	
337	Captain Raymond J. Lynott	30 May 1990	
338	Captain Darrell P. Zelko	30 May 1990	
339	Captain John W. Hesterman	21 Jun 1990	
340	Major John Steve 'Lefty' Farnham	21 Jun 1990	
341	Captain Lee J. Archambault	27 Jul 1990	
342	Captain Stephen W. 'Chappie' Chappel	26 Jul 1990	
343	Major Michael Christensen	26 Jul 1990	
344	Colonel Robert C. Huff	11 Sep 1990	
345	Lieutenant Colonel Bruce E. Kreidler	20 Sep 1990	
346	Major Donald P.J. Higgins	20 Sep 1990	
347	Captain John C. 'Pete' Peterson	20 Sep 1990	
348	Captain Matthew E. Byrd	16 Oct 1990	
349	Major Lee E. Huson	16 Oct 1990	
350	Captain Andrew W. Papp	10 Jan 1991	
351	Captain Greg L. Sembower	10 Jan 1991	
352	Captain Richard L. 'Rick' Wright Jr	11 Jan 1991	
353	Major Thomas D. 'TDY' Young	26 Feb 1991	
354	Squadron Leader Chris Topham (RAF)	27 Feb 1991	
355	Captain Skeeter Kohntopp	21 Mar 1991	
356	Captain Lee Conn	21 Mar 1991	
357	Captain Tony Seely	18 Apr 1991	
358	Captain Thomas P. 'Bulldog' Shoaf	18 Apr 1991	
359	Major Dave Brown	23 Apr 1991	
360	Captain Raymond A. Bivans	6 May 1991	
361	Major Douglas N. Campbell	7 May 1991	
362	Captain Tim Veeder	4 Jun 1991	
363	Captain Frank 'Vooter' Cavuoti	4 Jun 1991	
364	Captain Scooby 'Scob' Eiland	5 Jun 1991	
365	Captain Tony 'Lazer' Lazarski	5 Jun 1991	
366	Major Mike Daniels	9 Jul 1991	
367	Captain Scott S. Soto	9 Jul 1991	
368	Captain Mark A. Pope	9 Jul 1991	
369	Captain Mark S. Engeman	10 Jul 1991	
370	Colonel Raleigh T. 'Tom' Harrington	18 Jul 1991	
371	Major John D. Mackay	6 Aug 1991	
372	Captain John Massee	7 Aug 1991	
373	Captain Michael R. Kelley	7 Aug 1991	
374	Major James P. Joyce	28 Aug 1991	
375	Captain Dave M. 'Hendo' Henderson	28 Aug 1991	
376	Captain James M. 'Leekster' Leek	29 Aug 1991	
377	Captain Douglas E. 'Cout' Couture	2 Oct 1991	
378	Captain David M. Wooden	2 Oct 1991	
379	Major James R. Phillips	2 Oct 1991	
380	Major Thomas D. 'Tinker' Bell	14 Nov 1991	
381	Captain Barry D. 'Jekyl' Brannon	14 Nov 1991	
382	Captain Jeff W. Robinson	14 Nov 1991	
383	Major Richard A. Dunham	18 Dec 1991	
384	Major James P. Hunt	18 Dec 1991	
385	Captain Tony R. 'Dawg' Senna	19 Dec 1991	
386	Major David A. Adair	8 Jan 1992	
387	Captain Michael G. Hesley	5 Feb 1992	
388	Captain John P. Regan	5 Feb 1992	
389	Captain John S. Slaton	5 Feb 1992	
390	Captain Jonathan Bachman	18 Feb 1992	
391	Captain Michael J. Hilton	11 Mar 1992	
392	Captain Matthew P. McKeon	11 Mar 1992	
393	Captain John L. 'JMor' Moring	11 Mar 1992	
394	Captain John D. 'Dave' Silvia	12 Mar 1992	
395	Captain Jack G. Mayo	15 Apr 1992	
396	Captain George P. Biondi	15 Apr 1992	
397	Captain John G. Jerakis	15 Apr 1992	
398	Captain Zane F. Morris	16 Apr 1992	
399	Brigadier General Lloyd 'Fig' Newton	25 Apr 1992	
400	Lieutenant Colonel Robert K. Marple	20 May 1992	
401	Captain Charles E. 'Chuck' Osteen	20 May 1992	
402	Captain John B. Mills	20 May 1992	
403	Captain Robert 'Bobcat' Concannon	8 Jul 1992	
404	Captain Mark 'Drink' Drinkard	9 Jul 1992	
405	Captain Marcus 'Coop' Cooper	9 Jul 1992	
406	Captain Charlie 'Tuna' Hainline	10 Jul 1992	
407	Captain Richard J. 'Rich' Steckbeck	4 Nov 1992	
408	Captain Shayne H. 'Shotgun' Doering	4 Nov 1992	
409	Captain J. Hugh 'Huge' Burns	4 Nov 1992	
410	Captain Glenn C. Baugher	4 Nov 1992	
411	Captain Joseph M. 'Haiji' Skaja Jr	5 Nov 1992	
412	Captain Michael E. Newman	2 Dec 1992	
413	Captain John B. 'Snake' Pechiney	2 Dec 1992	
414	Captain Brian N. 'Rotor' Willett	2 Dec 1992	
415	Captain Kevin 'KC' Smith	2 Dec 1992	
416	Captain Gregory A. Eckfeld	9 Dec 1992	
417	Captain William Berg	7 Jan 1993	
418	Captain Michael Leclair	7 Jan 1993	
419	Captain Parrish Olmstead	7 Jan 1993	
420	Captain Dwayne 'Bags' Taylor	7 Jan 1993	
421	Captain David Bromwell	11 Jan 1993	
422	Captain Peter C. Hunt	7 Apr 1993	
423	Captain Lawrence G. Alicz	7 Apr 1993	
424	Captain Braden P. Delauder	7 Apr 1993	
425	Captain Damian J. McCarthy	21 May 1993	
426	Captain Jacob N. Shepherd	21 May 1993	
427	Captain Kevin L. Smith	21 May 1993	
428	Captain Michael W. Richey	17 Aug 1993	
429	Captain David Stischer	18 Aug 1993	
430	Captain William T. Davidson	18 Aug 1993	
431	Captain Russell C. Howard	18 Aug 1993	
432	Major Pitt M. Merryman	16 Nov 1993	
433	Captain Gregg Nesemeier III	16 Nov 1993	
434	Captain Christopher R. Williams	16 Nov 1993	
435	Major Dave Schemel	11 Jan 1994	
436	Squadron Leader Ian Wood (RAF)	11 Jan 1994	
437	Captain Bryan K. 'BK' Knight	11 Jan 1994	
438	Captain Philip A. Smith	12 Jan 1994	
439	Captain Kenneth J. Vantiger	15 Feb 1994	
440	Captain Joseph H. Kopacz	15 Feb 1994	
441	Captain Russell A. Vieira	15 Feb 1994	
442	Lieutenant Colonel William Crabbe	6 Apr 1994	
443	Captain John Ostromecky	6 Apr 1994	
444	Captain Rem Edwards	6 Apr 1994	
445	Thomas J. Palmer	14 Jun 1994	
446	Captain Francis M. Brown	14 Jun 1994	
447	Captain Todd J. Flesch	14 Jun 1994	
448	Captain James A. Marks Jr	15 Jun 1994	
449	Lieutenant Colonel Roy Y. Sikes	19 Jul 1994	
450	Captain Gregory P. Butler	19 Jul 1994	
451	Captain Hoyt D. Whetstone	19 Jul 1994	
452	Lieutenant Colonel Kurt A. Cichowski	23 Aug 1994	
453	Lieutenant Colonel Michael S. Roller	23 Aug 1994	
454	Major Gary R. Woltering	23 Aug 1994	
455	Major Daniel S. Gruber	24 Aug 1994	

This 410th Test Squadron aircraft is marked for Lt Col Steve Green, the commander of the Palmdale-based trials unit. In 1994 he became the first F-117 pilot to pass the 1,000-hour milestone on the type.

Saab JAS 39 Gripen

The JAS 39 programme has
been a Swedish *cause célèbre* –
one which holds the future of
the Swedish air force and the
nation's 'hi-tech' aerospace
industry in its hands. Often
threatened with cancellation,
now, after serious delays and
very public setbacks, the JAS 39
Gripen is on course to become
Sweden's prime combat aircraft
for the next century.

*Above: Gripens in their natural environment.
When the JAS enters service with F7, it will be
replacing the elderly AJ 37 'attack' Viggens. The
load-out on the aircraft nearest the camera is
optimised for an anti-shipping and air-to-ground
mission, with Sidewinders for self-defence.*

*Left: Saab's original JAS concept (the Saab 2110)
was of an even more slender, needle-nosed
design. The models illustrated the aircraft's
multi-role capability – one carries AAM armament
and the other has Rb 15 ASMs. It is interesting to
note that no centreline pylon is in evidence.
Regrettably, it seems no Gripen will ever wear the
Flygvapnet's splinter camouflage, although the
early models appeared in both air defence grey
and the splinter scheme.*

At the 1981 Paris Air Salon, Saab revealed
glimpses of a radical new combat aircraft
design, which it hoped would be
Sweden's new fighter for the 1990s. The previous
year the Swedish government had formally
launched the competition to find a successor to
the Viggen by establishing the JAS programme
(Jakt Attack Spaning – fighter attack, reconnaissance). Saab and several other major Swedish
defence companies joined forces as IG (Industri
Gruppen) JAS to develop a new multi-role
combat aircraft. The oldest AJ 37 Viggens were,
by then, approaching their 10th birthday, but
while the Viggen had been intended as a family
with mission-specific variants, the new aircraft
would be expected to undertake the entire range
of Viggen missions using a single common airframe.
While Saab had long been the sole supplier of
combat aircraft to the Swedish air force (Svenska
Flygvapnet), it was by no means assured that it
would be awarded the JAS contract, as the

General Dynamics (now Lockheed) F-16, the
McDonnell Douglas F/A-18 and the proposed
Northrop 'big-wing' F-5S were seen as likely
competitors. Indeed, the F-16 and F/A-18 were
both flown and evaluated by Swedish pilots.

In June 1981, IG JAS submitted its Saab 2105
proposal. The slender, single-engined aircraft
was of cropped canard configuration, with a surprisingly small fuselage pinched and tapered
behind the cockpit and engine intakes. It was a
radical departure from the B3LA that only a few
years previously Saab had hitherto expected to
be its next major project, and owed much to
developments initiated in the mid-1970s.

At the end of 1975, many of the Swedish air
force's front-line units were still operating the
J 35 Draken. The 'first generation' Viggens
(attack AJ 37 and reconnaissance SF/SH 37)
were appearing in increasing numbers, while
earlier that year Saab had received the formal
go-ahead for the more advanced (in terms of

radar and avionics) JA 37 'fighter' Viggens. The
Flygvapnet would need to replace its Saab 105
trainer/light attack aircraft, and it was also essential that a potential successor to the AJ 37 should
enter the planning stage as soon as possible.

Saab began work on preliminary studies of an
improved Viggen, the A20, and an all-new
attack aircraft, the B3LA ('B' signified a new
design, and 'LA' light attack). While intended as
a Saab 105 replacement, the boxy B3LA was a
sophisticated design with a supercritical wing.
Roughly equivalent in size to today's AMX, it
was designed around advanced avionics systems
and weapons systems, many of which were also
in their early stages. These included an Ericsson-
developed FLIR and a new D80 main computer,
along with IR-homing Saab B83 ASMs. It
would be required to operate from semi-prepared
air strips no longer than 3,000 ft (914 m) and
from remote dispersal sites in the same way as
the AJ 37, with the minimum of support. The

choice of powerplant fell between the Rolls-Royce RB199 and the General Electric F404. Work continued in earnest from 1976 until the B3LA's rapid cancellation in 1979. This was largely due to the incoming government's hostile attitude to combat aircraft development; however, the Supreme Commander of the Swedish armed forces then presented a convincing case for an entirely new aircraft, the JAS project, on the grounds that it would replace and not merely supplement the Viggen.

The Swedish proposal

The JAS Industry Group submitted a design for an unstable, single-seat, single-engined, fly-by-wire, delta-winged aircraft, with an all-moving canard – the Saab 2110. This was the final evolution of the original RB199-powered Saab 2105 and the comparable, but F404-powered, Saab 2108. On the way to this final proposal, Saab's design teams produced a total of three potential design configurations. The Saab 2102 was a conventional, single-engined swept-wing design with fixed lateral intakes, a mid-set wing and LERXes (leading-edge root extensions). It was roughly similar in size and appearance to the Saab 2105, though it lacked canards. The wing arrangement made the aircraft too bulky to be suitable. The more complex Saab 2107 was again single-engined but with the intake located above the fuselage in the style of North American's YF-107A or the Mikoyan 701. It featured a dramatically swept wing, a low-set tailplane and air-to-air missiles recessed under the fuselage.

For reasons of cost, simplicity and effectiveness, the now-familiar delta-canard layout of the Saab 2105 was adopted. Thirty per cent of its 8.8-ton (8-tonne) clean take-off weight was to be of composite materials, including the wing, wing boxes, foreplanes, fin and access hatches. All would be manufactured by Saab. The General Electric F404 turbofan, proven in the F/A-18 Hornet (but modified and uprated), was chosen as the powerplant.

IG JAS

The breakdown of workshare among the partners was settled with Saab gaining 65 per cent, Ericsson 16 per cent, Volvo-Flygmotor (which became Volvo-Aero in 1994) 15 per cent and FFV four per cent. At 1981 prices, the FMV predicted that the project would cost SeK 24,000 million (£2,250 million), of which SeK 4,000 million would be allocated to weapons, FLIR and reconnaissance equipment. This would comprise 23 per cent of the Swedish defence budget, but would repay that investment with running costs far lower than those of the Viggen. The significance of this project was not lost on the Swedish aerospace industry – without the project, the industry would perish. Saab was heavily committed to the military sector, having built over 4,000 fighters almost exclusively for the Swedish air force since 1937. Although diversification into civil markets had begun (chiefly through the SF 340 commuter airliner co-produced with Fairchild), its expertise lay

with combat aircraft. To further its case, IG JAS firmly undertook to build an aircraft that would be approximately half the size of the Viggen yet capable of carrying the same loads, with comparable or improved performance and at two thirds of the Viggen's cost. Furthermore, IG JAS had to accept a fixed-price contract for development and initial production while guaranteeing performance 'as advertised'. The Swedish government further raised the stakes by insisting that it could no longer support Saab through military purchases and that the company must achieve a 50/50 split between military and commercial aircraft within 10 years. Such harsh stipulations would see the Gripen become a double-edged sword for Saab.

Changing times

Development contracts between the FMV (Försvarets Materielverk – Sweden's Defence Material Agency, or procurement establishment) and IG JAS for the newly designated JAS 39 were signed on 30 June 1982, following the passing of a development authorisation bill by the then Centre-Liberal coalition government. The Social Democratic Party component of this government had long been opposed to the project and, indeed, to Sweden building any further 'advanced (combat) aircraft'. The public mood changed with repeated Soviet underwater special forces incursions around the Swedish coastline, particularly when a 'Whiskey'-class submarine very publicly ran aground at the Karlskrona naval base. While Sweden's neutrality continued to have complete cross-party and public support, opinions differed on just how this should be achieved and maintained. The JAS contracts

divided the SDP; many were mindful of the employment benefits the programme would provide, while the late Olaf Palme (leader of the SDP) stated that the project might soon become "an airborne version of the *General Belgrano*" – the Argentine cruiser sunk by a Royal Navy submarine during the Falklands conflict. Steps were made to postpone a decision until after the general election of 1982, which the incumbent government won. The Social Democrats then 'revised' their position to one of support for the Gripen, and in the event only the Communist Party and 10 SDP dissenters voted against the JAS bill.

The contracts signed (worth SeK 11.5 billion, then $1.87 billion) covered the development of five prototypes and an initial production run of only 30 aircraft. Options for an additional 110 were also undertaken. In September 1982, following a competition, the name Gripen (meaning Griffin (Gryphon) – a mythological winged creature with the torso of an eagle and the hindquarters of a lion) was selected.

The four IG JAS partners began to refine the earlier Saab 2110 design. The new aircraft had to fill the capable shoes of the Viggen with a much smaller, more versatile and more advanced airframe. The Gripen is claimed by Saab to be the first inherently unstable production canard fighter and features 35 computers interlinked via three MIL-STD-1553B databuses. A Viggen (the second prototype AJ 37, 37-52) refitted with a much simplified fly-by-wire control system to gain experience for the JAS 39, and dubbed the ESS JAS, first flew on 14 September 1982, at the hands of Tord Grims. The Gripen's inherent instability is the key to its agility and

small size. Its designers set aside conventional aerodynamic considerations by building an aircraft that is inherently unstable in pitch. It can only be flown by an advanced electronic flight control (fly-by-wire) system. Smaller servo-actuated control surfaces controlled by the computer must move consistently faster than a human could manage. The smaller wing (and airframe) that this permits reduces further costs.

Gripen takes shape

Sweden's unique operational demands play a major part in its basic layout. The Gripen's canard configuration allows it to exceed the payload and performance targets set by the Flygvapnet. The high-lift delta wing is further augmented by the addition of canards. The Gripen has a simple cropped-delta wing, with 45° of leading-edge sweep. Its canard foreplanes are swept at 43°. The dog-toothed wing is augmented by two leading-edge flaps linked with the four drooping elevons through a full-authority triplex digital FBW system. In flight, the active leading-edge flaps further reduce the Gripen's turning circle by increasing lift – deploying only when the aircraft is manoeuvring hard or at low speed. The trailing-edge flaps of the Gripen perform the opposite function to those on an inherently stable aircraft: instead of lowering the nose, the flaps raise the Gripen's nose (particularly when it is manoeuvring at low speed), increasing the tendency to pitch nose-up and improving agility.

The success of the Gripen depends on it being a complete, credible replacement for the entire Viggen family. While Saab was responsible for the most obvious part of the project – the airframe – the Gripen, like any modern combat aircraft, is nothing more than an expensive taxi without the systems that enable its pilot to fly and fight. As the single-seat JAS 39 is intended to be truly multi-role, enormous effort was expended by the other JAS partners in providing

Right: The first JAS 39 Gripen, 39-1, was unveiled at a ceremony at Saab's Linköping home, south of Stockholm. Despite all efforts the aircraft was still unfinished, and only its starboard side was revealed to the assembled crowd.

Right: The first JAS 39 Gripen, 39-1, was unveiled at a ceremony at Saab's Linköping home, south of Stockholm. Despite all efforts the aircraft was still unfinished, and only its starboard side was revealed to the assembled crowd.

the latest and best technology to provide the best possible performance, reduce pilot workload and make the Gripen a turning point in multi-role fighter design.

The key to the Gripen's performance is its powerplant. Volvo Aero shares assembly and testing of the F404 engine, designated RM12, with its original American manufacturer, General Electric. The RM12 had a projected dry rating of 12,150 lb (54.05 kN), or 17,800 lb (79.18 kN) with a new Volvo/GE afterburner, to give the Saab 2110 all-altitude supersonic performance even with fixed rectangular intakes. The RM12 (F404-400) is a two-shaft augmented low-bypass ratio turbofan, with a three-stage fan and a seven-stage compressor, both incorporating variable stators and driven by single-stage turbines. The afterburner, which boasts a fuel-activated, variable-area nozzle, is fully modulating from minimum to maximum augmentation. The engine can be 'slammed' from idle to full afterburner in three seconds. Sixty per cent of engine components are supplied by GE to Volvo at its Trollhättan plant, but Swedish design input has been such that many RM12 changes are featured in the newest F404-402 engines.

Advanced radar

Ericsson was tasked with developing a new multi-mode, pulse-Doppler, X-band radar. The resulting PS-05 (PS-05/A in its definitive form) has triple the processing capacity of the existing PS-46/A radar fitted to the JA 37, but only 60 per cent of the volume. Ferranti (now GEC-Ferranti) had some initial input, using technology developed for its Blue Vixen radar of the BAe Sea Harrier F/A.Mk 2. The UK company still builds the antenna pedestal. In return, Ericsson provided and continues to supply the Blue Vixen's exciter, waveform generator, signal and data processors and their associated software routines. GEC's current involvement with the EFA 2000's ECR 90 radar is viewed with wry interest by some in Sweden. The PS-05/A's lightweight planar array is a small, conventional, mechanically-driven unit, which utilises FM

pulse-compression for long-range detection. Its low sidelobe design offers increased radar efficiency, while minimising the effects of both ground clutter and hostile ECM. The radar utilises high-, medium- and low-pulse repetition frequencies (PRFs) to fulfil its multi-mission specification. Air-to-ground missions, navigation and terrain avoidance demand a low PRF, which offers track-while-scan capability, sea search and high-resolution ground mapping. In MTI (Moving Target Indicator) mode, the PS-05 has demonstrated its ability to pick up targets as small as cars. For the Gripen's prime air-to-air role, medium and high PRFs offer improved long-range target acquisition, multi-target track-while-scan and search capability. The radar and Gripen fire control system will ultimately integrate both missile and gun armament. At the moment, similar but less advanced systems in the JA 37 allow the pilot to fly a 'hands-off' forward hemisphere gun attack on certain airborne targets. With a target selected, the Viggen radar in effect 'flies' the aircraft to set up the correct firing solution, then tracks the cannon shells in the air for fire-correction. Ericsson claims the Gripen will further improve on this ability for faster, more manoeuvrable targets, using also a helmet-mounted sight under development by FFV.

Two PS-05 prototypes were built – one to be tested on a laboratory rig, the other in a converted AJ 37. MTBF (Mean Time Between Failure) for the PS-05 is set at 170 flying hours. The radar feeds an Ericsson-designed and -built 32-bit SDS-80 main computer system which has its roots in that intended for the B3LA. While the Viggen's central computer has an information processing capability of 2-3 million operations per second (MOPS), the Gripen will be capable of some 6-7 MOPS. Five D-80 onboard computers are carried to make up SDS-80: one as the main systems computer; one as a radar signal and data processor; two for the cockpit displays; and one dedicated to ECM. Ericsson chose a version of Pascal (Pascal/D 80) as its programming language, not a 'cutting edge' one but a known quantity which would not spring unnecessary surprises on the developers. The latest version, D 80E, is far more compatible with ADA, the USAF's (and increasingly an industry) standard programming language. The new PS-05/A radar was

The Gripen in its final form differed in several ways from the first airframe mock-up, which was shown in 1986. Most noticeable was the larger tail (enlarged to house the electrical rudder-actuating servos), which for the first time featured an Ericsson radar warning receiver.

tested over the course of almost 250 flights in a modified Viggen (37-51), until January 1992.

The HOTAS cockpit has three 5- x 6-in (2.7- x 15.2-cm) Ericsson EP-17 multi-function cockpit displays and a Hughes-developed wide-angle (28° by 22°) holographic HUD. Ericsson first flew such a diffractive optics HUD as early as 1977 in its own Sk 37 testbed. Diffractive optics remove the need for a collimating lens, as in other HUDs. Collimation, or long-range focusing, is done completely in the combiner unit beneath the HUD screen itself. Using a holographic mirror, which is a different shape to the glass in the HUD, and a special gel on the HUD combiner, 3-D imagery can be shown. The 'key-hole' effect of standard HUDs, where the pilot has to move his head around to see all the information on display, is done away with. All

imagery is focused directly in the pilot's line of sight, but the Gripen pilot can 'look around' it (while still looking forward), if necessary. The HUD optically compensates for the curvature of the aircraft's canopy, while its extremely bright symbology is produced by a narrow wavelength of green light from a stroke CRT.

It was planned to integrate an Ericsson FLIR with the radar and avionics, but issues of cost soon saw it deleted, with the option of adding such a (podded) system in the future. The radio panel and warning displays are located beside the main displays, on the side consoles, to the left and right of the cockpit, respectively. The raster-scanned monochrome (green) cockpit displays (which can fulfil each other's functions in the event of failure) dominate the main panel. Display symbology is driven by a display processor (DP) – one of the Gripen's main Ericsson D 80 computers – integrated with the avionics through three doubly-redundant MIL-STD-1553B databuses. This system processes all sensor information and converts radar scans into images, while maintaining the digital map memory.

Display technology

The three displays are all full-raster screens, which means they build up a picture in lines, pixel-by-pixel, like a normal TV screen but at a higher resolution. In fact, each of the three screens is a multi-sync display that can change resolution for differing functions. TV images from the Rb 75 seeker head (for example) are shown at 525 lines (per inch), standard displays at 675 lines and high-resolution images from the (planned) IRLS or FLIR at 875 lines – all at a frequency of 30 Hz. The DP is divided into two units, one driving the FDD and HSD, the other the MSD and HUD.

From Batch 2 aircraft, Ericsson hopes to offer full-colour cockpit displays, based on active-

matrix LCDs. LCDs are lighter, cheaper, brighter and clearer than CRTs; indeed, their contrast increases with higher ambient light. In this research they are working closely with Lockheed-Sanders, which is developing similar systems for the F-22 and F-16 MLU. Such displays are at the cutting edge of cockpit technology and still pose a technical challenge. The most difficult problem to overcome is how to produce an effective display that remains visible under all lighting conditions from all directions. Sources at the Mikoyan design bureau claim to have a system with high-contrast colour LCDs fully-developed and ready for use in the MiG-29M. Ericsson is more reserved in its claims, and pilot experience so far indicates that colour displays may be an unnecessary luxury and even a distraction, particularly in combat if the pilot is 'greying out'.

To input his own information, such as target selection for the Rb 75 or a change of way-point, the pilot can use a cursor that can be moved right across all three screens. This is another feature shared by the MiG-29M. The cursor is controlled by an X-Y switch on the throttle. The functions of each display can also be controlled by an array of 10 buttons along the sides, while brightness and contrast are automatically adjusted according to ambient light levels by two photo-sensitive cells on each MFD unit and one near the HUD.

Keeping the pilot informed

Standard flight instrumentation is presented on the left-hand screen, the flight data display (FDD). Four conventional analog instruments are fitted as back-ups. The central screen, or horizontal situation display (HSD), presents a computer-generated map of Sweden, with five variable scales, which can show man-made features such as built-up areas (with names and landmarks) and even power lines, to aid navigation and low flying – these features disappearing as the aircraft gains height once more. Ericsson pioneered the development of digital maps and less-sophisticated systems have been operational in the Viggen for over 15 years. A 3-D map is planned for the HUD, providing the pilot with perspective views of the oncoming terrain.

The HUD displays and the computer-generated attitude indicators on the FDD have been designed (thanks to Saab input) with impressive attention to detail. For example, in a loop the attitude indicators which appear as straight lines on conventional displays are curved, bending out as the aircraft nears the vertical and returning to straight lines (like the horizon outside) as the aircraft becomes level again. The artificial horizon on the FDD performs in a similar fashion, as it is covered in curved arrows which clearly illustrate the Gripen's flight attitude. The third cockpit screen, the multi-sensor display (MSD), is devoted to target information from the aircraft's radar (and FLIR) in synthetic symbolic form. Information from all the pilot's displays can be recorded on a standard (analog) video cassette to aid immediate pilot debriefing. Ericsson is working with the French firm Schlumberger to develop a similar digital system to provide instant access to reconnaissance data. The chief problem is how to compress the required data over the course of a mission without losing information or degrading playback quality. As part of the Gripen's training and mission debriefing system, all aircraft will carry a TV camera mounted ahead of the HUD, and film from this can be combined with HUD imagery back on the ground to provide a detailed record of the flight.

Involvement from abroad

Although the Gripen is an unmistakably Swedish aircraft, several foreign manufacturers are involved, chiefly to reduce costs. Apart from the engine and the composite wings of the first three prototypes (the latter supplied by BAe), the major non-Swedish components include the JAS 39's Microturbo APU and Intertechnique fuel system. The landing gear is the responsibility of UK-based A. P. Precision Hydraulics. A Martin-Baker S10LS rocket-powered, zero-zero ejection seat replaces the Saab systems used in all previous Flygvapnet combat jets. Also in the cockpit, the INS is provided by Honeywell and the fly-by-wire control system itself was developed by Lear Siegler. Hymatic Engineering, in the UK, provides the environmental control system and Dowty contributes elements of the hydraulic system. The one-piece windscreen and port-hinged canopy are built by Lucas Aerospace. Finally, the aircraft's 27-mm cannon is a product of Germany's Mauser-Werke.

In April 1983, a newly-elected Riksdag (Swedish parliament) gave the go-ahead for production of 30 Series 1 JAS aircraft as an affordable answer to the Flygvapnet's need for a third-generation combat aircraft. New facilities were built by Saab at Linköping to cope with the demand. The projected requirement was for 350 Gripens, with a service entry by 1992, rather than 1990 as originally hoped, equipping between 21 and 23 squadrons.

Engine tests began in 1984, and five test rigs had accumulated over 800 running hours by June 1985. A full-size mock-up was completed

Gripen 39-1 lands at Linköping after an early test flight. Saab shares the airfield's single runway with a civilian airport and, particularly in recent years, the Gripen has had to further share this space with Saab 340 and Saab 2000 test flights.

by early 1986, differing from the initial drawings by being a more stocky and box-like design, while retaining its small size. The Gripen is still surprisingly slender, resulting in low drag at high subsonic and supersonic regimes. The earlier, narrow fin seen on models and provisional drawings was replaced by a thicker, broader-chord fin, more akin to that of the Viggen. The original design was too small to accommodate the necessary rudder hydraulics or servos, and the new fin also gained an RWR. Saab went to great lengths in testing its unbuilt aircraft by constructing a fully-functional fuel system in a total-freedom, all-moving rig and another rig with a FBW system 'flying' its hydraulic control surfaces under commands from the simulator cockpit. The hydraulic system is a significant contributor to Saab's quest to find ways to reduce the Gripen's overall weight – using a higher than normal hydraulic pressure and smaller pipes, and carrying less fluid.

Two static airframes (39-51 and -52) were built for fatigue testing at Linköping. The first 'entered service' in 1991 to undertake a programme of some 16,000 hours until 1998. Eighty-four hydraulic jacks, including one inside the wing, simulate 56 different missions 'flown' by a computer, which subjects the airframe to all the stresses and strains of a lo-lo-lo attack mission or a high-level intercept, from

In less than two months, 39-1 undertook six test flights – on the last of these the aircraft crashed on landing and the pilot (Lars Rådeström) was lucky to escape. 39-1 was equipped with few production avionics systems and a standard 'metal' cockpit, but its loss was still a profound blow.

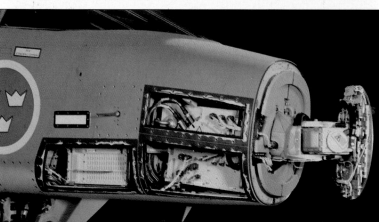

Left: The standard cockpit with its EP-17 MFDs first appeared in Gripen 39-4. The X/Y input switch for the pilot's displays is visible above the throttle grip, although the stick has been redesigned since this picture was taken.

Right: FFV Aerotech has designed a new g-suit for the JAS 39 pilot. Each fully-fitted suit is tailored for individual pilots and can be quickly tested for integrity with a compressor. More complicated than traditional 'bladder' suits, it enables pilots to function better at loads of up to 9 g.

Left: Ericsson treats the PS-05/A radar with secrecy, and many details of its design are still classified.

Below: The Gripen boasts Martin-Baker S10LS ejection seats – the world's first lightweight rocket-powered seat.

take-off to landing. After 1,000 hours the Gripens are inspected, and thus far have been cleared to 240 per cent of the official requirement, which includes a completely inspection-free service life of 3,000 hours. Two forward fuselage sections were completed and used for ejection seat trials on rocket sled, birdstrike and lightning resistance testing. Birdstrike protection is taken very seriously by the Flygvapnet, and all its operational flying areas have been mapped by ornithologists to record known concentrations and migration routes. At operational units, a daily 'bird forecast' is provided during pre-flight briefings.

Work continued at a steady pace throughout 1986. Out of the limelight, the project was troubled by rising costs, which threatened its future. Saab was troubled by the Gripen's rising weight, which it struggled to reduce. Volvo Flygmotor delivered the first uprated (Growth II) 18,100-lb (80.5-kN) RM12 engine to Saab in March 1987. By that time, the RM12 had logged 3,000 hours of ground-running including crashworthiness and birdstrike tests (which saw the fan blades strengthened). In September, the Viggen PS-05/A radar testbed made its maiden flight.

Flygvapnet and Bas 90

The Swedish air force pressed on with its plans for Gripen operations. The Bas 90 (Base 90) plan was unveiled in 1987 as an extension of Sweden's well established practice of operating combat aircraft from isolated road-strips. Bas 90 covered the provision of 24 air bases during the 1990s, with four additional 'V90' runways. Resembling ordinary roads, these 800- x 17-m (2625- x 55-ft) lengths of reinforced concrete and asphalt were linked to the central main runway and aircraft stands by a network of small taxiways and access roads for servicing vehicles. Hides for aircraft are provided in the surrounding trees, and in time of war small numbers of aircraft (four to six) would be dispersed to each location and concealed while under the protection of dedicated ground forces. In such circumstances each dispersed location would be the responsibility of a base battalion. Headquartered at the wing's main base, these battalions number some 800 during peacetime and increase to 2,000 when mobilised.

Individual aircraft are serviced and rearmed by a six-man team of one officer and five conscripts, the latter nevertheless well trained and intimately familiar with their given tasks. The Swedish air force relies on its 'Hunter' units – heavily armed six-man teams – to secure the base perimeter. Each team also works with a dog and includes a combat medic, resulting in a cohesive and effective fighting unit. Thus protected from 'interference', aircraft can be rearmed and refuelled (with a 10-minute turnaround time) away from the vulnerable air bases that most air forces are tied to, while all the time remaining under the command of Sweden's integrated air defence system.

The first aircraft was rolled out at Linköping on 26 April 1987, Saab's 50th anniversary. At the ceremony, Saab would allow only one side (starboard) of the Gripen to be seen – the aircraft was unfinished and had a much simplified cockpit. Five prototypes were to be built and the first was predicted to fly in late November/early December that year. An unexpected delay of over one year was then imposed by problems with the FBW control system's software package, which posed yet another challenge to

the still mooted 1992 in-service date. The FBW system was by now the responsibility of GEC Astronics, a newly-founded division of Britain's GEC Avionics which had acquired the original developer, Lear Siegler Astronics, although work continued in the United States.

Gripen in the air

It was not until 9 December 1988 that Gripen 39-1 first flew (for a total of 51 minutes) in the hands of Stig Holmström, who had already spent over 1,000 hours in the JAS 39 simulator. The aircraft survived a critical funding review in January of the following year, when the threat of an off-the-shelf purchase, instead of the Gripen, finally subsided. The flight envelope was quickly expanded as the prototype reached 36,000 ft (11000 m) and a maximum speed of Mach 1.2. A major set-back was suffered on the sixth flight when a failure of the flight control system caused the aircraft to veer off the runway and cartwheel while landing at Linköping, on 2 February 1989. Fortunately, the pilot, Lars Rådeström, was unhurt but for a broken arm. Detailed analyses by both Saab and the government's Accident Investigation Board traced the cause to pilot-induced oscillation caused by flaws in the pitch control routine of the FBW

control software. The official statement read "the accident was caused by the aircraft experiencing increasing pitch oscillations (divergent dynamic instability) in the final stage of landing, the oscillations becoming uncontrollable. This was because movement of the control stick in the pitch axis exceeded the values predicted when designing the flight control system, whereby the safety margins were exceeded at the critical frequency." In other words, the computers failed to control the aircraft's pitch at low speed, either because they overcompensated for air data sensor input or failed to keep up with the amount of information being input and became over-saturated.

The Gripen is inherently unstable, particularly at low speeds. While this makes it an admirable dogfighter, test pilot Stig Holmström was already on record as saying he felt the control system was 'too sensitive' after previous flights. The crash highlighted a serious handling problem in conditions of moderate near-ground turbulence in an aircraft specifically designed to operate in bad weather and high crosswinds. Saab immediately doubled its FCS development team to 60.

Major software corrections were undertaken in the United States by Calspan, with a modified Lockheed NT-33A (using Swedish and

Saab JAS 39A Gripen

1 Pitot head
2 Vortex generator
3 Radome
4 Radar scanner
5 Scanner tracking mechanism
6 Radar mounting bulkhead
7 Flush aerial
8 Ericsson PS-05/A multimode pulse-Doppler radar
9 Front pressure bulkhead
10 Yaw vane
11 Incidence vane
12 Cannon muzzle blast trough
13 Electro-luminescent formation lighting strip
14 Rudder pedals
15 Control column, triplex digital fly-by-wire control system
16 Triple CRT cockpit displays
17 Instrument panel shroud
18 Frameless windscreen panel
19 Hughes wide-angle HUD
20 Canopy cover, hinged to port
21 Martin-Baker S10LS zero-zero ejection seat
22 Canopy electric actuator
23 Cockpit rear pressure bulkhead

33 Avionics equipment compartment, access through nosewheel bay
34 Cockpit rear avionics equipment shelf
35 Starboard canard foreplane
36 Strobe light
37 Air conditioning equipment bay
38 Heat exchanger exhaust duct
39 Canard foreplane hydraulic actuator
40 Foreplane pivot mounting
41 Single 27-mm Mauser BK27 cannon
42 Port navigation light
43 Ground equipment test panel
44 Formation lighting strips
45 Canard foreplane composite construction
46 Cannon ammunition magazine
47 Upper communications aerial

51 Dorsal fairing cable and pipe ducting
52 TACAN aerial
53 Starboard wing integral fuel tank
54 Pylon mounting rib
55 Starboard two-segment leading-edge flap
56 Wingtip missile installation
57 Outboard elevon
58 Inboard elevon
59 IFF aerial
60 Engine bleed air spill duct
61 Formation lighting strips
62 Engine compressor intake
63 Secondary power system equipment bay
64 Inboard elevon hydraulic actuator
65 Microturbo APU
66 Volvo Aero RM12 afterburning engine

71 Radar warning antenna
72 ECM equipment fairing
73 Fintip VHF aerial
74 Tail navigation light
75 Carbon-fibre composite rudder
76 Rudder hydraulic actuator
77 Afterburner duct
78 Nozzle actuator
79 Variable area afterburner nozzle
80 Port airbrake panel
81 Airbrake hydraulic jack
82 Port inboard elevon

85 Port outboard elevon
86 Wingtip missile rail
87 Rb 24 Sidewinder (AIM-9J) air-to-air missile (Rb 74/AIM-9L on service aircraft)
88 AEW antennas, fore and aft
89 Port two-segment leading-edge flap
90 Rb 71 (BAe) Sky Flash air-to-air missile (AIM-120 AMRAAM on service aircraft)

95 Leading-edge flap powered hinge
96 Port wing integral fuel tank
97 Wing rib construction
98 Inboard pylon mounting rib
99 Mainwheel leg strut
100 Hydraulic retraction jack
101 Wingroot attachment fittings
102 Mainwheel leg breaker strut

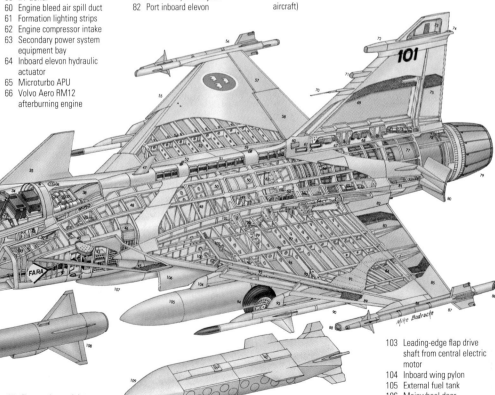

24 Engine throttle lever
25 Lower UHF aerial
26 Nosewheel leg door with taxiing light
27 Twin nosewheels, aft retracting
28 Hydraulic steering controls
29 Cannon muzzle
30 Boundary layer splitter plate
31 Fixed-geometry air intake
32 Boundary layer duct heat-exchanger air intake

48 Fuselage integral fuel tankage
49 Hydraulic reservoir and equipment bay
50 Wing panel attachment machined fuselage main frame

67 Fin attachment joints
68 Automatic flight control system equipment
69 Carbon-fibre composite fin construction
70 Artificial feel system pressure sensor

83 Elevon carbon-fibre composite construction
84 Outboard elevon hydraulic actuator in ventral fairing

91 Wing panel carbon-fibre skin
92 Outboard pylon mounting rib
93 Outer wing pylon
94 Port mainwheel

103 Leading-edge flap drive shaft from central electric motor
104 Inboard wing pylon
105 External fuel tank
106 Mainwheel door
107 Fuselage centreline external fuel tank
108 Saab Rbs 15S air-to-surface anti-ship missile
109 MBB DWS 39 sub-munitions dispenser

Above: Linköping's main runway was painted to resemble one of the Swedish air force's 'road' strips, as used at BAS 90 air bases. These special 800-m x 17-m (2625-ft x 55-ft) lengths of motorway and their associated road-side dispersals are a surprisingly common sight when travelling around Sweden.

Below: A major part of the JAS 39 'flight' trials involved establishing operating (landing and take-off) procedures for these much restricted runways. Of crucial importance to future operations is the aircraft's ability to come to a halt in time, without the benefit of a thrust reverser as found in the Saab Viggen.

American pilots) in a programme of 78 flights (74.6 hours). Over 350 landings were made to simulate the conditions experienced during the crash and to further explore the FCS performance. The front cockpit was fitted with a Gripen control stick and two pilots were always carried, both as a safety measure and to ease the workload. Errors in the original FBW system – dubbed version 3.13 – were identified and corrected, resulting in the 'final' version 5.4. However, the whole process caused another 15 months' delay

before the second prototype flew on 4 May 1990, putting the programme some three years behind the original (much revised) schedule. Arne Lindholm, who piloted Gripen 39-2 on its maiden flight, stated that the aircraft felt stable and that the FCS was much smoother than the first aircraft, which he had flown twice. This flight was unfortunately cut short by the failure of the cooling system for the FCS electronics and the aircraft returned to Linköping after only 14 minutes. Lindholm was assigned all the flying

in 39-2 following understandable criticism that the ill-fated 39-1's six flights had been spread between three different pilots.

Edition 7 FCS software was then under development, progressing to 7.3 and then 7.6, finally utilising the leading-edge slats. The standard for production aircraft was expected to be Edition 9. Like the prototype, Gripen 39-2 again carried a minimum avionics fit but was also fitted throughout with strain gauges. By mid-September 1990, 14 flights had been made, as opposed to the predicted year's end total of over 100, and service deliveries were reluctantly set back to 1993 rather than 1992.

Getting back to speed

After two investigations the FMV underscored its commitment to the JAS 39, and ultimately the government compensated Saab for the prototype's loss. Studies progressed for a projected two-seat JAS 39B aircraft originally begun in July 1989, the single-seat programme continued, and on 20 December 1990 the fourth aircraft, 39-4, became the third to fly. This aircraft was the first JAS 39 to carry the production avionics fit, but had no radar. Gripen No. 3, 39-3, made its maiden flight on 25 March 1991 with full standard avionics, display and radar, having been delayed by engine tests. It was followed by 39-5 on 23 October 1991. By then, 39-2 had been fitted with a modified FCS for further envelope expansion (high-*g* and high-speed testing), while 39-3 became the weapons testbed.

By now, much was made of the Gripen's export potential (the proposed JAS 39X), which some industry sources hoped could equal, if not exceed, Swedish acquisitions. Despite (or perhaps because of) the severe export restrictions then placed on Swedish military products, Austria, Denmark, Finland, Norway and Switzerland were seen as the potential customers.

Flight tests soon revealed that drag, in clean configuration, was 10 per cent lower than expected. By late 1990 it was revealed that all was not well with the initial RM12 installations. The engine suffered slow-thrust build-up (thrust droop) caused by differential expansion of the high-pressure turbine casing and single-stage

Although each wheel of its Goodyear landing gear is fitted with carbon brakes and anti-skid ABS systems, the Gripen relies on its canards, in free-flow, for aerodynamic braking once on the ground.

air-cooled turbine. These problems had previously been identified by Volvo-Flygmotor and were expected to be rectified in production aircraft. The afterburner lining also proved to be lacking in durability, and several solutions from heat-resistant ceramics to drilling holes in the casing were proposed – the second option was eventually chosen. None of these problems affected flight tests, however, unlike continued compressor blade cracking caused by resonance at certain points in the thrust range. The blades had to redesigned. Part of the problems stemmed from the increased thrust requirements demanded of the RM12 compared to the original F404. The Swedish engine has had its turbine inlet temperature increased to 105°F (41°C) and fan airflow increased by 10 per cent. It is a heavier engine than the F404 (due in part to 'beefing up' the fan and inlet against bird strikes), but still boasts an impressive specific fuel consumption of 0.84 lb/h/lb (23.9 mg/Ns) dry and 1.7 lb/h/lb (50.67 mg/Ns) with afterburner.

Star performer

Despite everything, airfield performance was soon found to be above specification and Gripens have repeatedly demonstrated their ability to operate from a standard Bas 90 runway. With a 10-kt (11.5-mph; 18.4-km/h) headwind and an AoA of 12°, the aircraft can come to a halt within 1,476 ft (450 m). In freeflow, the canards are the primary brakes, deployed from a landing speed of 136 mph (220 km/h). Rotated through 90°, they generate enormous drag and force the nosewheel onto the ground. The Gripen is also fitted with lightweight carbon brakes on all three undercarriage units and two rear-fuselage lateral airbrakes. The Viggen relies heavily on its thrust reverser to operate effectively from the small road strips, even smaller taxiways and forest dispersal sights. The Gripen's lack of such a system is partly offset by its small size, but operational experience may force some revisions of its V90 operations.

In October 1991, Saab submitted its costing proposal for the JAS 39B operational trainer and the follow-on Batch 2 order for 110 single-seat aircraft. That same month, the FMV issued its second report on the JAS 39. In the aircraft's

For over seven months in 1990, 39-2 was the sole Gripen in the air. With all flying in the second Gripen allotted to Arne Lindholm alone, 39-2 soon became involved in early stores carriage and separation testing.

favour was its lower-than-calculated drag, the solving of many RM12 hitches, the continued good performance of the FCS and the much acclaimed cockpit displays. Other milestones included flight testing to 9 *g* and the first missile firing (an Rb 74), while radar development work continued. However, problems were encountered with the APU, fuel system and the environmental control systems. The Microturbo APU had a TBO of mere hours and was failing with monotonous regularity. Ultimately, a replacement APU (from Lucas Aerospace) was mooted to replace the current units. By January 1992 the flight test programme had reached 300 flights and the FMV reconfirmed its belief that the JAS 39 would meet all its technical goals.

Export drive

From 31 March 1992 Saab was reorganised into distinct Military Aircraft, (Civil) Aircraft and Service Partner divisions. Thus, Gripen development, manufacture and marketing became the responsibility of Saab Military Aircraft, which remained the aircraft division's chief development department. Its immediate marketing efforts were directed towards Finland, and its 'DX' competition to replace elderly Saab Drakens and MiG-21s. Potential candidates for the 67-aircraft (finally 64) order were the Mirage 2000-5, F-16, F/A-18, MiG-29 and JAS 39 Gripen. As early as October 1990, Saab

After a major delay the second Gripen flew, albeit for a brief 14 minutes, on 4 May 1990 in the hands of Arne Lindholm, Saab's chief military test pilot. The Gripen was by then fitted with a much revised version of the original FCS – Version 5.4 – but it proved to be still far from perfect.

had submitted a proposal to supply 25 aircraft (including five JAS 39Bs) with an option for a further 20, for delivery in 1996. The Ilmavoimat (Finnish air force) undertook detailed flight tests of all the aircraft involved and, as a result, Finnish pilots became involved with an aircraft that had hitherto been a closely-guarded Swedish preserve. Over 250 Gripen sorties were undertaken by two Finnish test pilots (with a loaned aircraft) before the F/A-18A was selected in May 1992, with 57 aircraft to be assembled locally by Valmet as part of a substantial offset deal Saab could not match.

Another potential Gripen customer, Switzerland, was also lost to the F/A-18 in a 34-aircraft order that forced a national referendum. Interest from Hungary came in the form of a visit to Saab by a delegation in mid-1992; however, in October 1993, the cash-starved Hungarian air force began to take delivery of 28 MiG-29s by way of debt repayment from the former Soviet Union, ending hopes of any JAS 39 order. In each case, the air forces had specified that they would prefer a twin-engined design with effective air-to-ground capability.

Right: Observed by a centreline camera pod 39-2 lets fly a Sidewinder. The Flygvapnet chose the Rb 74 Sidewinder (AIM-9L) in favour of the indigenous Saab 372 (Rb 72), cancelled in 1978. Sweden also possesses older Sidewinder versions, the AIM-9B and AIM-9J, both known under the Rb 24 designation. Surprisingly, the more expensive RB 74s were used for test firings.

39-2 was equipped with a minimal avionics fit, but the airframe was fully strain-gauged. As a result it was involved in most of the early JAS 39 weapons trials. In this photograph the aircraft is seen with a load of three 135-mm Bofors M70 rocket pods and a pair of high-speed cameras to record the rocket firings.

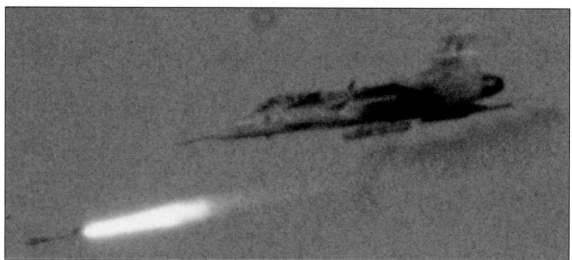

June 1992 saw the final go-ahead for the Flygvapnet's 96 Batch 2 JAS 39As and 14 JAS 39Bs (excluding one prototype) plus spares, for an adjusted cost of SeK 60.2 billion. Production was scheduled to begin in 1996 and to continue through to 2002. From that budget, 28 per cent of the funds were devoted to airframe development, 36 per cent to production, 15 per cent to weapons and 23 per cent to other associated costs such as the training systems. An integral part of the training programme is the two-seat JAS 39B, which finally gained formal approval. Tasked primarily with conversion and tactical training, the JAS 39B operational trainer will have a performance equivalent to that of the single-seater but, because its centre of gravity has been moved forward relative to the JAS 39A, the two-seat Gripen will be less manoeuvrable. Structurally, there is a 40 per cent change from the JAS 39A, including a 25.8-in (65.5-cm) forward fuselage stretch. Five thousand new elements have been incorporated, the gun has been deleted and fuel capacity has been slightly reduced. The rear cockpit is identical to the front, barring a HUD, but HUD imagery can be monitored on the head-down displays.

Meanwhile, 566 JAS 39A flights had been notched up by 31 August 1992, including further weapons tests at the Vidsel test range, in northern Sweden. The first production Gripen 39-101 was undergoing ground running tests prior to delivery, while 39-102 had left final assembly. In November 1992, an offer of Gripen licence-production was made to the Italian government as an alternative to the far more expensive EFA programme. Between 100 and 200 JAS 39s were covered in the prospective deal, but Italy held to its EFA commitment and has recently decided to lease surplus RAF Tornado ADVs as an interim measure. At the same time, Saab proposed the establishment of a dedicated foreign sales agency to support the expanding Swedish defence industry in its search for new markets abroad. The four Gripen prototypes were finally joined by 39-101 on 4 March 1993, when it made its 44-minute maiden flight (and the Gripen's 594th), piloted by Reino Lidvik. Equipped with a limited telemetry system, 39-101 filled the gap left in the test programme since the loss of the first prototype in 1989.

A second setback

A milestone in the test programme was reached on 21 April 1993, when the 1,000th test flight took place. 39-102 became the first Gripen to be handed over to the Flygvapnet at Linköping on 8 June 1993, being delivered to F7 at Såtenäs later the same day. By the end of June, 1,122 test flights had been completed, aircraft 39-103 to -108 were in final assembly, and

39-109 to -122 were on the line. On 18 August, 39-102 was lost in a dramatic crash during an air display over Stockholm, with the pilot (Lars Rådeström again) ejecting dramatically but safely. On exiting a roll, the pilot lost control of the aircraft – within 6.2 seconds the Gripen had stalled at a dangerously low altitude and Rådeström was left with no option but to abandon the aircraft. Saab later announced that the accident was caused by "the flight control system's high amplification of stick commands in combination with large, rapid stick movements by the pilot. This led to the stability margin being exceeded, and the aircraft entered a stall." A contributing factor was the late display of the STYRSÄK (maximum elevon deflection) warning that the FCS was becoming saturated, giving the pilot too little time to react. Flying was suspended until 29 December 1993, after the fitting of further updated flight control software. It was later revealed that a similar situation had occurred in the Gripen simulator but was deemed to be outside the aircraft's anticipated envelope.

FCS fault finding

The first Gripen crash was blamed on the control system responding too slowly to stick commands, and the system was redesigned as a result. The second crash was attributed to the aircraft being oversensitive to stick movements. Rådeström was applying rapid, maximum stick force in several directions in an attempt to regain control of his aircraft. This rapid motion caused signal feedback in the FCS which interfered with the pitch limitation system. Testing of Edition 9.11 of the FCS had revealed a condition dubbed 'superstall', whereby repeated large stick movements would forfeit control of the aircraft. Alarmingly, this condition was considered to be outside the operational envelope – if it did occur the aircraft's systems would alert the pilot in time, it was believed – and so was not incorporated in the flight manuals. Simulations revealed that such a situation would be quickly remedied by the FCS, if the pilot released the stick and let the aircraft stabilise itself, although this was hardly an ideal solution. Instead, the FCS was again revised and changes have been made to the design of the stick, which has been enlarged and reshaped.

All test aircraft are now flying with Edition 10.2 of the FCS software, which continues to impose restrictions on the flight envelope. Edition 11, for series aircraft, is the next step and is still a challenge. Simulator tests began in late 1994 for a period of five to six months and, once validated, Edition 11 will be retrofitted to all aircraft. Two inflight system failures – including a main computer crash – have underlined the efficacy of the Gripen's back-up systems. The three-channel digital FCS has a three-channel analog back-up, which kicks in if two of the digital channels malfunction. The back-up system, which can also be activated by the pilot, disables the canards (locking them in neutral position) and makes the Gripen neutrally stable.

By mid-1994, after over 1,400 flights, the remaining Gripens had completed 65 per cent of the total flight test programme, verifying 95 per cent of their contractual obligations. Weapons tests have included Rb 74 (AIM-9L) firings at 6 g, Rb 75 (AGM-65) firings at 3 g and successful separations from DWS 39, Rbs 15F, cannon pods and external tanks. Arming the Gripen has become one of the more involved issues in recent years. Basic armament for all roles includes an integral 27-mm Mauser BK27 cannon recessed under the port centre fuselage and two wingtip-mounted Rb 74 or other IR-homing AAMs, supplemented by four underwing and two ventral pylons for external stores. Original plans had called for the installation of the 30-mm Oerlikon KCA cannon, as fitted to the JA 37. This weapon was replaced by the current gun on the grounds that it was too large and heavy and would produce unacceptable airframe vibration. The electrically-driven BK27 was originally developed for the Panavia Tornado, weighs 220 lb (100 kg) including the barrel, and fires at 1,000 or 1,700 rpm.

'Attack' Gripen

When the Gripen enters service it will initially replace AJ 37 'attack' Viggens. The JAS 39 will be the first operational aircraft to carry the DWS 39, a development of Deutsche Aerospace's (DASA) DWS 24 stand-off submunitions dispenser. The FMV had invested approximately SeK 700 million ($113 million) in co-development with MBB (now DASA) by

Gripens 39-4 and 39-5 flew out of sequence – on 20 December 1990 and 23 October 1991, respectively, with 39-3 taking to the air on 25 March 1991. With the arrival of 39-5, the full range of tests could be carried out in earnest, as this was the first aircraft fitted with the PS-05/A radar.

the time a launch order was placed in October 1991. Seventy per cent of final production will be undertaken in Sweden and FFV Aerotech, at Malmen, is already assembling and machining components. The DWS 39 is unpowered, unlike the planned DWS 24, gliding after launch to its target up to 6 miles (9.6 km) away at a height of 150 ft (45 m). DWS 39 weighs 1,450 lb (657 kg) and measures 11.5 ft x 2 ft (3.5 m x 0.6 m). It relies on GPS navigation with a radar altimeter and four tail-mounted control fins to find its (pre-programmed) target. Travelling at a speed of Mach 0.4, DWS 39 needs only 50 seconds to cover a 6-mile (9.6-km) range and the glide weapon is designed to be accurate to within 30 ft (9.1m). Launch height is not imperative – recent USAF tests (for F-16 qualification of the weapon as the AFDS/Autonomous Free-flight Dispenser System) have seen it travel over 6,000 ft (1828 m) downrange, having been released from only 600 ft (182.8 m) at an offset angle of 26.5°. Release at high altitude and high subsonic speed (up to Mach 0.95) would provide DWS 39 with a formidable radius of action, perhaps up to 12 miles (19.5 km). Once over the target the weapon can lay a pattern of bomblets covering a swathe 3,000 ft x 1,000 ft (914 m x 304 m).

Typical sub-munition loads could include 24 runway denial bomblets, 96 cluster munitions, 120 anti-tank mines, 504 SB44 bomblets or 1,848 M42 GP bomblets. 'Smart' sub-munitions such as the SADARM or German SMART anti-tank weapons are another future option. Sweden acquired the TV-guided AGM-65A/B Maverick, as the Rb 75, and these have since been modified to improve image resolution against typically 'dark' northern European scenery. While published sources quote the 'short-range' Rb 75 as having a reach of 1.8 miles (3 km), experienced Swedish sources claim an effective range against a small (tank-sized) target of at least twice that. In a less advanced vein, standard Swedish M50- and M60-series

80- to 600-kg (175- to 1320-lb) HE/fragmentation bombs and Bofors M70 13.5-cm rocket pods are also available.

Sea strike

In the anti-shipping role, the Gripen's primary weapon is the Saab Rbs 15F medium-range ASM. Following on from the Rb 04 and 05, the Rbs (Robot – missile) 15F is the air-launched version of a weapon which originally equipped Swedish navy fast patrol boats. A Microturbo TRI-60-3 turbofan extends the ASM's maximum range to an impressive 55 miles (90 km) with a 440-lb (200-kg) armour-piercing HE warhead. The 14-ft 2-in (4.35-m) missile, with its 4.5-ft (1.4-m) wingspan, uses INS for mid-course guidance, switching to an active radar seeker for the terminal phase. It became operational with the Flygvapnet in 1989. In April 1994, Saab Missiles was awarded a contract to upgrade all the Swedish navy's Rbs 15s to Mk III standard, making them more ECCM resistant with an improved target seeker and central computer, while increasing the weapon's range. Such improvements will ultimately be incorporated on the air-launched version. Rbs 15F may well form the basis for Sweden's proposed ASOM (Autonomous Stand-Off Missile) for use against hardened targets (with a much heavier penetrator warhead) and a much improved imaging infra-red/terrain comparison guidance system. Saab is currently discussing co-operative development with other European and US manufacturers.

A joint programme may also provide the ultimate solution to one of the Gripen's more vexed armament problems, namely the provision of a new BVR missile. At present, Flygvapnet JA 37s rely on the BAe Dynamics Sky Flash (Rb 71 in Swedish parlance). With more medium-range missiles entering service with active terminal homing, and with 'fire-and-forget' capability fast becoming a reality, Sky Flash's 1970s-vintage semi-active seeker is becoming increasingly anachronistic and could expose the Gripen to a shot from a better-equipped adversary before it reaches the effective range of its own missiles. Despite several improvement programmes instigated since it entered Swedish service in 1978, it became obvious that Rb 71 would be a less than satisfactory long-term option for the Gripen. As a result, the Rb2000 requirement was issued by the FMV for a new BVR missile with an IOC in the year 2000. BAe proposed the Sky Flash 90 (Active Sky Flash) or Rb 71A, and later a ramjet-powered Rb 73 for the JAS 39. Thomson-CSF agreed to provide the missile seeker and Deutsche Aerospace contributed a new fragmentation warhead. Active Sky Flash has now fallen into abeyance, as all involved parties examine other options. FMV funding for the project ended in 1987.

Saab and British Aerospace have ties going back many years that have recently been elevated to a more formal basis. Work on Active Sky Flash led the two to a completely new,

advanced BVR AAM. This is the S225X ('S' for stealth and 'X' for experimental), which was unveiled in model form at the 1992 Farnborough show. In addition to British (BAe Defence Dynamics Division and GEC-Marconi Dynamics) and Swedish firms, Alenia and Thomson-CSF are involved, with the possibility of a tie-up with MATRA in the future. Formal work began between BAe and Saab in June 1992 on a weapon with Sky Flash-style mid-section fins and with four moving control fins replacing the older fixed tail. Current models show a slender missile with conventional rear control fins and without any mid-fuselage fins. Saab sources believe any production missile would be further refined with a new tail and more advanced aerodynamic controls. The missile will have a stealthy (low power output) active radar seeker, digital datalink and either rocket or ramjet propulsion. Effective range could be up to 62 miles (100 km), with a projected in-service date of 2002. S225X is intended as an option for the JAS 39, Eurofighter EFA 2000 and, indeed, any customer denied the US AIM-120 AMRAAM. The ramjet-equipped S225XR would further improve the missile's stand-off range and flight performance. This version has been primarily driven by the UK

In 1990, long before its first flight, a largely unpainted 39-5 undertook test firings of its Bk 27 cannon at Linköping. As seen here, the aircraft has not yet been fitted with its radar nose and carries a very interesting prototyope Ericsson FLIR pod on the shoulder pylon – perhaps for vibration testing in association with the gun. The blue tubing provides additional avionics air-cooling and the wingtip Sidewinder is of note.

MoD's SR(A) 1239 requirement for a future medium-range AAM. With a go-ahead received, Saab anticipates that the S225X and S225XR could be ready in five to eight years, respectively.

In the United States, Hughes is conscious of the pressing need for foreign AMRAAM sales

The delivery of the first Gripen to the Flygvapnet (39-102) was a major milestone, and Saab celebrated the event in grand style. 39-101 displayed for the assembled crowd before taking part in a unique flypast of four generations of indigenous Swedish fighters. The aircraft involved (Gripen, Viggen, Draken and Lansen) were an effective statement on Saab's history and its future.

After the ceremony marking its formal handover, 39-102 flew straight to F7 at Såtenás, escorted by a pair of AJ 37s. 39-101 had been on static display at Linköping the same day, before joining the four-ship flypast. Included with the weapons loadout displayed around it were examples of the Sky Flash and MATRA MICA. The MICA had been seen by many as a leading candidate for the Gripen's new BVR missile, but now seems to have been totally excluded from future plans.

to keep USAF acquisition costs down, and is working hard to integrate the AIM-120 into Sweden's plans for the Gripen. In August 1994, the FMV announced a buy of 100 AIM-120 AMRAAMs to serve as an interim BVR missile for the JAS 39 force, and letters of offer and acceptance were signed with the US government on 1 September. Form and fit tests with the Gripen and AMRAAM were actually undertaken in 1990 and prior to that (in the mid-1980s) contacts between the US government and Ericsson ensured that the PS-05 radar would be fully compatible with the new US weapon (as it is with the MATRA MICA).

Both Raytheon and Hughes build the AIM-120 for the US DoD, so-called 'lead-follower production'. This situation arose because the original US service requirement alone was for 24,000 AMRAAMs and two suppliers in competition would reduce costs. Production, currently standing at 100 per month, is split roughly 50/50 between the two, although Hughes has full design and technical leadership of the project. AIM-120s will be released to Sweden as an assisted direct commercial sale from the USAF, beginning in January 1998. This is the first such

sale, which circumvents the restrictions placed on normal FMS supply channels whereby an 'R&D surcharge' is placed on foreign customers, thus raising the price. In the case of AMRAAM this is worth some $114,000, or 25 per cent of the missile's unit cost. Flygvapnet AMRAAMs will be drawn from Lot 10 production (Lot 8 deliveries are currently underway) and will be complete by December 1998. Swedish defence sources have stated that these missiles will be 'second-grade, NATO-standard AMRAAMs, not up to the full USAF specification'. Hughes disagrees, saying that they will be full-standard AIM-120Bs drawn from the USAF inventory, although they do admit that certain highly-sensitive items of software will be removed. All FMS AIM-120s differ from their US counterparts in that they have the capability to be ground-launched, as in the Norwegian NASAMS system. Saab Missiles will be involved in developing the Gripen AMRAAM datalink.

The AMRAAM option

The AMRAAM purchase, much smaller than the 500 expected, was made in favour of the MATRA MICA or BAe Active Sky Flash. Ericsson has already developed a MICA datalink, and will not be involved in similar work to integrate the AMRAAM. While the likelihood of an AMRAAM buy had been privately acknowledged for some time, there is a feeling in some quarters that the AIM-120 purchase may be something of a dead-end as it cuts the Gripen off from (at least) one European missile partner which it may need to develop a more advanced long-range weapon, such as the S225X, in the future. Hughes sources disagree strongly. They point out that AMRAAM development has cost some $3.8 billion over 14 years, with much US government support. The missile has been tested exhaustively under intense jamming and countermeasures situations (not to mention combat), in association with the USAF and USN, that no other manufacturer can hope to rival.

Work on a ramjet-powered AMRAAM began 14 years ago and Hughes has invested $80 million in research so far, along with Atlantic Research Corporation and Hercules. Furthermore, within six months Hughes expects to sign a new international MoU with European partners in three or four nations. The way would then be open to build a next-generation AIM-120,

Production line

Gripens are assembled in five stages on the Linköping factory floor. At Station 1, the front fuselage is fitted with the bulk of the 15,000 smaller components that go into each aircraft. This includes both foreign- and Swedish-sourced parts, while the fuselage assemblies themselves are built at an ancillary Saab plant near Linköping. By the end of this process the Gripen is 50 per cent complete. At Station 2 the fin and 2,000 remaining components are added before the largely complete aircraft moves to Station 3 for electrical testing. Hydraulic tests are undertaken at Station 4. The RM12 engines, delivered in large reusable canisters from Volvo Aero, at Trollhättan, are finally installed at Station 5. RM8 installation for the Viggen took two days, but the Gripen requires only three to four hours before it can be rolled into the paint shop.

Fly-by-wire system

The JAS 39 relies on a series of electrical servos connected to the canards, leading edges, flaps, rudder and airbrakes to move these control surfaces. This replaces conventional mechanical linkages controlled directly by the pilot's stick and rudder pedals.

Air-to-air missile armament

The Gripen has a maximum of four underwing pylons for AAMs, plus the wingtip rails. Its primary BVR armament, upon entering service, will be the Hughes AIM-120B AMRAAM and, depending on what launchers are chosen, a potential load of eight could be carried. The wingtip rails are dedicated to the Rb 74 Sidewinder. This version, equivalent to the AIM-9L, can be differentiated from the earlier Rb 24 (AIM-9B/J) by its pointed, double-delta control vanes. In 1991 pilot Arne Lindholm encountered disquieting in-flight vibrations and, on landing, discovered that fins had broken off a dummy Sidewinder. As a result test flights were undertaken using 'finless missiles'.

Air-to-surface armament

This aircraft carries a typical loadout for operational Gripens, consisting of two Rb 75 Mavericks on the outer pylons and a pair of larger Rbs 15F anti-ship missiles. Rbs 15F is descended from Saab Missiles' earlier Rb 04 ASM, with a new cruciform tail replacing the former wings and endplate fins. The new weapon's chief advantage lies in its air-breathing Microturbo TRI-60-3 turbofan which provides a formidable stand-off range of some 90 km (56 miles). Rb 04 relied on a simple solid rocket motor. Launched from high altitude, Rbs 15F descends to sea-skimming height to use its radar altimeter. For the terminal attack phase, the missile switches from INS guidance to its own active radar seeker.

Saab JAS 39A Gripen

39-102 was the first JAS 39A to be delivered to the Flygvapnet. Two months later the aircraft was lost in a dramatic crash over Stockholm harbour during a display for the city's annual water festival – a victim of 'superstall'. Miraculously, it fell on a small island, missing the substantial crowds that had gathered to watch. The pilot, Lars Rådeström, ejected and his parachute was entangled by trees, leaving him dangling over the water. He is now the chief test pilot for the Saab 2000.

Other weapons

The Gripen's prime weapon against ground targets will be the MBB-designed DWS 39 sub-munitions dispenser. The Gripen can also call on the Flygvapnet's array of M50- and M60-series HE bombs or Bofors M70 six-round rocket pods.

Electronic warfare suite

Self-protection of the Gripen is one of the least discussed elements of the entire JAS programme. Quite how the stated aim of enabling the Gripen to operate effectively in a hostile ECM environment (while defending itself from enemy aircraft) will be achieved is not yet clear. Ericsson is prime contractor for the aircraft's EW fit. The system under development is believed to be dubbed Erijammer 300. This is a somewhat misleading name, as it refers to an integrated system rather than just an individual pod. The Gripen will rely on at least one ECM pod (mounted to starboard on its shoulder pylon) for full protection allied with onboard systems and underwing countermeasures dispensers.

Colour schemes and markings

Gripens delivered to the Flygvapnet thus far all wear a two-tone air defence grey scheme, similar to that applied to JA 37s. The lack of toned-down national markings is less surprising, bearing in mind Sweden's continuing neutral status. The wing number (in this case F7) is carried on the nose, while a two-digit tactical code – derived from the last two numbers of the aircraft's serial (39102) – is applied in Dayglo self-adhesive numbers.

Undercarriage

The Gripen's undercarriage legs are a product of A. P. Precision Hydraulics. The nose gear retracts rearward and, like all the other wheels, is fitted with carbon brakes.

perhaps with a ramjet, that would offer a new warhead with a much increased 'no-escape' zone and longer range. Hughes would be willing to offer development of the 'back end' (motor and fuselage fins) for this S225X/XR rival to European firms (with the UK predominant), while investing in improving the 'front end' (computer and seeker systems) itself.

In Swedish terms, this could involve Volvo-Aero as engine builders and perhaps Ericsson in software development, along with Saab Missiles. Such an improved AMRAAM for the US, independent of any other programme, is under consideration for the year 2000. A European deal would speed this up by four to five years, while both sides would obtain a better weapon for less money. Needless to say, Hughes feels that any UK involvement would absolutely preclude parallel development of the rival S225X. With S225X still firmly a paper project, Hughes feels that it is holding all the cards and will be the world's chief supplier of advanced long-range AAMs for the foreseeable future.

AIM-120 and AJS 37

Future Swedish AIM-120 buys are seen as purely a matter of time, not least because the Flygvapnet plans to integrate the missile with the JA 37. The attack Viggen fleet is already

undergoing the AJS 37 upgrade, which makes the AJ 37 compatible with new JAS 39 weapons systems. This will make the type the perfect 'lead-in trainer' for the first Gripen pilots, who will all be drawn from the AJ 37 community. At some stage the Gripen will replace the JA 37 force and, in typical Swedish fashion, it makes sense to pave the way for that transition also.

The Gripen is designed to operate in a highly active, electronic-resistant environment and thus to be jam-resistant and ECCM-capable. Active systems have been designed by Ericsson, although little is publicly known of them. Ericsson has much experience in providing podded EW and ECM systems to the Flygvapnet and its latest product, the A100 Erijammer, has won orders from Switzerland and Canada. The Gripen's system will be Ericsson's first integrated EW suite and the manufacturer is tight-lipped about the specific capabilities of its system. The overriding factor is cost, and Ericsson plans to deliver aircraft with a level of equipment that in its view may not be complete but which can be upgraded as funds allow. An onboard threat library assembled from Sweden's own 'national technical means' and outside sources will be accessed by the aircraft's RWR. Threat information is displayed via the cockpit MFDs and countermeasures are automatically selected.

Above: Sweden has given much thought to defence from attack by sea. It has a well-equipped 'white-water' navy and a series of coastal gun and missile emplacements. In time of war the Gripen would be tasked with anti-shipping missions, while other aircraft would establish air superiority over any beachhead.

Right: The Gripen is still subject to handling restrictions, and at the time of writing an angle-of-attack limit of only 20° was in force. The addition of new filters in the FCS should see this situation improve later in 1995.

The Gripen will be fitted with integral chaff/flare dispensers in its four underwing weapon pylons and missile rails. The choice of such countermeasures was thus dictated, to a degree, by the choice of BVR missile. With AIM-120 selected, Swedish sources say the choice of launcher still lies between the US- and UK-developed systems. US sources say the Gripen will be equipped with a US-built launcher, such as the LAU-127 family. Already the Celsius Tech BOP/B six-round flare dispenser has been acquired and fitted to the outboard pylons of at least one Gripen, so only a decision on a chaff dispenser (undoubtedly another Celsius Tech system such as the BOL) seems to remain.

Gripen flying was briefly suspended between 14 January and 15 February 1994, after Volvo

identified blade failure in an RM12 low-pressure fan caused by defective fuel injectors and leading to uneven fuel flow and vibration. This was cured after the problem was traced to a blockage in three of the fuel nozzles. With deliveries resumed, 20 engines have so far been handed over. Ten complete aircraft were planned to be delivered to the Flygvapnet by the end of 1994 (although, by September, only 39-104 to -107 had been handed over). All of these aircraft remain unflown, at Linköping, where the first maintenance teams from F7 are being trained on the type. Thirty mechanics are temporarily based there and the first ground crews have now been qualified. By 23 August 1994, 1,428 flights (over 1,100 hours) had been undertaken by the Gripen fleet, with Saab aiming for full flight clearance after 2,200 flights.

Contractor changes

Much development work is still being done and several major changes are in prospect for the Gripen. After a decision taken in 1993, development of the FCS for Batch 2 aircraft has now been transferred to Martin-Marietta (now Lockheed-Martin) which, in addition, is working on the Saab 2000 airliner. Saab still remains the author of the FCS software. Responsibility for the HUD has also changed hands, with production now being undertaken by Kaiser Electronics in California. The first HUD was handed over in June, and Ericsson reports that the transfer of equipment and processes has gone smoothly. When the first aircraft was delivered to the air force in 1993 it was not spin qualified, and this will remain the case until 1995. In late 1994, the Gripen was still limited to an angle of attack of only 20° while development of new non-linear filters to reduce phase lag (delays in response to control input which result in PIO) was underway, again scheduled for completion in 1995.

Saab is experiencing delays in the Gripen's built-in test equipment which is currently taking two minutes to perform a complete systems diagnostic instead of the five seconds planned for series aircraft. Live firing vibration tests remain to be completed, although EMP testing with a 25-mW transmitter and reflector system has been finished at Linköping. In addition, all aircraft systems have been temperature tested down to -4°F (-20°C). By the end of 1994, 19 pilots had flown seven aircraft. This includes seven Saab, four FMV and two Flygvapnet pilots who are all currently active. Three other Saab and a single FMV pilot are no longer involved in flight tests, along with the two Finnish evaluators.

JAS 39C and Batch 3

Saab is still working hard to sell the Gripen abroad, in a marked reversal of former policy. At Farnborough in 1992, Swedish Defence Minister Anders Bjoerck revealed SAF plans for a so-called upgraded 'Turbo Gripen', or JAS 39C, for a third Swedish production batch. This would have an uprated RM12 turbofan, Ericsson D80E computers and more weapons, for both potential export and for further Flygvapnet deliveries to replace the last of some 350 Viggens. The JAS 39C has now become closely aligned with the export JAS 39X. Questions have been raised over US restrictions on Gripen exports. The RM12 engine is essen-

tially a US product but Volvo stated that it fully expects US approval to 'market' the Gripen in the near future. What this means in practical terms is not completely clear, but the Swedish perspective is that '40 per cent of a sale is worth more than 100 per cent of no sale', as General Electric would receive 'royalties' from any Gripen export.

In any case, Volvo Aero and Saab are seriously considering a complete change of powerplant for Batch 3 Gripens. The current choices lie between the SNECMA M88-3 (Rafale), Eurojet EJ200 (Eurofighter 2000), General Electric F414 (F/A-18E/F) and an 'RM12 plus' with an enhanced turbine and new afterburner. Taking any engine intended for a twin-engined design, as all the above are, and integrating it into the Gripen is not seen as a major undertaking, chiefly requiring inlet/intake changes to increase the airflow. Volvo has already completed Phase 1 studies, which include full engineering blueprints. Phase 2 studies (for lifecycle costs and integration detail) are due to start in mid-1995, with a final decision on a new engine expected in 1997 – at the same time as an official go-ahead for Batch 3 Gripens. Such deliberations may be a serious proposal to improve the Gripen, or a means of persuading the US to

Below: The release of this picture in 1994 gave the first public clues of the final ECM fit for the JAS 39A. An Ericsson-designed jamming pod can clearly be seen under the starboard intake. While it bears a passing resemblance to other podded Ericsson products, such as the Erijammer A100, it is an obviously more complex item. The dummy pod (carried along with dummy weapons) is similar to early designs for the Erijammer 300, which were reportedly shelved some time ago.

Above: The Gripen has a straightforward wing design, with a composite wing box. Its leading-edge flaps are powered by Lucas Aerospace 'geared hinge' actuators and deploy only at low speed or when manoeuvring.

Right: The Gripen has a clean take-off weight of only 8800 kg (18,740 lb), resulting in a thrust-to-weight ratio of one. MTOW increases to about 12500 kg (27,560) with a full stores load.

agree to a more favourable RM12 export arrangement. It may also be the case that a re-engined JAS 39 will be driven by exports rather than domestic purchases. In any case, Volvo remains committed to further powerplant development, even including the possibility of a supercruise RM12.

Gripen exports are also increasingly wedded to its AMRAAM capability. In the weeks before the Swedish missile buy was agreed, US authorisation for a Gripen/AIM-120 export to any AIM-120-approved customer was sought and obtained, and also has full backing from Hughes. This 'approved' list currently stands at 17 nations and is only added to when a formal application for AMRAAM is made. Much rumoured but never mentioned potential Gripen customers include Brazil and Chile. The prime candidate as far as Saab is concerned is Austria, which has frequently underlined its AMRAAM requirement. The Austrian air force currently operates two squadrons of J 35Ö Drakens, armed with Swedish-built AIM-9P-3 Sidewinders. Saab is a favoured contender to replace these aircraft and, given Austria's strong commitment to the EU in the recent referendum, a non-European purchase seems very unlikely. The Liberal Party, the largest opposition group,

Above: The two-seat JAS 39B trainer is progressing towards an October 1995 roll-out date and is projected to be in service by 1998. At 14.8 m (48 ft 6¾ in), it is 70 cm (27½ in) longer than the JAS 39A.

Below: The selection of the AIM-120 for the Gripen answered some questions about the type's future, but raised more. Strangely, Gripens have had 'AMRAAM'-labelled suspension points on their underwing pylons since 1991, at least.

By late 1994 all the Gripens delivered to the Flygvapnet since 39-102 remained unflown at Linköping while crews of mechanics were trained on them. At the same time, a specially set up air force team, TU 39, was developing operational procedure, at the nearby air base of Malmen.

is strongly pro-NATO and WEU, while the government remains outwardly opposed to military alliances. It is not unthinkable that this policy may change following the October 1994 elections, in which the SDP/People's Party coalition was returned, but with a much reduced majority. All concerned realise that a decision for a new fighter must be made within 12 months, and the Gripen seems a front-runner.

With a planned production rate of 20 aircraft a year from 1996, Saab could delay Flygvapnet deliveries to meet the needs of another customer. The first Gripen took 604 days to complete; today, this time has been cut to 200 days (only 1,460 factory personnel are employed at Linköping). It often has been reported that Saab and British Aerospace will strike a marketing agreement to offer the Gripen to customers who need more than a Hawk 200 but less then Eurofighter 2000, or who need an interim EFA or a low-cost complement. What is certain is that once the Gripen is firmly in service with the Flygvapnet, export chances will increase accordingly.

Gearing up for operations

By late 1994, 10 Gripens were in final assembly, with another 10 (including some Batch 2 aircraft) on the line. Saab expects to deliver 140 aircraft between 1993 and 2002. These will replace eight squadrons of AJ 37 Viggens, but there will then be a need to replace the younger JA 37s in the air defence role. The two remaining squadrons of J 35J Drakens will have been long disbanded by then. Go-ahead for 140 Batch 3 aircraft, in whatever final form they take, is anticipated by Saab in 1996. The first Swedish squadron (F7's 2 divisionen, 'Gustaf Blau') will begin conversion by October 1995. F7 Skaraborgs Flygflottilj, as the Flygvapnet's 'attack OCU', will be the centre of the Gripen world for years to come. Pilots are already flying the AJS 37, which will provide a pool of aircrew for the JAS 39. Ground training facilities are also taking shape. An elaborate new three-story, three-winged training centre is due for completion by October 1995. Hangarage for eight aircraft is also under construction. The eventual unit complement will be 15-20 Gripens, with a similar number of pilots, per squadron. New pilots will progress from text book studies to a PC-based system to the multi-mission trainer. This fixed-position trainer replicates the Gripen cockpit, with a screen arrangement providing 180° views for the 'pilot'. The ultimate domed, all-moving, full-mission simulator will be in operation by 1999. This system will provide realistic flight and combat simulation with a tactical environment system capable of generating 400 objects (images) around the pilot. F7 expects to have an effective training system up and running by October 1995, and to be fully operational by April 1996. The ultimate training system is the two-seat Gripen itself.

The prototype JAS 39B (39-800) was largely complete at Linköping by September 1994, with 39-801 and a fatigue test airframe (39-71) taking shape. 39-800 entered final assembly on 31 August 1994. Its schedule after that includes a roll-out in October 1995, first flight in 1996 and delivery in 1998 after a 200-hour test programme. Ejection seat sled tests commenced in the US in July 1993 and are now progressing with Martin-Baker in Northern Ireland.

Already Saab has a modification programme in hand to recall the initial 30 Batch 1 aircraft and update their software to Batch 2 standard. These will feature a PP12 processor for the EP17 MFDs, replacing the current EP1 and EP2 units which are twice the size and weight. The next landmarks for the JAS 39A will be the addition of the TARAS tactical radio system, approval of a reconnaissance system and upgrades to the EW suite. The third element of the Gripen mission, reconnaissance, will be commissioned in 1995. Then, Ericsson expects an FMV requirement to be issued for a podded system. Once the official requirement has been finalised, the Swedish electronics firm can apply some or all of the systems it has under development. It expects the most likely option to be for an infra-red linescan (for which it will integrate a Honeywell IRLS), with additional electro-optical sensors such as a FLIR. Ericsson had undertaken substantial development of its own FLIR designs. A reconnaissance pod would be carried on the Gripen's starboard 'shoulder' pylon. In years to come Ericsson expects to further develop the PS-05/A into an electronically scanned, fully phased-array unit. Radical advances are also heralded for the Gripen's FCS. While Saab says little attention is being paid to

Future plans for the Gripen may include a complete re-engining for export JAS 39Xs and for the final Swedish Batch 3 purchase (for 140 aircraft) keenly anticipated by Saab.

any thrust-vectoring developments, the potential for an even more manoeuvrable Gripen lies in uncoupling the canards to move independently of each other.

By 1996/97 the first Gripen squadron will finally be operational and will provide the key to the type's future success. The Gripen has already weathered the storm of two unfortunate and public accidents, which have focused attention on the aircraft's only major weakness, and one which has already largely been solved. A successful service introduction will, however, be essential if the programme is to survive unscathed and uncut, and if the aircraft is to find any export customers.

The Gripen equation

Swedish requirements dictated from the outset that the Gripen would be single-engined with a small, densely packed airframe. Combat experience has always highlighted the vulnerability of and attrition suffered by single-engined aircraft, while small size has become progressively less important than true versatility and multi-mission capability. Prospective customers have to juggle financial benefits with operational realities. While the Gripen is deservedly compared with the next generation of combat aircraft – Eurofighter, Rafale and even F-22 – it will face stiff competition from the F/A-18 and from comprehensively upgraded and structurally refurbished surplus F-16s, as well as from the latest Russian superfighters. Several of the customers that Saab once viewed as the most likely prospective purchasers for the Gripen have bought other types, and only Austria remains. The aircraft will continue to appeal to those nations denied US or European equipment or unwilling to risk relying on a fickle US or a notoriously unreliable Russia for continuing spares support.

Above all, the Gripen is a victim of history, appearing just at the wrong time. When it was designed, no-one could have guessed that the world situation would change so much. In the Cold War of the mid-1980s, the Gripen looked set to steer a sure-fire course between the superpowers, selling to air forces who had no other choices. That situation disappeared almost overnight, leaving the Gripen to compete in a world awash with advanced fighters, where everything is for sale. The Gripen is, however, so well tuned to Swedish national needs that in Flygvapnet service it seems likely to have a long and auspicious career, the latest in an extensive line of distinctively Swedish fighters. Although the Gripen is late and over budget, and although problems do still exist with the revolutionary FCS at the heart of the aircraft and it will initially operate with some restrictions, the Gripen remains a magnificent achievement. It is, above all, a truly modern multi-role fighter, an ambitious project for a superpower or a major grouping of advanced nations, let alone for a single, sparsely peopled nation on the periphery of Europe.

Further development of the Gripen's FCS is now in the hands of Martin-Marietta (Lockheed-Martin) and 1995 should see the resolution of most of the Gripen's lingering performance headaches. Over the next 15 years Saab anticipates a growing market for aircraft such as the JAS 39, and the company firmly believes that it will be the one collecting the orders.

Red Stars

Had the Cold War ever turned hot, five Soviet armies would have rolled across the East German border and smashed their way across the North German Plain, supported by heliborne assaults by organic Army Aviation forces. In the air, mass formations of bombers and fighters would have poured through sanitised 'corridors' punched through NATO air defences by specialised defence suppression aircraft, to cause maximum damage to NATO's vulnerable rear areas. The Warsaw Pact air armies would have included Czech, Polish and East German aircraft, and even Soviet aircraft brought forward from bases in Poland and in Russia itself, but at the heart of the aerial armada would have been the 16th Air Army. This force, permanently stationed in East Germany, included 20 regiments of fast-jet fighters, fighter-bombers and reconnaissance aircraft, and was a flexible, highly-capable tactical air force in its own right, manned by Russia's best pilots, and equipped with the very latest aircraft and weapons.

For the entire period of the Cold War, the USSR maintained massive forces in East Germany. If the Cold War had turned hot, these forces would have been the spearhead of the Warsaw Pact's advance. They were therefore equipped with the latest equipment and manned by Russia's finest soldiers and airmen. Many Russians who served with the so-called Western Group of Forces (also known as the Group of Soviet Forces in Germany) would be offended by such a summary, preferring to see themselves as the defenders of socialism and the Motherland against a potentially aggressive West, and as worthy successors to those who had courageously resisted Hitler in what Russians still refer to as the 'Great Patriotic War'.

Although the Western Group of Forces consisted of no less than five powerful armies, perhaps its greatest strength was in the air. The 16th Air Army represented a tactical air force of tremendous capability, consisting as it did of some of Russia's most historic air force units, equipped with the latest and best aircraft types. These were flown by the very best pilots, trained to a higher standard than almost any other element of the Soviet armed forces, and maintained at constant readiness, with frequent realistic exercises to maintain the edge. If the 16th Air Army's true purpose was

Wings swept fully forward, an Su-24MR 'Fencer-E' from the 11th ORAP at Welzow thunders over the Baltic during a training sortie. Although Su-24 bombers were withdrawn from the 16th Air Army in 1989, the type remained in Germany in the reconnaissance role, and East German airfields would have acted as forward operating bases for Su-24 bombers from Poland, the Ukraine and Russia.

over Germany

Red Stars over Germany

Photographs taken in East Germany before reunification are extremely rare. This is the very first photo of the Su-24 'Fencer-Cs' based at Grossenhain to be published. The 7th Bombardirovchnyi Aviatsionnaya Polk (Bomber Aviation Regiment, abbreviated to BAP) fulfilled the nuclear strike role until withdrawn to Stary Konstantinov in the Ukraine during 1989, for political reasons. The regiment's partner in the 128th Bombardirovchnyi Aviatsionnaya Diviziya (Bomber Aviation Division) was the 727th BAP at Brand, withdrawn at the same time.

The Yak-28 'Brewer-E' was finally withdrawn from service with the 16th Air Army during early 1989, but one was retained at Werneuchen as an instructional airframe. The type was replaced by the MiG-25BM 'Foxbat-F' in the defence suppression role with the 931st RAP. Werneuchen's MiG-25BMs were quickly withdrawn after the reunification of the two Germanies, since they were among the most secret aircraft on charge with the 16th Air Army, and it was felt undesirable to expose them to the cameras and prying eyes of the hordes of aircraft spotters who descended on the former East Germany. It is believed that they were first withdrawn to Osla, in Poland, before being pulled back further to Russia itself.

entirely defensive, then it performed its task to perfection. By deterring NATO aggression (considered as a real threat by many Russians, however impossible in reality) for more than 40 years, its airmen kept their Motherland safe, emerging from the Cold War unbeaten.

It is almost impossible to divine exactly what the USSR's real ambitions were during the Cold War period. Different leaders made very different public statements about the Soviet vision of the future, and the same individuals sometimes said very different things to different audiences. Although a stated doctrine of peaceful coexistence can be traced back as far as Beria, this was not supported by Soviet actions, and the whole concept of coexistence with the West was treated as a new and revolutionary idea by later politicians.

Although Russia was merely one of many Soviet Republics until the establishment of the CIS on 8 December 1991 (a looser confederation of the three big former Soviet states – Byelorussia, Ukraine and the Russian Federation – was soon joined by more states), it was the largest and most populous state within the USSR. It was also the industrial powerhouse and political centre of the Soviet Union, in which Russian interests were always paramount. The outlook of the USSR was that of Russia itself, and the terms Russian and Soviet are thus often interchangeable.

Many historians ascribe a certain understandable paranoia to Russia, founded on many past broken alliances and invasions by supposed friends. Russia saw the wartime alliance between the USSR and the Western allies as being never more than a fragile expedient aimed at the overthrow of Nazi Germany. Until 1941, British newspapers, for example, had reviled Stalin in much the same tones as they insulted Hitler, and the Soviet Union had been seen as

another foul dictatorship, the bully of the 'plucky Finns' and unfortunate Poles. The USSR was aware that Germany had pressed hard for a separate peace with Britain before invading the Soviet Union, and that such a separate peace had also been sought at the end of the war. Such attitudes and events led to no small measure of suspicion. From Russia's point of view, Britain and the USA had not done nearly enough to help Russia against Germany, had delayed the opening of a Second Front and had provided insufficient aid, and that of mediocre quality.

Mutual suspicions were further exacerbated after the war. While Britain and the USA saw the 'spheres of influence' agreed to at Yalta as being rather vague, Russia considered its spheres of influence to be legally-agreed possessions, and resented what it saw as Western interference when it encouraged the installation of friendly puppet regimes in Eastern Europe. On the other hand, while Russia did not

With a Guards badge emblazoned on its intake, a MiG-27D 'Flogger-J' of the 19th GvAPIB comes in to land at Mirow-Lärz, on the final stage of its long, flat, fast approach. Traffic lights were essential on the road which ran past the Mirow threshold.

intervene in the Greek civil war (Greece was, after all, agreed as being within Britain's sphere of influence), the USSR could not help but be appalled by the way the Greek Communists were put down, in a manner which seemed to typify the Western allies' attitude to socialism in general. The differing attitudes to the defeated enemy were also of crucial importance. Stalin watched in horror as the three Western allies combined their zones of Germany, and rapidly began to rebuild German industry and infrastructure. The Soviet Union stripped its sector of Germany of its productive capacity, and exacted massive payments of reparations. The USSR saw the formation of NATO in 1949 as the establishment of an anti-Soviet alliance. The final straw came with the rehabilitation of Nazi Germany (which joined NATO in 1955) as a bulwark against the USSR and its fraternal allies.

A slide into hostile confrontation was inevitable, and it may only have been the threat of the atomic bomb which prevented an outbreak of real fighting. The Western allies had a clear vision of what the Cold War was about (however vague they may have been on detail): the defence of Western Europe and its core values of liberty, equality and democracy against the Communist threat, and the need to prevent the spread of Communism in the wider world. The USSR declared no such simple philosophy. There were from the start those hardliners to whom the spread of Communism (or more accurately Leninism or Stalinism) to the rest of the civilised world was a sacred duty, while others took a more pragmatic view and were concerned to defend the gains of the revolution against what they saw as an aggressive and potentially hostile West.

Thus, the posture of the Soviet armed forces during the Cold War was determined by a government which may not have had a clear view of what its 'war aims' were, and which certainly presented two major strands of thought to the world. NATO always saw the Warsaw Pact (formed in 1955, but effectively no more than a formalisation of existing military co-operation agreements dating from the late 1940s) as a simple Russian-led military power, hostile to

the West, expansionist in outlook and likely to invade parts of Europe if NATO ever let its guard drop. Even as late as the 1980s, the Western allies seem to have regarded Russia as a potential danger, restrained from aggression only by a combination of economic and military realities, but actively working to destabilise Western governments and ready for military action if ever the potential rewards outweighed the potential risk. This was probably an oversimplification, not least because while there were those in Russia who justified such fears, their influence waned as time passed, and by the 1980s it is fair to say that most Russians saw themselves as

The front-line regiments in East Germany were proud of their heritage, and frequently had retired aircraft as gate guards. Sometimes these aircraft were displayed at the main gate of a particular base, while at other airfields they guarded the readiness platform. This camouflaged MiG-21SMT 'Fishbed-K' was more unusually located, standing in the domestic site of Nobitz (Altenburg), close to the base school and Zvensoviet building. Before it received a regiment of MiG-29s direct from Russia, Nobitz had been a MiG-27 fighter-bomber base.

Above: A MiG-29 taxis past the Wittstock control tower. Although the tower bristles with communications antennas, the 16th Air Army frequently operated 'radio silent', and small shelters built beside the runways usually housed a bored conscript with a flare gun whose job was to give take-off and landing clearance. Airfield radar was truck-mounted, allowing a regiment to decamp swiftly to a forward location if necessary. All Russian tactical aircraft are designed to be compatible with captured NATO ground support equipment.

the potential victims of Western Imperialist aggression, and genuinely believed the Warsaw Treaty organisation was a bulwark against potential American hostility.

Whatever the underlying philosophy of the Russian government, its armed forces maintained an overtly offensive posture (as did those of the 'defensive' NATO alliance), especially in Germany. Although the Cold War's real battles were fought outside Europe, between client states supported by the two superpowers, Germany was always the front line in the Cold War. Tension between the two superpower blocks facing each other over Germany led directly to the Berlin Airlift, and to successive crises, big and small.

Unlike Western democracies, Russia and its allies always had a formal military doctrine, an officially recognised and agreed system of views relating to the 'essence, aims, character and means of waging any possible war'; in other words, a formal war plan. Until the early to mid-1980s, Warsaw Pact military doctrine assumed a major Warsaw Pact strike against NATO in Europe, usually justified as

being the response to the NATO attack which, it was said, would accompany dying capitalism's inevitable final gasps.

However such an attack was to be justified, documents unearthed when the two Germanies were reunited give a good idea of how military operations might have progressed. Any war would have been fought vigorously and ruthlessly, and would have opened with a surprise nuclear attack against NATO installations in Germany. Exercise maps marked the German/Dutch border as being the 'limit of strategic and operational tactical nuclear strikes', presumably in the hope that NATO's doctrine of flexible response would keep the extent of nuclear strikes within the borders of the two Germanies. The first wave would have included some 320 warheads, including 60 missiles armed with 200-kT warheads. Airbursts would have been used where possible to minimise fall-out and contamination, but the effects would have been nightmarish, quite conceivably leaving every major NATO command and control facility, weapons storage area and air base in ruins.

Warsaw Pact armies would then have fought through Germany in their NBC (nuclear, biological, chemical) kits and well-sealed tanks and APCs (armoured personnel carriers), with Germany occupied within an estimated three days. The offensive then would have rolled on to the Channel and the Pyrenees. This kind of attack would have involved an estimated 12,000 tanks and 25,000 APCs.

Such plans were not merely part of a warped 'nightmare'. After the collapse of the old East German regime, the West German authorities found temporary occupation currency printed and stored ready to replace the Deutschmark, together with identity papers for some 300,000 East German administrators, and even new traffic signs for use in Germany, Holland and Belgium. They found field marshal's shoulder-boards waiting to be issued

to East Germany's highest ranking officer, and thousands of invasion medals, minted and ready for issue. German inspectors found that Warsaw Pact forces were maintained at a high degree of readiness, with some units ready to move at 45 minutes' notice, and most ready for war within two hours of the orders being given, a far cry from the creaking inefficiency which Western military leaders had always assumed. Units were constantly exercised and vehicles were kept armed and ready to go.

During the 1980s, the offensive nuclear doctrine gave way to a doctrine of conventional defence, in which the use of conventional weapons was preferred and in which defending existing territory was accorded a higher priority than capturing NATO-held territory. This change in doctrine was masterminded by Marshal Nikolai Ogarkov, who also led a drive for improved quality in conventional weapons. The new doctrine was actually drawn up by Minister of Defence General Yazov, the Warsaw Pact's Commander-in-Chief Marshal Kulikov, and General Moiseyev. The new doctrine almost certainly ended Warsaw Pact consideration of nuclear-first use as an option, but whether it really ended the use of massive counter-attack as a defensive tactic is open to question. After reunification, a senior Bundeswehr officer was able to question his former East German opposite number and asked the other what his defensive plans had been. "Antwerp," was the East German's reported reply! These radical ideas were also enthusiastically embraced by the new Soviet leader, Mikhail Gorbachev. The policy placed an increasing emphasis on manned aircraft, since the neutralisation of NATO air power (once regarded as the task of nuclear missiles) remained a high priority, not least because this was the area in which it was felt that NATO could severely erode the Warsaw Pact's numerical advantage on the ground.

Towards the end of its time in Germany, the 16th Air Army ceased to be a Soviet asset and instead formally became an element of the armed forces of the new CIS (Confederation of Independent States). In reality this meant a transfer to Russian control. Outwardly, the change was manifested by the appearance of Russian tricolour flags outside many bases, and by the application of red, white and blue markings on many aircraft. This Grossenhain-based MiG-27 goes even further, with the old double-headed eagle of the Romanovs superimposed on the Russian flag. The red and white object behind the aircraft's rudder is a scarecrow, a common sight on Russian military airfields.

Far left: The flight director (senior air traffic control officer) and the navigation/operations officers are seen here at their stations in the Wittstock control tower.

Left: The landing control officer sits in front of his radar screens, monitoring the progress of inbound aircraft and ready to assist with a GCA talkdown should it be necessary. The somewhat makeshift appearance of the equipment reflects the ease with which the equipment can be moved to a forward operating base, if required.

Red Stars over Germany

Each MiG-29 base in Germany had a crude, no-motion simulator, essentially a procedures trainer but with basic visual displays. In NATO air forces, several bases operating a common aircraft type would share a much more sophisticated full-motion simulator, but individual pilots would have less access to such a piece of equipment. The Soviet regiments in Germany also had a very high proportion of two-seat trainers, for instrument flying training and hack duties.

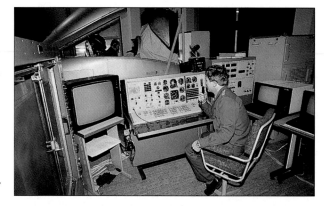

At the very heart of any Warsaw Pact campaign in Europe, whether offensive or defensive, would have been the Soviet armed forces, and at the core of those were the forces already stationed within East Germany. The Russian deployment in East Germany cannot be understood without reference to World War II, not least because the bases and units in place as the Cold War drew to a close were the direct descendants of those that had advanced into Germany in 1945. Thus, the armies, divisions and regiments based in Germany in 1990 were mostly those same units that had smashed through a battered Wehrmacht in the early months of 1945. In most cases their garrisons were in the positions where they had halted in May 1945, or to which they had advanced or retreated in order to conform to the dictates of the Yalta and Potsdam treaties.

Army Aviation

By October 1990, the Soviet armed forces in East Germany consisted of a declared total of 363,690 military personnel, with 5,880 tanks, 9,790 armoured vehicles, 4,624 artillery pieces, 625 combat aircraft and 698 combat heli-

Right: Although they were housed in modern hardened aircraft shelters, aircraft underwent maintenance in the large hangars at each base. These were mostly decorated with colourful posters exhorting the engineers to attain their socialist targets, and other such sentiments. Here, a Wittstock-based 'Fulcrum-A' undergoes radar tests.

Below: A blue-coded MiG-29 undergoes maintenance in one of Wittstock's hangars, inherited from the airfield's Luftwaffe days. The aircraft has had its ejection seat, canopy and starboard engine removed.

copters. These horrifyingly large totals may even have been underestimates. It was found, for example, that East Germany's declared total of 2,800 APCs for CFE talks was far short of the actual 8,200 such vehicles that it had on charge. The 1,000 Soviet barracks, airfields and other military facilities allegedly represented 10 per cent of the area of the German Democratic Republic!

The ground forces were divided between two Guards Tank Armies, a Guards 'Shock' Infantry Army and two Guards Infantry Armies, with separate direct-reporting missile brigades and an artillery division. Virtually all of these units have the Krasnonamennaya (Red Banner) honorific within their title, and some also have 'Order of Lenin' or 'Order of Suvarov' in the full unit title (these are omitted for clarity henceforth). The 1st Gvardeiskaya Tankovaya Armiya (Guards Tank Army, abbreviated to GvTA), headquartered in Dresden, included the 20th 'Prikarpatsko-Berlinskaya' Gvardeiskaya Motostrelkovaya Diviziya (Guards Motor Rifle Division, GvMD), the 9th 'Bobrujsko-Berlinskaya' Tankovaya Diviziya (Tank Division, TD), and the 11th 'Prikarpatsko-Berlinskaya' Gvardeiskaya

Tankovaya Diviziya (Guards Tank Division, GvTD). The 2nd GvTA, headquartered in Furstenburg, included the 16th 'Umanskaya' GvTD, the 21st 'Taganskaya' GvMD, the 94th 'Swenigorodsko-Berlinskaya' GvMD, and the 207th MD (Motor Rifle Division). The Magdeburg-based 3rd Guards Shock Infantry Army included the 7th 'Kijevsko-Berlinskaya' GvTD, the 10th 'Marshal of the Soviet Union R. A. Malinkovski' GvTD, the 12th 'Umanskaya' GvTD, and the 47th 'Nischnedneprovskaya' GvTD. The 8th Guards Infantry Army (Gvardeiskaya Obchevoyskovaya Armiya, GvOA) was headquartered at Weimar-Nohra, parenting the 27th 'Omsko-Novoburgskaya' GvMD, the 39th 'Barvenkovskaya' GvMD, the 57th 'Novoburgskaya' GvMD, and the 79th 'Saporoschskaya' GvTD. Finally, the Eberswalde-Finow-based 20th GvOA comprised the 35th 'Krasnogradskaya' MD and the 90th GvTD, while the 6th 'Berlinskaya' GVMD, Berlin's garrison, reported directly to Western Group of Forces headquarters.

After the Great Patriotic War, senior politicians upbraided the Red air forces for exaggerating their contribution to

An element of Mil Mi-24 'Hinds' takes off for the transit home from their base at Brandis, festooned with auxiliary fuel tanks and 20-round 80-mm rocket pods. Orange intake filters identify the aircraft as belonging to the 1st Eskadrilya of the 485th OVP. The introduction of the Mil Mi-24 marked a major increase in capability for the helicopter regiments, and prompted a major reorganisation, including the re-establishment of Army Aviation.

Many of the ways in which the 16th Air Army actually operated seem strange and even primitive to Western eyes, although such curious practices were generally founded on sound operational reasons. Here, the Mirow runway is lit by truck-mounted searchlights, which would have been just as much at home lighting a forward airstrip. Many of the airfields in East Germany had runways flanked by barrels of used diesel oil, which would have been burned as a primitive 'fog-clearing' measure.

Wing

The Su-17M-4 wing pivots at about 25 per cent span, simplifying fuselage design and construction, and minimising the number of changes to the basic Su-7 from which the swing-wing Su-17 was derived. The outboard position of the pivots also minimised the effect of wing sweep on handling, and reduced movement of the centre of pressure of the wing, thereby enhancing stability in pitch during wing sweep. Thus, the Su-17M-4 has a fixed inner wing, built up around a main box spar and incorporating main undercarriage bays, the cannon bays, high-pressure air bottles and ammunition boxes. Pylons are attached to these fixed wing sections. The moving outer wing panels (which incorporate integral fuel tanks) move in and out of the hollow wing glove section of the fixed inner wing, with strips of fluorocarbon plastic (similar to Teflon) providing lubrication. The wing pivots consist of bearings in the fixed and moving sections of the wing, with guides and an auxiliary roller. The pivot is lubricated by grease which is fed into it under pressure as the wing is swept. The inboard section of the wing incorporates slotted flaps, with simple hinging flaps and leading-edge slats on the moving outboard sections.

Armament

Unusually, this Su-17M-4 carries UB-32-57 57-mm rocket pods underwing, 57-mm rockets having largely been replaced by the newer 80-mm S-8 rocket, in the 20-round B-8M pod, during the late 1980s. Underfuselage, the aircraft has a pair of Kh-25MP anti-radar missiles (known to NATO as the AS-14 'Kedge'). Unguided rockets are an excellent weapon for destroying radar or SAM sites once the guidance radar has been shut down.

Sukhoi Su-17M-4 'Fitter-K'
20 Aviatsionnaya Polk Istrebeitelei-Bombardirovchikov
(20th Fighter-Bomber Regiment)
Gross-Dölln (Templin)
Germany, April 1994

Perhaps the most colourful of the Su-17M-4s assigned to the 20th APIB was Yellow 27, which received a gaudy red and white sharkmouth on its nose and a top hat silhouette on its rudder during 1993. The significance of these very individual markings is not known. Some other aircraft assigned to the regiment wore squadron badges (a polar bear for the first *eskadrilya*, a bat for the second, and a diving eagle (later replaced by a two-headed Romanov eagle in Russian colours) for the third. The third squadron was also a Guards unit, and its aircraft wore the distinctive laurel wreath and red banner Guards badge on the nose, just behind the intake lip. The regiment used yellow code letters, thinly outlined in red (although two aircraft had non-standard Dayglo orange codes). Four main blocks of codes seem to have been allocated, perhaps with one block per squadron and with an extra block for the two-seat trainers. Established in Finland on 10 November 1939, the 20th APIB equipped with MiG-15s in 1951 before moving to Poland and then to Germany, flying from Frankfurt on Oder, Damgarten and Parchim. MiG-17s were received in 1953, and Su-7Bs in 1964. The unit had been based at its present home of Gross Dölln since 1954, and is believed to have been the first Soviet unit to receive the Su-17M 'Fitter-C', in 1976. Upon its departure from Gross Dölln on 5 April 1994, the regiment flew its aircraft to Taganrog for scrapping or reallocation to the navy. The unit itself was due to convert to the Su-24 at Kamienka, prior to an eventual move to Penza.

Radar

Allegations that the MiG-29's Phazatron N-019 radar was a simple copy of the Hughes AN/APG-65 were refuted when the first photographs of its antenna were published. The radar, allocated the ASCC reporting name 'Slot Back', uses a primitive-looking, bin-like inverse-cassegrain antenna similar to that used on the radars fitted to the MiG-21 and MiG-23, and N-019 is quite probably derived from those radars. A coherent pulse-Doppler radar, N-019 has a range/discrimination performance broadly comparable to equivalent Western radars, but poor processing capacity limits the number of targets that can be simultaneously tracked or attacked to 10 and one (later two), respectively. When NATO evaluated the MiG-29s it inherited from East Germany, the N-019 was found to be much more capable than had been believed, but some unexpected weaknesses were also revealed. As a BVR fighter, however, the early-generation 'Fulcrum' enjoyed significant advantages over the F-16 and a broad parity with the F-15A.

IRST

The MiG-29's KOLS is part of the Geofizika S-31 electro-optical complex developed specifically for the fighter, and has been described as an 'optical radar', emphasising its potential as an alternative to radar for target detection, tracking and engagement. It consists of an active laser for rangefinding, collimated and synchronised with an infra-red search and track system which allows highly-accurate, emission-free angular detection and tracking of airborne targets.

Mikoyan MiG-29 'Fulcrum-A'
968 Istrebeitel'nyi Aviatsionnyi Polk
(968th Fighter Aviation Regiment)
Nobitz (Altenburg)
Germany

Previously home to the MiG-27-equipped 296th Aviatsionnyi Polk Istrebeitelei-Bombardirovchikov Polk (Aviation Regiment Fighter-Bomber), Nobitz assumed the fighter role during 1989, when the 'Floggers' relocated to Grossenhain, replacing a withdrawing regiment of Su-24 bombers. The MiG-27s were themselves replaced at Nobitz by the 968th Istrebeitel'nyi Aviatsionnyi Polk (Fighter Aviation Regiment) which arrived from Russia with its MiG-29s. At least one of the regiment's three squadrons used MiG-29 'Fulcrum-As' drawn from the earliest production batch, which lacked the fin leading-edge extension fairings which housed upward-firing chaff/flare dispensers, and which had distinctive ventral fins beside the engine nacelles, under the horizontal tail. This squadron's aircraft were unusual in that they carried a unit badge below the cockpit even when they arrived in Germany. Guards badges were fairly common, and aircraft 'excellence awards' factory or OKB badges were by no means rare in the WGF, but unit badges were generally not used until after the withdrawals began.

Armament

The MiG-29s assigned to the 16th Air Army were used primarily in the air-to-air fighter role, and as such carried a mix of short-range IR-homing and long-range semi-active or IR-homing missiles on their six underwing pylons. Initially, the standard short-range missile in use was the R-60 (AA-8 'Aphid'), but this was soon replaced by the more agile, longer-range R-73 (AA-11 'Archer') which has been described by senior Luftwaffe officers (who inherited R-73s from the former East German air force) as being superior to the latest and projected AIM-9 Sidewinder variants. The missile owes its capability to a combination of powerful aerodynamic controls (rudder-like tabs on the rear fins and all-moving forward control fins) and a vectoring rocket nozzle. The standard medium-range missile carried by 16th Air Army MiG-29s was the R-27 (AA-10 'Alamo'), available in IR-homing and semi-active radar-homing versions, and considered by some analysts to be superior to the AIM-120 AMRAAM in some respects. The MiG-29 carried two of these powerful missiles, sometimes carrying one with each type of homing (the IR missile giving a passive, emission-free BVR capability) or sometimes with two semi-active radar-homing missiles. A lightweight GSh-30l single-barrelled 30-mm cannon is fitted in the port LERX, with 150 rounds of ammunition. The use of laser ranging makes the cannon exceptionally accurate, and in later MiG-29 variants the ammunition tank was of reduced capacity, 150 rounds being considered too much for most conceivable circumstances.

Powerplant

The Su-17M-4 is powered by a single Lyul'ka AL21F-3S single-spool axial-flow turbojet rated at 112.5 kN (25,290 lb st) with afterburner, or 78 kN (17,534 lb st) in maximum dry power. The engine has a 14-stage compressor, with 10 stages of variable pitch stators, a 12-tube annular combustion chamber, a two-stage turbine, and a fully-variable afterburner nozzle, whose variable 'petals' are entirely hidden within the fixed jetpipe. The throttle has fixed 'stops' for stop, idle and maximum dry power, and for minimum and maximum afterburner, and also mounts radio, airbrake navigation and weapons controls. Bleed air from the engine is used for air conditioning, some pneumatic systems and for fuel tank pressurisation. Air for the engine enters the pitot nose intake, flowing around the fixed conical centrebody, and then being split to flow around the cockpit before re-merging (at bulkhead 34) to flow into the engine's compressor. Engine access is obtained by removing the entire rear fuselage and tail unit from bulkhead 34a. Auxiliaries are mounted below the engine.

Tail unit

The all-moving tailplane rotates around half-axles and is built around separate front and rear sections. The front section has the leading edge, a main spar, eight braces and 12 ribs, while the rear section has 15 ribs. An 8.4-kg (18.5-lb) anti-flutter weight projects from the leading edge, just inboard from the tip.

Undercarriage

The conventional tricycle undercarriage had single wheels on each unit. The mainwheels were each fitted with four disc brakes, and were braked automatically during retraction. The nosewheel was self-aligning. All three units were hydraulically actuated, although a pneumatic extension system was available for emergency use.

Colour scheme

The Su-17M-4s of the 16th Air Army wore a three-tone camouflage of green and brown. The actual shades used differed considerably, and there was no uniform pattern. Yellow 27 was one of the lighter-painted Su-17M-4s, with two shades of brown, other aircraft using one dark brown colour and two dark greens.

Fuel
The Su-17M-4 carries its fuel in four fuselage and two wing tanks, which can all be filled from a single point on the dorsal spine, above the No. 2 tank, although the wing tanks also have their own fillers for use if the pump which takes fuel to them from the No. 2 tank is inoperative. The No. 3 tank serves as a collector tank. The fuselage and underwing hardpoints are plumbed for the carriage of 820-litre (180-Imp gal) or 1150-litre (253-Imp gal) auxiliary tanks.

Cockpit
The Su-17M-4 cockpit is covered by a rearward-hinging clamshell canopy, whose centre frame incorporates a simple electrically-heated periscope to augment the two mirrors carried on the forward frame. Even the single-seater has a hood for instrument flying training, which automatically deploys if the aircraft descends below a certain height, or if the altimeter fails, or if ejection is initiated. This dome-shaped hood is of braced fabric, and hinges over the pilot's head pneumatically from its stowage on the starboard side of the canopy. The heavily-framed windscreen has three silicate glass layers, and is reinforced by plastic, making it extremely birdstrike-resistant. The quarterlights are acrylic and 12 mm thick, like the opening part of the canopy. Aluminium armour of 18-mm thickness is fitted into the cockpit sides.

Cannon
The Su-17M-4's built-in armament consists of a pair of belt-fed NR-30 30-mm cannon, each with 80 rounds of ammunition, mounted in the innermost part of the root of the fixed, inboard wing glove. The fuselage skin adjacent to each muzzle is protected by a crude steel (or perhaps titanium on some later aircraft) panel. The internal cannon can be augmented by a variety of cannon pods, including the SPPU-22-01, which contains a GSh-23L twin-barrelled 23-mm cannon equipped with traversable barrels for strafing. These pods contain 260 rounds of ammunition and can be mounted to fire backwards or forwards. When carried under the wing gloves, barrel depression is controlled directly by the PrNK-54 weapons system. The pods can also be carried under the belly of the Su-17M-4 but, in this position, barrel depression is preset and fixed.

Avionics
The Su-17M-4 differed from earlier 'Fitter' variants in being equipped with a more advanced avionics suite, with PrNK-54 weapons/navigation system fed by long-range RSDN (similar to LORAN) and A-312 (similar to TACAN). The aircraft also has a new CVM20-22 navigation/weapons-aiming computer and equipment for the defence suppression role. The latter included a BA-58 radar transmission registration system, which could pinpoint and identify hostile radar emissions, and then cue anti-radar missiles (especially the Kh-58 (AS-11 'Kilter') onto their targets. This was housed in a bulky 'bathtub' fairing which could be scabbed on below the fuselage. Delta NM pods, carried underwing, were associated with the guidance of other missiles. Late-series Su-17M-4s, like this aircraft, have a TV system for guidance of TV missiles, with a display unit on the starboard side of the cockpit.

Cockpit
The MiG-29 has been criticised because it has a fairly old-fashioned cockpit, with conventional analog instruments, and without any modern multi-function display screens. Many fighter pilots, however, feel that more modern cockpits (like that of the F/A-18) tend to over-saturate the pilot with information, reducing situational awareness. The arguments are not clear cut.

Fuel
One of the most serious shortcomings of the original MiG-29 was its limited range and endurance, which has been addressed in more recent variants by adding to internal fuel capacity. In the basic 'Fulcrum-A', fuel is stored in four fuselage and two wing tanks. Figures released by Mikoyan, MAPO and Mikoyan general designer Rostislav Belyakov all differ slightly but, according to the manufacturer, the wing cells contain 660 litres, tank No. 1 contains 650 litres, No. 2 contains 870 litres, No. 3 contains 1810 litres and No. 3a contains 310 litres. This gives a total of 4300 litres, which can be augmented by carriage of a 1500-litre ventral fuel tank. The cannon cannot be fired when this tank is being carried (except on later variants, or on modified aircraft), limiting its usefulness.

Unit insignia
The winged swept-star insignia seen here was carried by only one of the 968th IAP's three squadrons. Applied in red and blue, the device was based on the insignia carried by the Yak-3s, Yak-7s and Yak-9s of a Frontal Aviation Air Corps during the Great Patriotic War. The links between the wartime unit and the 968th IAP remain uncertain, however. One of the squadron's MiG-29UBs was sent to Wittstock, retaining the winged star badge and leading to some confusion. Squadron markings were later applied to some aircraft from Zerbst and Wittstock, while Alt Lonnewitz, Köthen and Merseburg applied Guards badges to their MiG-29s.

Handling

The MiG-29 enjoys unrivalled high-Alpha handling, making the aircraft a particularly formidable opponent in a close-in, low-speed turning fight. The flight control system has a sophisticated aileron-rudder interconnect. At higher angles of attack, this progressively reduces aileron deflection, while increasing rudder deflection in response to the pilot's sideways deflection of the control column to command roll. Additionally, the flight control system has no hard limits, so that it is possible, in extremis, to exceed maximum g and maximum Alpha simply by applying extra stick force to pull-through the synthetic 'stick-stop'. High angle of attack behaviour is sufficiently benign that the pilot can be confident that exceeding the stated Alpha limit will not result in immediate departure, but will merely make it progressively more likely that the aircraft will eventually depart. This allows the pilot to make temporary excursions into the 'tatty corners' of the envelope with some confidence, whenever tactical circumstances demand it. Thus the MiG-29 pilot can pull more g, or go to a higher angle of attack in order to boresight an enemy fighter, evade a missile or avoid a hillside, while Western fighter pilots simply cannot override their aircraft's hard limits.

The MiG-29 in Germany

By 1990 the MiG-29 was numerically the most important front-line aircraft in the 16th Air Army, equipping eight of the nine fighter regiments. The aircraft was also in service with the Soviet forces in Czechoslovakia and Hungary, and was entering service with most of Russia's Warsaw Pact allies. From their bases in East Germany, air defence-configured MiG-29s of the 16th Air Army had a radius of action which covered the whole of Germany, most of Holland and Belgium, and an important swathe of northern France. Had war broken out, their targets would have included allied fighters and fighter-bombers, as well as high-value assets like tankers and AEW platforms.

Ventral fins

Ventral fins were applied to the first MiG-29 prototype after its maiden flight, and were retained on the first production batches of single-seat MiG-29s. The introduction of overwing chaff/flare dispensers in fairings which led forward from the fin leading edge extensions was accompanied by deletion of the ventral fins.

Keith Fretwell

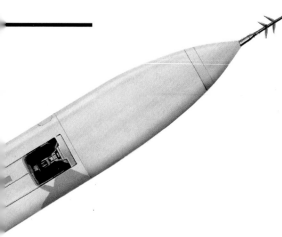

Radar

The Su-24MR's nose accommodates the antennas for an RLS BO Shtik synthetic aperture sideways-looking radar, optimised for terrain mapping, and with MTI capability, on either side of the aircraft's track. The radar gives a resolution of between 5 and 7.5 m, and looks at an area between 4 and 28 km out from the aircraft centreline. The whole nose was painted white in order to give the aircraft the same external appearance as the bomber Su-24M. A forward-looking Relief terrain-following radar is housed in the tip of the nose of the Su-24MR, as part of the integrated NK-24MR navigation system, which also incorporates A-035 Impuls radio altimeter, DISS-7 Doppler, MIS-P INS, CVU Orbita-10-058R digital computer and SAU-6 autopilot.

The map on the right shows all of the *fast-jet airfields, helicopter bases and motorway strips regularly used by the 16th Air Army, and by Russian Army Aviation, during the final years in East Germany. Airfields and other facilities used by East German units are not shown here. Red triangles show the location of the various army headquarters, stars mark airfields, and circles mark motorway strips. The official names actually used by the Western Group of Forces are given first where they differ from the names used in the West, which are given in parentheses. The headquarters of the 16th Air Army at Zossen-Wunstorf controlled two geographical corps, each with fighter and fighter-bomber divisions, and with direct-reporting transport, reconnaissance and Shturmovik units not assigned to the corps structure. The Northern Air Corps was headquartered at Wittstock and controlled a fighter division (regiments at Eberswalde, Pütnitz and Wittstock) and a fighter-bomber division (Gross-Dölln, Lärz and Neuruppin). The Southern Air Corps was headquartered at Wittenberg and controlled two fighter divisions (regiments at Altes Lager, Köthen and Zerbst, and at Alt Lönnewitz, Merseburg and Nobitz) and a fighter-bomber division (Brand, Grossenhain, and Finsterwalde). The reconnaissance division controlled units at Allstedt, Sperenburg, Welzow and Werneuchen, while the transport division controlled units at Sperenburg. Brandis and Tütow were the two Shturmovik bases. From their bases in East Germany, Soviet MiG-29s could range over the whole of West Germany, most of Holland and Belgium, and could even reach air base targets in northern France. MiG-27 fighter bombers could attack virtually every airfield in West Germany. Army helicopter regiments were controlled by the individual armies. Thus, the 1st GvTA at Dresden controlled units at Allstedt, Brandis and Dresden, while the 2nd GvTA at Fürstenburg controlled units at Damm and Werneuchen. The 3rd OA at Magdeburg had helicopter units at Borstel and Neuruppin, the 8th GvOA at Nohra had units at Nohra, Altes Lager and Hassleben, and the 20th GvOA at Eberswalde had aviation units at Mahlwinkel and Gross-Dölln. A regiment at Parchim maintained a detachment at Lärz, while one at Brandis had a detachment at Merseburg. The helicopter units at Gross-Dölln moved there from Prenzlau. In time of war, many regiments from Russia and Poland would have moved forward to operate from German bases, with Gross-Dölln, Wittstock, Damgarten and Altes Lager all being known to be potential FOLs for strategic and tactical aircraft not usually based in Germany. The 16th Air Army itself may even have moved forward in time of war, perhaps using captured airfields in the eastern part of the Federal Republic.*

Built-in systems

The Su-24MR is a true multi-sensor reconnaissance platform, with podded radiation, laser and Elint sensors, and built-in SLAR, optical, TV and IR reconnaissance systems. Reconnaissance data from the IR, TV, laser and radiation reconnaissance sensors can be datalinked to the Posrednik truck-mounted interpretation/exploitation complex. Permanently installed sensors include an AP-402 panoramic camera (with f3.5 90.5-mm lens), an AIST-M TV sensor, a forward-oblique A-100 camera (with 100-mm lens) in the bottom of the port engine intake, and a Zima IR reconnaissance set.

Defensive systems

As a reconnaissance derivative of the Su-24M 'Fencer-D' (Russia's most advanced in-service tactical bomber), the Su-24MR has a superb integrated defensive aids system, with SPO-15 Bereza RHAWS, LO-82 Mak-UL missile plume detector, L-101G or L-102G Geran-F active jammer, APP-50A Avtomat-F chaff/flare dispenser and a Neon-F jamming aids control unit. This, plus the aircraft's superb performance, confer a high degree of survivability.

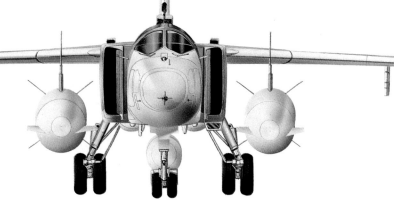

Alternative equipment

Instead of the Shpil-2M pod illustrated here, the Su-24MR could carry a Tangazh electronic reconnaissance pod on the centreline. This small, slab-sided pod identifies and locates pulse and continuous wave emitters operating in the 0.8 - 300 cm and 2.8 - 3.6 cm wavebands. It was often seen under 11th ORAP Su-24MRs.

i Su-24MR 'Fencer-E'

Vitebskii' ORAP

w

any, 1992

wears the white codes of the 11th Otdelnyi Razvedyvatnyi Aviatsionnaya Polk (11th Independent
e Aviation Regiment) which was based at Welzow from 1954, operating the Ilyushin Il-28, the Yakovlev
m 1986, the Su-24MR in the tactical and theatre reconnaissance roles. From 1988 until 1991, the regiment
le squadron of Su-24MP 'Fencer-Fs', variously described as an EW escort jamming, Sigint or Elint platform,
wo squadrons of Su-24MRs. In 1970 (the centenary of Lenin's birth) the Byelorussian Komsomol youth
esented the regiment with a red banner, an event thereafter commemorated by the application of a small
* the regiment's aircraft.

KEY

★ Air forces airfields
☆ Army Aviation airfields
✦ Air forces/army airfields
● Motorway airstrips
☆ Disused airfields
▲ Army headquarters
▮ Major towns

Fuel
The Su-24MR's internal fuel capacity of 11700 litres in four internal tanks can be augmented by the carriage of external tanks, of 3000-litre capacity on the wing glove pylons, and/or of 2000-litre under the belly.

Radiation monitoring
The Efir-1M radiation reconnaissance pod is intended to monitor surface or airborne radioactive contamination, recording information on tape and transmitting data back via a narrowband radio. Only 3 m long, the pod is usually carried under the starboard wing, often balanced by an AAM (typically an R-60/AA-8 'Aphid' IR-homing missile) to port. Su-24MRs in Germany seemed to carry an Efir-1M as part of their standard loadout.

Laser reconnaissance
The largest of the reconnaissance pods carried by the Su-24MR is the Shpil-2M. Intended for low-level reconnaissance by day or night, the equipment provides 0.25 m resolution from 400-m altitude, and scans an area equivalent to four times aircraft height, producing an image of almost photographic quality. Data can be immediately datalinked to the ground station.

Sukho
11th '
Welzo
Germ

This Su-24MR
Reconnaissanc
Yak-28 and, fr
included a sing
alongside the
organisation p
badge to one o

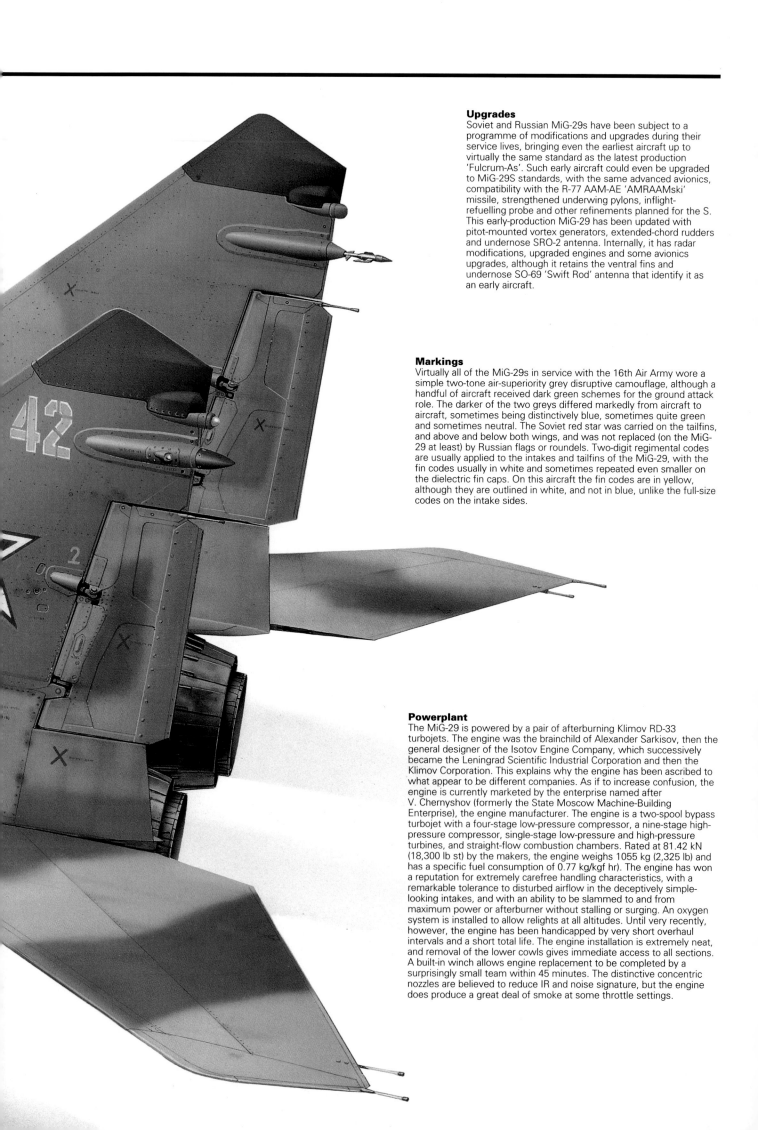

Upgrades

Soviet and Russian MiG-29s have been subject to a programme of modifications and upgrades during their service lives, bringing even the earliest aircraft up to virtually the same standard as the latest production 'Fulcrum-As'. Such early aircraft could even be upgraded to MiG-29S standards, with the same advanced avionics, compatibility with the R-77 AAM-AE 'AMRAAMski' missile, strengthened underwing pylons, inflight-refuelling probe and other refinements planned for the S. This early-production MiG-29 has been updated with pitot-mounted vortex generators, extended-chord rudders and undernose SRO-2 antenna. Internally, it has radar modifications, upgraded engines and some avionics upgrades, although it retains the ventral fins and undernose SO-69 'Swift Rod' antenna that identify it as an early aircraft.

Markings

Virtually all of the MiG-29s in service with the 16th Air Army wore a simple two-tone air-superiority grey disruptive camouflage, although a handful of aircraft received dark green schemes for the ground attack role. The darker of the two greys differed markedly from aircraft to aircraft, sometimes being distinctively blue, sometimes quite green and sometimes neutral. The Soviet red star was carried on the tailfins, and above and below both wings, and was not replaced (on the MiG-29 at least) by Russian flags or roundels. Two-digit regimental codes are usually applied to the intakes and tailfins of the MiG-29, with the fin codes usually in white and sometimes repeated even smaller on the dielectric fin caps. On this aircraft the fin codes are in yellow, although they are outlined in white, and not in blue, unlike the full-size codes on the intake sides.

Powerplant

The MiG-29 is powered by a pair of afterburning Klimov RD-33 turbojets. The engine was the brainchild of Alexander Sarkisov, then the general designer of the Isotov Engine Company, which successively became the Leningrad Scientific Industrial Corporation and then the Klimov Corporation. This explains why the engine has been ascribed to what appear to be different companies. As if to increase confusion, the engine is currently marketed by the enterprise named after V. Chernyshov (formerly the State Moscow Machine-Building Enterprise), the engine manufacturer. The engine is a two-spool bypass turbojet with a four-stage low-pressure compressor, a nine-stage high-pressure compressor, single-stage low-pressure and high-pressure turbines, and straight-flow combustion chambers. Rated at 81.42 kN (18,300 lb st) by the makers, the engine weighs 1055 kg (2,325 lb) and has a specific fuel consumption of 0.77 kg/kgf hr). The engine has won a reputation for extremely carefree handling characteristics, with a remarkable tolerance to disturbed airflow in the deceptively simple-looking intakes, and with an ability to be slammed to and from maximum power or afterburner without stalling or surging. An oxygen system is installed to allow relights at all altitudes. Until very recently, however, the engine has been handicapped by very short overhaul intervals and a short total life. The engine installation is extremely neat, and removal of the lower cowls gives immediate access to all sections. A built-in winch allows engine replacement to be completed by a surprisingly small team within 45 minutes. The distinctive concentric nozzles are believed to reduce IR and noise signature, but the engine does produce a great deal of smoke at some throttle settings.

Bases of the 16th Air Army and Army Aviation

Baltic Sea

Schleswig-
Holstein

Pütnitz (Damgarten)

Kavelsdorf

Tütow (Demmin)

EAST GERMANY

POLAND

NEU BRANDENBURG

Damm (Parchim)

Lärz (Mirow)

FURSTENBURG

Wittstock

☆ **Prenzlau**

WEST
GERMANY

Netzeband

Neuruppin

Gross-Dölln (Templin)

Eberswalde (Finow)

Borstel (Stendal)

Oranienburg

STENDAL

Vehlefanz

Werneuchen

Mahlwinkel

WEST BERLIN

EAST BERLIN

FURSTENWALDE

MAGDEBURG

Zossen-Wunsdorf

Friedersdorf-Skaby

Zerbst

Sperenburg

Cochstedt

Brand

Altes Lager (Juterbog)

Köthen

Alt Lönnewitz (Falkenburg)

Finsterwalde

COTTBUS

Welzow (Neu Welzow)

Allstedt

Merseburg

Ruhland

Osterfeld

Brandis

Grossenhain

Hassleben

LEIPZIG

Gallschutz

Ottendorf-Okrilla

ERFURT

Nohra (Weimar)

Nobitz (Altenburg)

Hellerau (Dresden)

DRESDEN

Hesse

Bavaria

CZECHOSLOVAKIA

69

The Mi-8 formed the backbone of the helicopter forces in East Germany, serving in huge numbers in a variety of roles, and in a wide variety of colour schemes. This is a basic Mi-8T 'Hip-C' transport.

eventual victory, reiterating the conventional wisdom that the ground forces remained pre-eminent, and that air power's sole contribution was to support army operations. For most of the 1950s and early 1960s, NATO's strategy of massive nuclear retaliation to any attack rendered the tactical air support role something of a potential irrelevance. Tactical air power thus remained very much a subordinate arm, with Frontal Aviation fighters and fighter-bombers being optimised for the interceptor role, and with close air support aircraft usually being half-hearted conversions of redundant interceptors. Such aircraft came under the command of the army commanders of military districts, Groups of Forces or Operational Manoeuvre Groups, but little importance was attached to their development and no purpose-built ground attack aircraft entered service until NATO's adoption of a doctrine of flexible response prompted the design of the Su-17, MiG-27 and Su-25, the first two of which were developed from fighter-interceptors. The proportion of Soviet military spending devoted to

Frontal Aviation (under whom support helicopters were still counted) trebled.

The development of the helicopter offered ground force commanders a new tool, which promised to be particularly useful for the direct support of ground forces, a promise which seemed to be fulfilled by US use of helicopters in Korea, British use in Malaya, Suez and Cyprus, and French use in Algeria. As soon as it reached maturity, the helicopter was pressed into Soviet military service in the transport and assault transport roles. As early as 1953 the Mil Mi-4 was in military service, and in 1956, at the Tushino air show, 36 of these aircraft demonstrated a mass assault. The Mi-4 was soon deployed with the Group of Soviet Forces in Germany, continuing to serve until its replacement in the transport role by the Mi-8, during the 1970s, when it was converted for use in the EW and armed assault roles. During the 1960s, the Mi-4 was augmented in Western Group of Forces service by the massive Mi-6 'Hook', which was for many years both the world's biggest and

Air and ground crew members, all armed with holstered pistols, swarm over their Mil Mi-2 'Hoplite'. The Mi-2 (designed by the Mil OKB in Russia but licence-built by PZL-Swidnik in Poland) served only in small numbers with the 16th Air Army, mainly in the liaison role, although a handful of the aircraft were Mi-2U trainers with full dual controls. Initially based at Hassleben, Templin and Werneuchen, the Mi-2Ts and Mi-2Us were eventually concentrated in the 41st OVE at Werneuchen. Armed sub-variants were produced and exported to some air forces, but none of these is believed to have been used by the Soviets in East Germany. The unit withdrew to Russia during the summer of 1993.

The cannon-armed Mi-24P 'Hind-F' augmented the Mi-24V in the first of the two independent regiments attached to each army, except the 225th OVP at Allstedt (attached to the 1st GvTA) which had not begun conversion from the Mi-24D to its intended mix of Mi-24Vs and Mi-24Ps. The Mi-24P was a derivative of the basic Mi-24V, with the same ATGM armament, but with the 12.7-mm machine-gun replaced by a twin-barrelled 30-mm cannon on the starboard fuselage side. This was intended to give the aircraft an accurate, powerful and cheap alternative to ATGMs for use against semi-soft or low value targets. Mi-24Ps could have operated together in pairs, or in four-aircraft flights, or could have operated in mixed sections beside Mi-24Vs, as circumstances dictated.

fastest helicopter. The introduction of the Mi-6 gave army commanders an aircraft with dramatic new capabilities: heavy artillery pieces, tactical missiles or light combat vehicles could be carried by air. The Mi-6A served with the Western Group of Forces in the transport role, but was augmented by two specialised sub-variants, the Mi-6VKP (Vozduzhni'i Komandni'i Punkt – Airborne Command Post) 'Hook-B' and the complementary Mi-22 (also known as the Mi-6BUS) 'Hook-C'.

The introduction of the Mi-8 during the early 1970s gave ground force commanders an agile, fast means of moving troops over the battlefield, landing them in the enemy rear when necessary. The addition of weapons to the 'Hip' transformed it into a flying tank, further increas-

Armeskaya Aviatsiya (Order of Battle 1990)

Units assigned to numbered Armies

UNIT	BASE	TYPES
1st Gvardeiskaya Tankovaya Armiya, Dresden		
225th OVP	Allstedt	Mi-24D, Mi-24V, Mi-8TB
485th OVP	Brandis	Mi-24V, Mi-24RKR, Mi-24K, Mi-8MT, Mi-8MTV, Mi 8VZPU, Mi-9
6th OVE	Hellerau	Mi-24RKR, Mi-24K, Mi-6VKP, Mi-22, Mi-8PPA, Mi-8T, Mi-8TB

The 485th OVP maintained a major Mi-8 and Mi-24 detachment at Merseburg until early 1991, when the MiG-29 base closed.

2nd Gvardeiskaya Tankovaya Armiya, Furstenburg		
172nd OVP	Damm (Parchim)	Mi-24V, Mi-24P, Mi-8TB, Mi-8MT
439th OVP	Damm (Parchim)	Mi-24V, Mi-24RKR, Mi-24K, Mi-9, Mi-8TB/MT
41st OVE	Werneuchen	Mi-24RKR, Mi-24K, Mi-6VKP, Mi-22, Mi-8PPA, Mi-8T, Mi-2T

The 439th OVP maintained a detachment at Mirow-Lärz until August 1992. The aircraft at Mirow-Lärz returned to Damm before their departure to Russia with the rest of the regiment.

3rd Gvardeiskaya Obchevoyskovaya Armiya, Magdeburg		
178th OVP	Borstel (Stendal)	Mi-24V, Mi-24P, Mi-8T, Mi-8TB, Mi-8MTV
440th OVP	Borstel (Stendal)	Mi-24D, Mi-24V, Mi-24RKR, Mi-24K, Mi-8T, Mi-8MT, Mi-8TB, Mi-9
9th OVE	Neuruppin	Mi-24RKR, Mi-24K, Mi-6VKP, Mi-22, Mi-8PPA, Mi-8K, Mi-9

The 9th OVE moved to Oranienburg in April 1991, on the closure of Neuruppin.

8th Gvardeiskaya Obchevoyskovaya Armiya, Weimar-Nohra		
336th OVP	Nohra (Weimar)	Mi-24V, Mi-24P, Mi-8TB
486th OVP	Altes Lager	Mi-24V, Mi-24RKR, Mi-24K, Mi-8TB, Mi-8MTV
298th OVE	Hassleben	Mi-24RKR, Mi-24K, Mi-6VKP, Mi-8T, Mi-2T

The 298th OVE's Mi-2Ts transferred to Werneuchen in August 1992, when the rest of the regiment departed.

20th Gvardeiskaya Obchevoyskovaya Armiya, Eberswalde-Finow		
337th OVP	Mahlwinkel	Mi-24V, Mi-24P, Mi-8TB, Mi-8MTV
487th OVP	Prenzlau	Mi-24V, Mi-24RKR, Mi-24K, Mi-8MT, Mi-8MTV, Mi-9

| 296th OVE | Mahlwinkel | Mi-24RKR, Mi-24K, Mi-6VKP, Mi-8PPA, Mi-9 |

The 487th OVP moved to Gross Dölln, and then to Werneuchen in 1991. Some aircraft from the 296th OVE relocated to Oranienburg during late 1991. An official (although error-filled) Russian order of battle for the Western Group of Forces gives the above squadrons under the 6th 'Berlinskaya' Gvardeiskaya Motostrelkovaya Diviziya, with no aviation units assigned to the 20th GvOA.

Direct-reporting units

UNIT	BASE	TYPES
113th OVE	Sperenburg	Mi-8MTV, Mi-24RKR, Mi-22, Mi-6VKP, Mi-8K
226th OSAP	Sperenburg	Mi-8T, Mi-8TL, Mi-8TB, Mi-8S, Mi-8PS, Mi-9
239th GvOVP	Oranienburg	Mi-6, Mi-8MT, Mi-MTV
292nd OERVE	Cochstedt	Mi-8SMV, Mi-8PPA, Mi-9, Mi-8T

The 239th GvOVP bears the honour title 'Belgorodsky'

Withdrawal timetable

225th OVP	April 1991	
9th OVE	April 1991	Oranienburg
486th OVP	1 August 1991	
296th OVE	May 1992	(Some aircraft to Oranienburg)
485th OVP	May 1992	
292nd OERVE	June 1992	
178th OVP	July 1992	
440th OVP	July 1992	
41st OVE	1/7 August 1992	
336th OVP	8/12 August 1992	
487th OVP	11/13 August 1992	
6th OVE	20 August 1992	
298th OVE	August 1992	(Mi-2Ts to Werneuchen)
172nd OVP	October 1992	Kaliningrad
439th OVP	October 1992	Kaliningrad
9th OVE	August 1993	
226th OSAP	From April 1994	
337th OVP	13/16 May 1994	Novosibirsk
113th OVE	From 28 May 1994	
239th GvOVP	By June 1994	

The exact role of the little known Mi-8K is uncertain. As far as can be determined, only two were deployed with the Western Group of Forces, this one operating from Sperenburg. The box-like fairing projecting from the cut-out in the clamshell doors is the type's main distinguishing feature, but its exact function remains unclear.

ing the scope of activities which helicopters could undertake. Further roles were found for the helicopter during the late 1970s, when EW, command post and Elint versions of the 'Hip' began to enter service, some of them replacing Mi-4 conversions, others filling roles that were entirely new to the helicopter. Versions of the Mi-8 deployed with Army Aviation in Germany included the basic Mi-8T 'Hip-C' military transport, together with the armed Mi-8TB 'Hip-E' and the square-windowed, passenger-configured Mi-8S 'Hip-C'. The Mi-8PS was a refined Mi-8S version optimised for the military VIP transport role, and saw service in even greater numbers. Further transport versions include the Mi-8MT 'Hip-H' (known as the Mi-17 in civilian or foreign military use) and the pres-

surised Mi-8MTV 'Hip-H'. Two final transport derivatives are the Mi-8TL (Transportniy Laboratorniy), one of which is used for crash-site investigation, and the little known Mi-8K, which has cut-outs in its rear doors and has been seen with an unidentified projection jutting out from this. This may merely be a means of carrying outsized loads (boxed main rotor blades) or may be some kind of retractable antenna or sensor fairing. At least two served with Army Aviation in Germany.

Known specialised Mi-8 sub-types operational with the Western Group of Forces included the Mi-8VZPU (Vozduzhni'i Zapasnoi Punkt Upravlenja – Aerial Reserve Post Director) 'Hip-D'. This version, also erroneously referred to as the Mi-8VKP, was a dedicated radio relay aircraft, and

The Mil Mi-8PPA is a dedicated jamming platform, allocated the reporting name 'Hip-K' by ASCC. The aircraft has a row of heat exchangers below the fuselage, with massive cross-dipole antenna arrays on the sides of the rear fuselage, and huge box-like fairings on the cabin sides. Large numbers were deployed in Germany, where active jamming would have had a major role to play if war had broken out. This example flew from Dresden-Hellerau. A later version exists, based on the Mi-17 airframe, and with more solid antenna arrays, but this was not deployed with the Western Group of Forces.

served with a number of units, as did the Mi-8PPA (Patanovchik Pamech Aktivni'i – Active Jamming Director) 'Hip-K', a dedicated communications jammer, and the Mi-9 'Hip-G' airborne command post. The Mi-8SMV 'Hip-J' was a dedicated Elint platform, and served only with a single squadron based at Cochstedt.

The most important and influential helicopter to enter Soviet military service during the Cold War was the Mi-24. In the absence of a dedicated fixed-wing ground attack aircraft, the heavily armed Mi-24 gave Soviet army commanders the *Shturmovik* it had lacked since the retirement of the Il-2. Fast, heavily armed and well-armoured, the Mi-24 could fulfil the same kind of role, but also had the flexibility to lift an eight-man infantry squad or an anti-tank missile team. Direct fire support (primarily using unguided rocket projectiles) became a vital helicopter role, such that by 1989 it was estimated that 25 per cent of direct fire support would be provided by helicopters, most of it directed at targets beyond the range of conventional artillery, or in support of formations operating in the enemy rear areas.

The basic 'Hind-A' entered service with the Group of Soviet Forces in Germany during 1974, 90 being divided between two regiments at Parchim and Stendal. A handful may even have been delivered to these regiments as early as 1973. The new Mi-24D 'Hind-D', with redesigned forward fuselage, augmented the 'Hind-As' from 1976. The further improved Mi-24V 'Hind-E', equipped with the new tube-launched AT-6 'Spiral' missile, followed in 1979.

It had virtually replaced the Mi-24D by 1989, although the type remained in use at Allstedt until 1991 and about eight examples remained on charge until the withdrawal from Stendal in 1992.

The introduction of the Mi-24 allowed the development of new tactics, materially contributing to the move towards faster-flowing assaults and airborne descents, and encouraging the development of a seamless system of close air support, with the careful co-ordination of Mi-24 helicopters, Su-25 ground attack aircraft, and MiG-27 or Su-17 fighter-bombers. It was the introduction of the Mi-24 that prompted the establishment in 1979 of a separate 'Army Aviation', which had been abandoned and became part of

Red Stars over Germany

The up-engined and updated Mi-8MT and Mi-8MTV 'Hip-H' (usually known as the Mi-17 in civilian or in foreign military service) was in service with the 16th Air Army in large numbers. The type's higher engine power made it a more useful tactical helicopter, and it was preferred to the Mi-8 by the front-line Army Aviation regiments. Many examples were fitted with scabbed-on cockpit armour and chaff/flare dispensers, and some were heavily armed for use in the assault role, with up to six rocket pods on the outrigger pylons. This red-coded Mi-8MTV served with the 6th OVE at Dresden Hellerau. This aircraft has a covered L-166V-11E Ispanka IR jammer mounted on the rear part of the engine fairing.

Frontal Aviation in 1942. Frontal Aviation retained control of fixed-wing close-support aircraft, but the operational control of helicopter units was passed directly to ground force commanders.

By 1990 each army had its own organic Armeiskaya Aviatsiya (Army Aviation) element, with a single headquarters squadron (actually designated as an Independent Helicopter Squadron) for liaison and command post duties, as well as two Independent Helicopter Regiments equipped with a standardised mix of 'Hips' and 'Hinds' (described below). All Army Aviation squadrons are further divided into *zveno* (flight) and *para* (pair) sub-units. The headquarters Otdelnyi Vertoletnyi Eskadriliya (Independent Helicopter Squadron, OVE) would have two liaison/utility-tasked *zveno*, each usually equipped with four Mi-8, Mi-17 or Mi-2 helicopters, or perhaps with one *zveno* operating Mi-8s and the other Mi-2s. One *zveno* would be assigned to reconnaissance, with a *para* of Mi-24RCh 'Hind-G1' helicopters (also known as the Mi-24RKR) for NBC monitoring and reconnaissance, and a second *para* of Mi-24K 'Hind-G2' fire-correction helicopters. Another *zveno* (or sometimes just a single *para*) would be equipped with the communications-jamming Mi-8PPA 'Hip-K'. Finally, the squadron would have a single command post *para*, with one Mi-6VKP 'Hook-B' and one Mi-22 'Hook-C'.

The first Otdelnyi Vertoletnyi Polk (Independent Helicopter Regiment, OVP) assigned to each army would have a straightforward assault/transport structure, with two

assault *eskadrilya* (squadrons) and a third transport *eskadrilya*. The assault *eskadrilya* each had five *zveno* with four Mi-24V 'Hind-E' or Mi-24P 'Hind-F' helicopters, sometimes with a mix of both types in mixed *zveno* or even mixed *paras*, with one aircraft of each type operating together. The latter arrangement is believed to have been extremely uncommon, except on an *ad hoc* basis. The third, transport squadron would have five *zveno* of Mi-8T 'Hip-C', Mi-8TB 'Hip-E' or Mi-8MTB 'Hip-H' transport helicopters, sometimes with a different sub-variant equipping different *zveno*.

The second OVE assigned to each army had a very different multi-role structure, with three identically equipped multi-role *eskadrilya*. Each had two *zveno* with a total of eight Mi-24V and/or Mi-24Ps, with two more *zveno* operating 'Hip' transport sub-variants. The fifth *zveno* had two *para* of Mi-24RKRs and two of Mi-24Ks, while a final *para* of communications relay Mi-8VZPU (sometimes known as Mi-8VKP) 'Hip-D' or Mi-9 'Hip-Gs' would complete each *eskadrilya*.

The 1st GvTA controlled the 225th OVP at Allstedt, the 485th OVP at Brandis, and the 6th OVE at Dresden Hellerau. The two regiments were both non-standard, the 225th having only 'Hind-Ds' and 'Hip-Es' (all red-coded), and the 485th having no Mi-24Ps among its otherwise standard complement of yellow- and orange-coded aircraft. The 6th OVE's aircraft wore yellow codes.

Helicopter units reporting to the 2nd GvTA were the

The Mil Mi-6 'Hook-A' provided heavy-lift support to the Western Group of Forces. Powered by a pair of 4,700-shp (3506-kW) Soloviev D-25V (TV-2VM) turboshafts, the Mi-6 is capable of 162 kt (300 km/h; 186 mph), which for many years made it the fastest helicopter in the world, as well as the largest. The aircraft is capable of carrying heavy underslung loads, and its capacious cabin can be reroled quickly and easily to allow the carriage of passengers, freight, stretchers or vehicles. Military Mi-6s were equipped with an Asanayev machine-gun in the heavily glazed nose. In East Germany, the heavyweight Mi-6s were seldom seen without their detachable stub wings.

Two specialised versions of the Mi-24 served with the Western Group of Forces. The Mi-24K is a dedicated fire-correction helicopter, with a massive oblique camera in the cabin, and an unidentified traversable electro-optical or TV sensor in the starboard chin position, usually covered by an upward-hinging door (seen closed here). The aircraft has no provision for ATGMs, and the guidance antenna pod below the port side of the nose is deleted. The Mi-24K does, however, frequently carry pods of unguided rocket projectiles under its anhedral stub wings. The front cockpit of the Mi-24K entirely lacks dual controls, and accommodates the sensor operator. The Mi-24K is known as the 'Hind-G2' to NATO, reflecting its similarity to the Mi-24RKR/RCh, with which it serves.

172nd and 439th OVPs, both based at Damm (Parchim), with red and yellow codes, respectively. The 439th included no Mi-24Ps, but maintained a detachment at Mirow-Lärz. Headquarters element was the 41st OVE at Werneuchen, whose yellow-coded fleet included some six Mi-2Ts, but no Mi-8PPAs.

The helicopter units of the 3rd Guards Shock Infantry Army consisted of the 178th and 440th Independent Helicopter Regiments, both based at Stendal and with white and red codes, respectively. The 440th was unusual in retaining eight Mi-24Ds alongside its Mi-24Vs. Headquarters unit for the 3rd Guards Infantry Army was the 9th OVE at Neuruppin (with red codes), which moved to

Oranienburg in April 1991, on Neuruppin's closure. This unit included at least one of the little-known Mi-8Ks.

The aviation elements of the 8th GvOA were the 336th OVP at Nohra, whose helicopters wore a mix of yellow and orange codes, the 486th OVP at Altes Lager (with white codes) and the 298th OVP at Hassleben, whose helicopters wore red codes, and included eight Mi-2Ts and no Mi-8PPAs or Mi-22s. Only a handful of Mi-24Ps were in use, all with the 486th.

The 20th GvOA could call upon the services of the 337th OVP at Mahlwinkel (with yellow codes), and the 487th OVP at Prenzlau (with blue codes), with a headquarters unit, the red-coded 296th OVE also at Mahlwinkel.

The Mi-24RKR 'Hind-G' is a dedicated NBC reconnaissance/monitoring aircraft, with soil sampling probes on each wing's endplate fin, and often with marker flag dispensers on the tailskid strut. The aircraft retains its nose-mounted gun turret, but lacks undernose EO and guidance pods.

The Western Group of Forces's sole Mil Mi-8TL (Transportniy Laboratornyi) was based at Sperenburg with the 226th OSAP and was believed to have been tasked with supporting aircraft accident investigation teams, for which it was presumably equipped with specialised equipment. Externally, the aircraft appears to have been almost indistinguishable from a standard transport-configured Mil Mi-8T 'Hip-C'.

The Czech-built Aero L-39 served with each of the 16th Air Army's two Sukhoi Su-25-equipped Shturmovik units, operating in the liaison, continuation and instrument flying training, and forward air control and FAC training. This aircraft carries a pair of 16-round 57-mm rocket pods, presumably loaded with white phosphorus rockets for target marking. Aero L-39Vs were also frequently detached to East Germany for target-towing duties.

The Prenzlau regiment moved to Gross Dölln to take over the old Tu-16/Tu-22 deployment ramp in about late 1990, then moved again to Werneuchen in late 1991. Some published orders of battle have suggested that these aviation units were actually assigned to the 6th GvMD, and not to the 20th GvOA, but this would seem very unlikely.

Reporting directly to Western Group of Forces headquarters were four more Army Aviation units. Sperenburg housed the 226th Otdelnyi Smechannyi Aviatsionnaya Polk (Independent Transport Aviation Regiment, abbreviated as OSAP), which included an Army Aviation *eskadrilya* with five *zvenos* operating a mix of yellow-coded Mi-8S, Mi-8PS and Mi-8T 'Hip-Cs' all used primarily for VIP and liaison flying. The squadron also included a pair of yellow-coded Mi-9s. Also based at Sperenburg was the 113th OVE, which operated three *zvenos* of Mi-8MTs, with a *zveno* of Mi-24RKRs and a *zveno* with one *para* of Mi-9s and a *para* with one Mi-22 and one Mi-6VKP. The squadron also parented one of the shadowy Mi-8Ks, with a cut-out in the rear doors, which may have housed a deployable sensor or may merely have allowed the carriage of outsized loads like spare rotor blades. The role of the squadron was believed to be to act as a wartime reserve, providing extra helicopters to other regiments, and provid-

ing an extra command element. These aircraft (apart from the red-coded 'Hooks') had yellow codes, but were augmented by 'Hips' from many other regiments.

Rather more specialised was the 239th 'Belgorodskii' GvOVP, whose 26 Mi-6s and 36 Mi-8MTs (all with red code letters) provided airlift support for the airborne and special forces assigned to the Western Group of Forces. Some sources suggest that the regiment reported directly to the 16th Air Army headquarters, but this cannot be confirmed, not least because only some of the Army Aviation units appear in the official Western Group of Forces order of battle released by the Russians before the final pull-out. The final direct-reporting Army Aviation unit was the Cochstedt-based 292nd Otdelnyi Eletronika Radiorazvedka Vertoletnyi Eskadriliya (Independent Electronic and Radio reconnaissance Helicopter Squadron, OERVE), whose red-coded complement included three *paras* with six communications-jamming Mi-8PPAs, a single communications relay *para* with two Mi-9s and *three* paras with six of the elusive and little known Mi-8SMV 'Hip-J' Elint aircraft. The squadron's specialised Mi-8 and Mi-9 sub-variants were augmented by straight transport 'Hips'.

Although assigned to the operational control of the army commanders, the Army Aviation units were manned by air

forces' personnel, and Frontal Aviation remained responsible for training and logistics support.

Air forces

In addition to the organic (rotary-wing) aviation assets directly attached to its armies, and the other direct-reporting Army Aviation units, the Western Group of Forces could call upon its own tactical air force. Reporting directly to the Headquarters of the Group of Soviet Forces in Germany and not subordinate to any of the five numbered armies was the 16th Red Banner Air Army, headquartered at Zossen-Wunsdorf. Formed mainly from Frontal Aviation tactical fighter, fighter-bomber and reconnaissance units, but also including Long-Range Aviation transport aircraft, the 16th Air Army controlled three fighter divisions and two fighter-bomber divisions (each with some three regiments), with a number of reconnaissance and transport units. At one time these divisions reported to intermediate Northern and Southern Tactical Air Corps, but these headquarters may have been inactive during 1991, since they do not appear in the incomplete (but official) Russian orders of battle which refer to that period.

The 16th Air Army was formed in August 1942 to support the Stalingrad Front, under the command of General P. S. Stepanov, who was replaced on 28 September by

General S. I. Rudenko. The 16th Air Army supported Russian counter-attacks at Stalingrad, and supported the Don Front's 65th and 24th Armies during the Winter Offensive of 1942. The organisation proved effective in combat and also adept at developing tactics and equipment. The Il-2 received its second, gunner's cockpit largely at the instigation of the 16th Air Army, which was also influential in the setting up of the radio control network for the defence of Leningrad.

Below: This landing Su-25 is slowed by its twin brake chutes.

Bottom: Another non-standard camouflage is seen on a 357th OShAP Su-25 at Tütow. The aircraft carries a cartoon rook emblem on the engine intake.

Red Stars over Germany

One of the two Su-25UBs assigned to the 357th OShAP at Tütow. Between October 1986 and November 1987, the regiment was based in Afghanistan, with one of its squadrons based at Kandahar and the other two at Bagram. One of the regiment's pilots, Konstantin Pavlukov, was made a 'Hero of the Soviet Union' and later killed himself with a hand grenade. The unit moved to Demmin in December 1988. During its service in Germany, the unit suffered some unfortunate incidents. On 12 April 1990, for example, one of the unit's Su-25s fired two air-to-surface missiles from the Tütow ramp: one exploded on the airfield and the other wiped out a nearby grain elevator.

The 16th Air Army played a major part in the Battle of Kursk (as one of three participating Air Armies), renovating 154 airfields for use during the battle. The 16th took part in attacks on Orle in July 1943, and attacked river crossings over the Dnieper.

From July 1944, the 16th Air Army supported the First White Russian Front, co-operating closely with the advancing tank armies as they pursued the retreating German 4th Army. The organisation played a part in the liberation of Baranovichi, and then in the Vistula offensive, before supporting the belated liberation of Warsaw in January 1945, by which time it included the 1st Composite Air Division of the Polish army. During 1945, the 16th Air Army supported Zhukhov's drive on Berlin, building 32 airfields, and adding hard runways to 15 more between 26 January and 7 February. When airfields became unusable due to the thick mud, the 16th Air Army used autobahn strips, paving the central reservation to give 75-ft (23-m) wide runways.

When Nazi Germany finally collapsed in May 1945, the 16th Air Army found itself occupying a host of airfields around Berlin, most of which had been among the defeated Luftwaffe's oldest and best-equipped aerodromes. Officers messes were quickly stripped of their 'eagle and swastika' decorations and were pressed into use for the Soviet pilots, while hangars which had once seen Messerschmitts and Heinkels were used for the maintenance of MiGs and Sukhois. Many of these former Luftwaffe

airfields survived in front-line use until the final withdrawals of 1992-1994, and at one time there were plans for some (notably Alt Lonnewitz) to be taken over by the new Luftwaffe.

Details of the deployment and basing of the 16th Air Army during the 1950s, 1960s, 1970s and even the early 1980s are uncertain. The only information coming out of East Germany on aircraft types and location was piecemeal or highly classified, and most of the orders of battle published before the fall of the Berlin Wall were remarkably inaccurate. Aircraft spotting was not encouraged! It is clear that for most of the Cold War period, the 16th Air Army was maintained at maximum strength, with the latest combat aircraft, and that there were few base closures or unreplaced unit withdrawals before the reunification of the two Germanies. The posture of the 16th Air Army fluctuated slightly, with reductions in offensive capability when circumstances dictated (when tension between the superpowers reduced), and with increases at other times. A regiment of Il-28 'Beagle' bombers, for example, was withdrawn with great publicity from Oranienburg on one occasion, while bombers from bases in the USSR have frequently been forward-deployed on 16th Air Army airfields.

Generally, though, it can be seen that the 16th Air Army's fighter regiments were among the first to transition from piston-engined Lavochkins and Yaks to the Mikoyan Gurevich MiG-15 'Fagot' (it is not thought that earlier jets like the MiG-9, or the competing Lavochkin La-15,

The Su-17M-4s of the 730th APIB at Neuruppin wore red nose codes, while the 'Fitters' of the 20th APIB at Templin wore yellow codes. The Su-17M-4's primary role in East Germany was defence suppression. Red- (or perhaps black-) coded Su-17M-3 'Fitter-Hs' were used by the 294th ORAP at Allstedt in the reconnaissance role. The blue and white badge on the nose of this aircraft is a logo often used by the Sukhoi OKB.

This Su-17UM3 of the 20th APIB has a small rhinoceros insignia painted on its tailfin. Like many trainer versions of front-line Soviet tactical aircraft, the Su-17UM3 has a very poor view from the rear seat, and on approach the instructor relies on a small retractable periscope. Soviet fast-jet regiments in Germany generally included a large number of two-seat trainers, reflecting in part the heavy commitment to training young pilots fresh from advanced training and basic type conversion. The fourth squadron of each regiment lacked aircraft of its own, and included only Third Class pilots working up to operational readiness.

reached Germany-based units), and its attack elements were among the first to receive Ilyushin Il-28 'Beagle' tactical bombers. Successive re-equipments brought MiG-17 'Fargos', MiG-19 'Farmers' and, during the early 1960s, 'MiG-21 'Fishbeds' to the fighter regiments, with older MiG-15s and MiG-17s passing to fighter-bomber units. The 1960s saw the conversion of all of the fighter regiments to the MiG-21, with many attack units converting to supersonic Su-7 'Fitters' and Yak-28 'Brewers'. Swing-wing aircraft like the MiG-23, Su-17 and MiG-27 replaced the older types during the 1970s.

Although the 16th Air Army existed to support the five Soviet armies based in Germany, its fighter elements had a disproportionate importance, with a vital peacetime role of preventing overflights by NATO reconnaissance aircraft. Inevitably described by the West as navigational errors, these deliberate overflights and penetrations did take place. After an initial period during which RAF Canberras and RAF-crewed RB-45s were able to use their altitude performance to avoid interception, the introduction of jet fighters by the Western Group of Forces made things more dangerous for the reconnaissance crews, and more subtle tactics had to be developed. A new generation of ultra-high-altitude reconnaissance aircraft introduced during the late 1950s allowed a limited resumption of direct overflights for a restricted period, before Soviet fighters with better high-altitude performance were deployed in East Germany. RB-57Ds (and later RB-57Fs) were operated from Rhein Main AFB under Operation Bordertown between 1959 and 1964 (when MiG-21s arrived). Even when overflights were impossible, there was an endless game of cat-and-mouse played between NATO aircraft and 16th Air Army

fighters, with the Western aircraft making feints (and sometimes actual penetrations), or sometimes accidentally or deliberately straying from the recognised air corridors to Berlin in order to trigger a Soviet reaction, which would then be recorded, timed and analysed.

These games were not without casualties, although the victims were often innocent aircraft which had genuinely strayed off course. During the Berlin Airlift, Russian fighters (mainly Yak-3s and Lavochkin La-9s, but even including some Il-10s) harassed the incoming and outgoing allied transport aircraft. Favourite tactics included head-on high-speed passes within the corridors and, over air-to-ground firing ranges, deliberate dives through the transport stream, firing cannon and machine-guns in front of oncoming transports. Forty-two such dive-strafe incidents were

Wearing a fur-collared, camouflaged two-piece flying suit, a combined seat/parachute harness, high-laced flying boots and the latest pattern flying helmet, this young 'Fitter' pilot proudly informed us that his squadron, the 20th APIB's third eskadrilya, was a Guards unit, as reflected by the insignia on the nose of his aircraft. The Su-17 is a popular aircraft with its pilots, and is affectionately nicknamed the 'Strizh' (Swallow).

Yellow 21 wears a Guards badge on its nose and, more unusually, a squadron badge on its fin. This consists of a yellow shield with the number 20 flanked by the initials G and D (in Western script), standing for Gross-Dölln. Above this is a blue bird of prey, with the number 3 superimposed, and a blue and white pennant. Some other 3rd Eskadrilya Su-17M-4s wore an entirely different badge, with a blue and white shield with XX (20) and 3 superimposed. This shield was itself superimposed on a double-headed Romanov eagle, wrapped around with a red, white and blue pennant.

Above: A MiG-27M of the Brand-based 911th APIB taxis past a World War II era Luftwaffe building at Nobitz. The bases in East Germany were an extraordinary combination of architectural styles, mixing Nazi and Soviet.

Right: A typical warload for the MiG-27K features 20-round B-8M 80-mm rocket pods and 250-kg cluster bombs, as well as the underfuselage 30-mm cannon.

reported by US pilots, with 14 more instances of gun fire in the vicinity of allied transports, and 54 instances of Soviet AAA. Ninety-six air misses were reported as a result of the Soviet fighters' close flying, and the Russians deliberately jammed allied radio frequencies on many occasions, and at other times chose to use them for fighter-to-fighter communications.

The Berlin corridors continued to be the setting for clashes and incidents even after the airlift. On 29 April 1952 an Air France DC-4 was shot up by Soviet fighters, which injured a stewardess and two passengers. On 12 March 1953 an RAF Lincoln (a type then frequently used by the RAF for Elint and Sigint missions) was attacked by a pair of MiG-15s near Kassell, in the US zone of Germany. Another Lincoln, from the Central Gunnery School, was shot

Sitting outside its typically well-camouflaged hardened aircraft shelter is a blue-coded MiG-27K 'Flogger-J2' of the 559th APIB at Finsterwalde, one of three MiG-27 units assigned to the Southern Tactical Air Corps' 105th ADIB. The division's other 'Flogger' units were the 911th APIB at Brand (equipped with the same sub-variant) and the 296th APIB at Grossenhain, equipped with the earlier MiG-27D/M 'Flogger-J'. The fourth MiG-27 unit in Germany was the 19th GvAPIB which partnered the Su-17M-4s of the 125th ADIB of the Northern Tactical Air Corps. The aircraft wears a small red 'Excellence' award on its nose.

down by MiG-15s later the same day. The Russians claimed that this aircraft was 75 miles (121 km) outside the Berlin corridor in which it was supposed to have been flying. At about the same time, a BEA Vickers Viking was attacked in the corridor but escaped unscathed. The pilot of a Belgian F-84 (H8-N) was luckier, being forced to land at Pütnitz after interception by based MiGs on 29 May 1958. An American military C-47 was forced down at Pütnitz on 20 May 1960, in similar circumstances. On 28 January 1964 a USAF T-39B on a radar navigation exercise was shot down over East Germany by Soviet fighters. Less than two months later a USAF RB-66C fell to the guns of Soviet MiG-19s from Pütnitz. When intercepted, it was 16 miles (26 km) over the wrong side of the East German border. Canadian TV personality Hughie Green (a former RAF pilot and keen private pilot) experienced the hazards of flying in the corridor when his Cessna 337 (perhaps mistaken for a US Army Cessna O-2) was attacked by MiGs.

The Soviets remained understandably suspicious of aircraft flying over East Germany, even those using the international airspace which formed the three corridors in and out of Berlin. Such suspicion was probably justified, since both the USAF and the RAF used the corridors for intelligence-gathering flights, using Elint, Comint and Sigint gear, sideways-looking radar and long-lens oblique cameras. The USAF's 7575th Operations Group at Rhein Main was tasked with Elint, Sigint and reconnaissance duties. Successively equipped with C-130A-IIs, C-130B-IIs and

C-130Es, one of the group's squadrons was specifically tasked with intelligence gathering within the Berlin corridor (Operation Creek Misty), which was also the main role of another group squadron equipped with C-97Gs. The RAF's No. 51 Squadron also operated in the Berlin corridor, using a variety of aircraft, including on-loan Varsities and Hastings. Seven SLAR-equipped RB-69s (converted Neptunes) which were operated by the USAF from Wiesbaden from 1957 on behalf of the CIA may also have made some flights in the corridor.

For most of the 1980s, the backbone of the 16th Air Army was provided by fighter regiments of MiG-23s (of various sub-types) based at Wittstock, Pütnitz (Damgarten), Alt Lonnewitz (Falkenburg), Merseburg, Zerbst, Köthen and Altes Lager (Juterbog), with a regiment of MiG-25 interceptors at Eberswalde (Finow) which parented a MiG-25 detachment at Wittstock. These had replaced MiG-21s during the mid-1970s. Reconnaissance MiG-25s were based at Parchim (a full regiment until about 1984) and Werneuchen (with Yak-28s and perhaps MiG-21Rs). Reconnaissance Yak-28s, MiG-25s and (from 1986) Su-24s were based at Welzow. MiG-21Rs were also based at Allstedt, close to the inner German border. The MiG-25 interceptors were intended to counter the USAF's SR-71 Blackbirds based at RAF Mildenhall, which began permanent operations from this location during 1982; when this detachment ceased operations in November 1989 before its return to the USA, the MiG-25s were redeployed to Rus-

In ferry configuration, with belly and underwing fuel tanks, a Grossenhain-based MiG-27 comes in to land, ventral fin folded away to prevent it from scraping the runway.

With a guards badge on its engine intake and a Mikoyan OKB badge on its nose, a yellow-coded MiG-27 of the 19th GvAPIB waits for clearance to line up on the Mirow-Lärz runway. The aircraft is armed with B-8M rocket pods under the wing gloves, each containing 20 80-mm unguided rocket projectiles. A runway controller's caravan is just visible behind the aircraft. From their bases in East Germany, 16th Air Army MiG-27s could have attacked targets over most of Germany, but could not have reached the Netherlands, Belgium or France.

Red Stars over Germany

The 16th Air Army used several styles of flying clothing, with different patterns of helmet, flying suit, jacket and boots. Here two pilots from the MiG-23-equipped 833rd IAP at Altes Lager demonstrate the heavyweight winter flying jacket, and one of the available types of leather jacket, which were favoured more for their image than their practical value. The pilot on the left wears high-laced flying boots, while his comrade has ankle-length boots. Both men wear the modern-pattern helmet, with its distinctive row of holes across the crown. Flying suits were issued in one-piece and two-piece form, in a variety of colours. Soviet flying kit is remarkably good, light, comfortable and protective. As time wore on, 16th Air Army pilots gained progressively less flying time, and were increasingly hindered by restrictions imposed by the new German government. Remarkably, morale held up well in spite of the various problems.

Although 16th Air Army tactical aircraft were accommodated in hardened aircraft shelters, routine operations were conducted from a conventional 'ramp' or hardstanding. Here, MiG-23UBs and MiG-23MLDs are prepared for a flying 'wave' at their base at Altes Lager. Despite its apparent obsolescence, the MiG-23MLD was popular with its pilots, and enjoyed a longer range than the more modern MiG-29. Israeli evaluation of the similar MiG-23ML found it to be an extremely effective tactical fighter, able to defeat the F-16 in some scenarios. The MiG-23MLD had a host of aerodynamic refinements, including notched wingroots and automatic wing leading-edge slats, and also featured a much improved defensive system, with extra upward-firing chaff/flare dispensers over the wingroots and an updated RHAWS.

MiG-27D standards and by similar newly-built aircraft known as MiG-27Ms (both versions are referred to as 'Flogger-J' by NATO) from 1982. The MiG-27s had a range of about 270 nm (310 miles; 500 km) with external fuel, and this gave them the ability to reach some Dutch airfield targets (Leeuwarden and Soesterburg, for example) and most airfields in West Germany. Su-17M 'Fitter-Ds' arrived at Gross Dölln (Templin) in 1977, and later at Neuruppin, and were replaced by the Su-17M3 'Fitter-H' from 1982. These aircraft had a longer range than the attack 'Floggers'. Between 1979 and early 1981, Gross Dölln hosted a regiment-sized detachment of Su-24 'Fencers' for operational evaluation, and two fully operational Su-24 regiments were deployed to Grossenhain and Brand (probably replacing Su-7s and Su-17s, respectively) from 1982.

Russia-based bombers were frequent visitors to Germany, both to reinforce the 16th Air Army in times of tension and to use the various German ranges. Tupolev Tu-16s, for example, were regular visitors to Damgarten, Gross Dölln and Oranienburg. A particularly large Tu-16 deployment was made in 1986, in the wake of the US raids on Libya, involving a reported total of more than 50 'Badgers'. This reflected the Soviet government's abhorrence of the operation, which was seen as a totally unjustifiable and undeclared act of war, made possible by the connivance of America's NATO allies. Gross Dölln also supported detachments by Tu-22 'Blinders' and Tu-22M 'Backfires'. There have even been reports of a Tu-160 deployment to Pütnitz.

The number of transport aircraft assigned directly to the 16th Air Army plummeted during the 1970s, due largely to the massive increase in helicopter numbers. Thus, the helicopter transport base at Furstenwalde actually closed in about 1977, its Mi-4 and Mi-6 helicopters redeploying to Oranienburg. This base had become rather quiet since the 1969/1970 departure of its transport regiment, which had operated some 12 An-8 'Camps' and 45 Lisunov Li-2 'Cabs' since about 1965. Henceforth, the 16th Air Army would have only a small fleet of its own transport aircraft, and these were based at Sperenburg.

During the late 1980s, the 16th Air Army underwent major changes driven by a number of factors. Between 1982 and 1987, USAFE had re-equipped its 12 Europe-based fighter squadrons with F-16s and F-15s, while the introduction of the Panavia Tornado in Germany-based RAF and Luftwaffe bomber squadrons marked a dramatic improvement in NATO's offensive capability. Tactical fighters with less range than the Tornado also added to the

sia. When the SR-71s made their north-to-south trisonic runs along the German border (taking care to stay well inside West German airspace), they were shadowed by the MiG-25s. On several occasions the 16th Air Army played host to PVO interceptors from Russia, with Su-15s deploying to Brand in 1976, for example, and with Su-27s deploying to the same base in 1991. The Su-27s based at Chojna and Kluczewo-Stargard in Poland also had forward operating base facilities at Pütnitz and Altes Lager.

Offensive capability was provided by three regiments of MiG-27 'Flogger-Ds', at Nobitz (Altenburg), Lärz (Mirow) and Finsterwalde. These replaced Su-7s and MiG-17s from 1977, and were themselves replaced by aircraft upgraded to

16 Vozdushnaya Armiya (Order of Battle 1990)

Southern Tactical Air Corps

UNIT	BASE	TYPES
6th 'Donezkaya and Segedskaya' Gvardeiskaya Istrebeitelnyi Aviatsionnaya Diviziya, Merseburg		
31st 'Nilopolskyi' GvIAP	Alt Lonnewitz	MiG-29, -29UB, -23UB
85th 'Sebastapolskyi' GvIAP	Merseburg	MiG-29, -29UB, -23UB
968th IAP	Nobitz	MiG-29, -29UB, -23UB
All three regiments use a mix of 'Fulcrum-As', 'Fulcrum-Cs' and trainers.		
126th Gvardeiskaya Istrebeitelnyi Aviatsionnaya Diviziya, Zerbst		
35th IAP	Zerbst	MiG-29, -29UB, -23UB
73rd IAP	Köthen	MiG-29, -29UB, -23UB
833rd IAP	Altes Lager	MiG-23MLD, -23UB
Both MiG-29 units operated a mix of 'Fulcrum-As', 'Fulcrum-Cs' and trainers.		
105th Aviatsionnaya Diviziya Istrebeitelei-Bombardirovchikov		
296th APIB	Grossenhain	MiG-27, -23UB
559th APIB	Finsterwalde	MiG-27, -23UB
911th APIB	Brand	MiG-27, -23UB

Northern Tactical Air Corps

UNIT	BASE	TYPES
16th 'Swirskaya' Gvardeiskaya Istrebeitelnyi Aviatsionnaya Diviziya, Merseburg		
33rd IAP	Wittstock	MiG-29, -29UB, -23UB
733rd IAP	Pütnitz	MiG-29, -29UB, -23UB
787th IAP	Eberswalde	MiG-29, -29UB, -23UB
Wittstock had only one or two 'Fulcrum-Cs'; Pütnitz had an even mix of 'Fulcrum-As' and 'Fulcrum-Cs'; Eberswalde had only 'Fulcrum-Cs' and trainers.		
125th Aviatsionnaya Diviziya Istrebeitelei-Bombardirovchikov, Rechlin		
19th GvAPIB	Mirow-Lärz	MiG-27, -23UB
20th GvAPIB	Gross Dölln	Su-17M3/M4, -UM3
730th APIB	Neuruppin	Su-17M4, -UM3
Gross Dölln completed transition to Su-17M4s only after departure of 730th APIB.		

Direct-reporting units

UNIT	BASE	TYPES
Theatre Reconnaissance Division, Welzow (?)		
11th ORAP	Welzow	Su-24MR/MP
294th ORAP	Allstedt	Su-17M3/UM3
931st ORAP	Werneuchen	MiG-25R (various sub-types)
390th ORAE	Sperenburg	An-12, An-26, Il-20, Il-22
Theatre Transport Division, Sperenburg		
226th OSAP	Sperenburg	An-12, An-24V, An-26, Tu-134A3
Independent Shturmovik Regiments		
357th OShAP	Brandis	Su-25, Su-25UB, L-39
368th OShAP	Tütow	Su-25, Su-25UB, L-39

Withdrawal timetable

294th RAP	April 1991	
730th IBAP	26 April 1991	Unknown destination, except 3rd Eskadrilya to Gross Dölln
931st ORAP	May 1991	To Welzow
85th GvIAP	May 1991	
11th RAP (3rd Esk)	5-7 June 1991	Su-24MPs to Chortkov, Ukraine
73rd GvIAP	July 1991	
968th IAP	8 April 1992	Possibly to Lipetsk
357th OShAP	28 April 1992	
833rd IAP	13 May 1992	Orenburg (or Totskoye?)
35th IAP	10 June 1992	
911th APIB	1 July 1992	Kanolovo, Byelorussia
931st ORAP	6 July 1992	Siberia
19th GvAPIB	22 March 1993	Orenburg
296th APIB	22 March 1993	Orenburg
559th APIB	22 March 1993	Morozovsk
787th IAP	11 May 1993	Ros, Byelorussia
11th ORAP	8 June 1993	Marinovka
31st GvIAP	8 June 1993	Zernograd
368th OShAP	8 June 1993	Budyennovsk
20th GvIAP	5 April 1994	Taganrog
33rd IAP	7 April 1994	Andreapol (via Pütnitz)
733rd IAP	11 April 1994	Andreapol (with 33rd IAP)
226th OSAP, 390th ORAP left in stages by 31 August 1994.		

threat. It has been pointed out, for example, that Danish F-16s could, in certain configurations, have dropped bombs on Moscow.

It was clearly time to upgrade the 16th Air Army's air defence units, and this was made possible by the delivery of new Mikoyan MiG-29s, which equipped eight of the nine fighter regiments (24 of 27 squadrons) and thereby redressed the balance. The first unit to receive the new fighter was the 33rd Istrebeitelnyi Aviatsionnaya Polk (Fighter Aviation Regiment) at Wittstock, which traded in its blue-coded MiG-23M 'Flogger-Bs' for white-coded 'Fulcrum-As' in January 1986. Regiments at Pütnitz, Zerbst, Köthen, Merseburg, Nobitz, Alt Lonnewitz and Eberswalde re-equipped between 1987 and 1989, replacing

One of the 833rd IAP's MiG-23MLDs completes its landing roll at Altes Lager (known as Juterbog during Luftwaffe days, and home to Messerschmitt Bf 109s, for example). The MiG-23MLD uses a single cruciform brake parachute. As the last MiG-23 front-line fighter variant, the MiG-23MLD was compatible with the R-73 (AA-11 'Archer' AAM) and may also have had provision for helmet-mounted sights.

With its red stars faded, and its paintwork patched and retouched, one of the MiG-23UBs assigned to Grossenhain's 296th APIB taxis out prior to its departure. MiG-23, MiG-27 and MiG-29 units all maintained large numbers of two-seat MiG-23UBs for training and as hacks. Reports that these aircraft were designated MiG-23UM, reflecting a removal of combat capability under the terms of the CFE treaty, are in error.

This Mirow-Lärz-based MiG-23UB wears a Guards badge and the same yellow codes as the regiment's MiG-27s. The instructor's periscope is raised when the aircraft is taxiing, and until the undercarriage is raised. It automatically deploys when the undercarriage is lowered again.

MiG-23MLDs (Pütnitz and Köthen), MiG-25s (Ebers-walde), and MiG-23Ms, while Nobitz was new to the fighter role. Single-seat MiG-29s from several production series were used by the 16th Air Army, including some from the earliest production blocks (these had ventral fins and no overwing chaff/flare dispensers), while others were brand-new, factory-fresh, big-spined 'Fulcrum-Cs'. The latter sub-type has no separate OKB designation, and differs only in having increased fuel capacity (between 75 and 240 litres/16 to 53 Imp gal, according to different Mikoyan documents) and perhaps a refined defensive aids sub-system. Many of the Germany-based MiG-29s were modified to partial MiG-29S standards, with provision for underwing fuel tanks and other improvements.

The ninth fighter unit in East Germany, the 833rd IAP at Altes Lager, retained the MiG-23MLD 'Flogger-K', and may have been scheduled to convert to the MiG-29 had the 16th Air Army stayed in Germany. Alternatively, it may have been decided that to retain one fighter regiment whose aircraft had a longer range than the MiG-29 would offer useful tactical flexibility. The MiG-23 had a radius of action of 1000 km (621 miles) in the fighter role, while the MiG-29 'Fulcrum-A' had a radius of only 640 km (398 miles). 'Only' is perhaps the wrong word to use, since a 640-km range from their East German bases would have allowed the 16th Air Army's MiG-29s to range over the whole of Germany and Holland, and the only Belgian air-field not in range would have been Koksijde. In north-east France, the bases at Reims, Metz/Frascaty, Toul/Rosières, Nancy/Ochey, Strasbourg/Entzheim and Colmar/Mayen-heim would all have been within range. The MiG-23MLDs and Polish-based Su-27s could have ranged even further.

The MiG-23 has often been underrated, and is most often compared with obsolete Western fighters like the F-4

Phantom. In fact, the aircraft is surprisingly capable, with good agility, a well thought out weapons system and excellent performance characteristics. The lightweight MiG-23ML and improved MiG-23MLD are particularly impressive aircraft. When Israel evaluated a defecting Syrian MiG-23ML, it found to its surprise that the 'Flogger' repre-sented a formidable opponent, capable of bettering the F-16A in some situations.

The 16th Air Army's reconnaissance and EW assets were upgraded at the same time, with Allstedt's MiG-21Rs giv-ing way to specially configured Su-17s and the last Yak-28s being retired from Welzow in 1986 (replaced by EW-configured Su-24MP 'Fencer-Fs') and from Werneuchen in 1988 (replaced by MiG-25BM 'Foxbat-F' defence suppres-sion aircraft). The introduction of the Su-17M3 'Fitter-H' in the reconnaissance role was a major improvement. Although the Su-17 lacked some of the MiG-21's outright speed and altitude performance, it was faster at low level, and had much better range and the ability to carry a greater load. The Allstedt aircraft were equipped with the massive KKR-ITA/2-54 reconnaissance pod. This contained day and night optical sensors, Elint equipment, and photoflash, chaff and flare cartridges. This basically gave one pod the capability of the four separate pods used by the regiment's old MiG-21Rs. (These were, for the record: the D pod for daylight photography with six A-39 cameras, an Ashtchafa strip camera, SPO-3R emitter detector and ASO-2 ECM; the R pod for active and passive radar reconnaissance with LYRA and MS-81 monitors and a single A-39 camera; the N pod for night photography; and the ED pod for Sigint/ Elint and ECM duties). In the fighter-bomber role, Neu-ruppin converted to the Su-17M4 'Fitter-K', with Templin following but reportedly not completing the process until the withdrawal of the Neuruppin aircraft allowed its third squadron to re-equip.

At the same time, tension between Russia and America was diminishing and the new General Secretary, Mikhail Gorbachev, was pursuing disarmament with some fervour. While attempting to solve the crisis facing Russian Com-munism with his programme of restructuring (*Perestroika*), Gorbachev also aimed to play the part of international peacemaker. His aim was to reduce the numbers of strategic nuclear missiles and to deflect the USA from its stated intent to develop 'Star Wars' anti-ballistic missile weapons under the Strategic Defense Initiative (SDI). Although claiming to act from altruistic motives in the realisation that we all are part of one interconnected world and fear the spectre of nuclear catastrophe, Gorbachev was probably motivated by terror of the potential expenditure that a renewed phase of the arms race would entail. Gorbachev was behind the 1987 Warsaw Treaty Organisation declara-

tion to the effect that it would never begin hostilities unless under armed attack, would never make the first use of nuclear weapons, that it had no territorial claims on any state in Europe or outside, and that it would ensure that the new defensive defence doctrine put forward by Ogarkov was accepted.

To add substance to these declarations it was felt that it would be politically useful to reduce the organisation's most visible offensive capability. Accordingly, the Su-24 strategic nuclear strike regiments at Brand and Grossenhain (which had reported to the 4th Air Army for operational control) were withdrawn and replaced by shorter-ranged new-generation MiG-27K 'Flogger-J2s' and MiG-27D/M 'Flogger-Js', one regiment redeploying from Nobitz, which became a fighter base with MiG-29s. The Su-24 regiments were not disbanded; instead, they redeployed to bases in the USSR, from where they would doubtless have returned to German or Polish bases in times of tension. In any case, their replacements were nuclear-capable MiG-27s, and it is also possible that each of the MiG-23 fighter regiments (and the new MiG-29 regiments which replaced them) included a nuclear strike squadron. In his book, the Soviet defector Alexander Zuyev (himself a MiG-29 pilot) revealed that his own MiG-29 regiment consisted of a first nuclear strike squadron, a second escort/sweep squadron and a third base defence squadron, and inferred that this was standard practice. The strike aircraft would have carried a single 30-kT RN-40 on the reinforced port inboard pylon. Such an arrangement may have existed in 16th Air Army MiG-29 regiments, since it was acknowledged at both Eberswalde

and Pütnitz that one of the three squadrons in each regiment was tasked with the fighter-bomber role, although it was not specified whether this then included a nuclear capability.

Thus, while the 16th Air Army appeared to be reducing its offensive capability, it was actually improving its short-range tactical attack and strike potential. From 1988, the 16th Air Army also gained two Otdelnyi Shturmovoi Aviatsionnaya Polk (Independent *Shturmovik* Aviation Regiment, OShAP), with Sukhoi Su-25s, while the Su-17 fighter-bomber regiments at Gross Dölln and Neuruppin began to convert from the Su-17M3 to the Su-17M4.

In the normal course of events, one might have expected to see the modernisation of the 16th Air Army continuing, perhaps with Su-27s replacing some of the MiG-29s and with the introduction of even newer aircraft types planned for the late 1990s. The Mikoyan MiG-29M, for example, with its extended range and multi-role capability, was developed almost specifically to meet the requirements of the Group of Soviet Forces in Germany, and might eventually have re-equipped the Su-17 and MiG-27 units, as well as those operating the basic 'Fulcrum-A' and 'Fulcrum-C'. Such a force would have dramatically increased the flexibility of the 16th Air Army, radically improving both air-to-air and air-to-ground capabilities, while appearing to mark a switch to an all-fighter force, without overtly hostile dedicated fighter-bombers. All such plans were thrown into disarray after 7 November 1989, however, when the Berlin Wall was torn down. Mikhail Gorbachev's *Perestroika* had had little effect in stimulating the stagnating Russian econo-

White 26, a Pütnitz-based early series MiG-29 'Fulcrum-A', carries an R-60 (AA-8 'Aphid') training round underwing. Many 16th Air Army 'Fulcrum-As' were replaced by 'Fulcrum-Cs' shortly before the reunification of the two Germanies, although more than half of the MiG-29s in Germany in 1990 were still 'Fulcrum-As', including perhaps 40 of the very early version with ventral fins, as seen here.

A well-worn early series MiG-29 lands at Nobitz. Aerodynamic and systems modifications brought these aircraft up to the same standards as later production 'Fulcrum-As', apart from the absence of overwing chaff/flare dispensers. One of the squadrons at Nobitz wore a swept winged star as its badge. This was applied below the cockpit on the port side.

Red Stars over Germany

The RAF uses the acronym QRA, and the USAF use the term 'zulu'. Whatever the language, the practise of maintaining fully-armed aircraft on quick-reaction alert extended east of the Iron Curtain. Here a 787th IAP 'Fulcrum-C' sits outside its shelter at Eberswalde, armed with two R-27 (AA-10 'Alamo') and two R-73 (AA-11 'Archer') AAMs underwing. The date was 14 November 1990, soon after the two Germanies were reunited, and when taking photographs over the fence at Soviet bases in Germany could be misinterpreted. The weather was typically East German, with a thick mist rendered sulphurous by the heavy pollution. The 787th IAP at Eberswalde was responsible for the defence of Berlin from the north, and had previously operated MiG-25s, whose task was to counter high-flying Mach 3 USAF SR-71 reconnaissance aircraft.

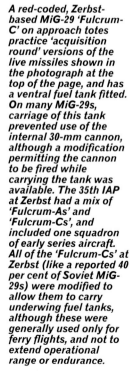

A red-coded, Zerbst-based MiG-29 'Fulcrum-C' on approach totes practice 'acquisition round' versions of the live missiles shown in the photograph at the top of the page, and has a ventral fuel tank fitted. On many MiG-29s, carriage of this tank prevented use of the internal 30-mm cannon, although a modification permitting the cannon to be fired while carrying the tank was available. The 35th IAP at Zerbst had a mix of 'Fulcrum-As' and 'Fulcrum-Cs', and included one squadron of early series aircraft. All of the 'Fulcrum-Cs' at Zerbst (like a reported 40 per cent of Soviet MiG-29s) were modified to allow them to carry underwing fuel tanks, although these were generally used only for ferry flights, and not to extend operational range or endurance.

my, or in combating the waste, inefficiency and corruption which Russia's over-centralised and bureaucratic system had encouraged, but his talk of democracy (by which he meant something quite different to the West European sense of the word) let genies out of several bottles. Perhaps most importantly, it unleashed a tide of demands for German reunification, which represented a nightmare scenario for Russia.

One of the pillars of Soviet policy in the immediate aftermath of World War II had been that Germany should be kept weak and powerless, and while some Russian politicians claimed that they could have accepted an independent, unified Germany it would have to have been totally demilitarised and de-Nazified, like a left-wing, less-heavily armed version of Austria or Finland. By the 1980s, the German Democratic Republic seemed to be one of Russia's most faithful and useful allies, and the prospect of losing it – let alone of having to face a more powerful Germany – was impossible to contemplate. Moreover, it was clear to some farsighted observers that the reunification of the two Germanies might set in motion a process that would destroy the Warsaw Pact, and even the USSR itself. Once the Czechs or the Poles or the Ukrainians saw the East Germans gaining the benefits of living under a Western democracy, where would it end?

As demands for reunification grew, the cohesion of the Warsaw Pact began to weaken, and the position of the Soviet forces in East Germany grew steadily less tenable. On 6 July 1990, a NATO summit in London saw a declaration that the Germanies would reunite, and on 16 July, Russia and Germany signed a historic accord, which paved the way for the 12 September signing of a formal treaty in Moscow. Under this, the USSR agreed to withdraw its troops from Germany while Germany agreed in return to grant financial aid in resettling the Soviet troops. Germany also agreed to reduce its own troop levels (370,000 men in the Bundeswehr) to allay fears of a new, militarily powerful, reunified Germany. The former Federal and Democratic Republics formally reunified on 3 October 1990.

The Cold War was over, and the Western Group of Forces had no longer had any role to play, except to wait for repatriation. Overnight, the entire environment changed for the Soviet forces, which went from dominance to the status of unwanted guests. The 16th Air Army suddenly faced restrictions on when it could and could not fly, and was forced to take into account considerations such as the impact of noise on the local community. The use of training ranges was severely curtailed, and all flying had to be co-ordinated by a Luftwaffe lodger unit at Zossen. The Germans are reported to have gradually imposed constraints on low flying and the carriage of live weapons, and the pretence that the 16th Air Army was still an operational force

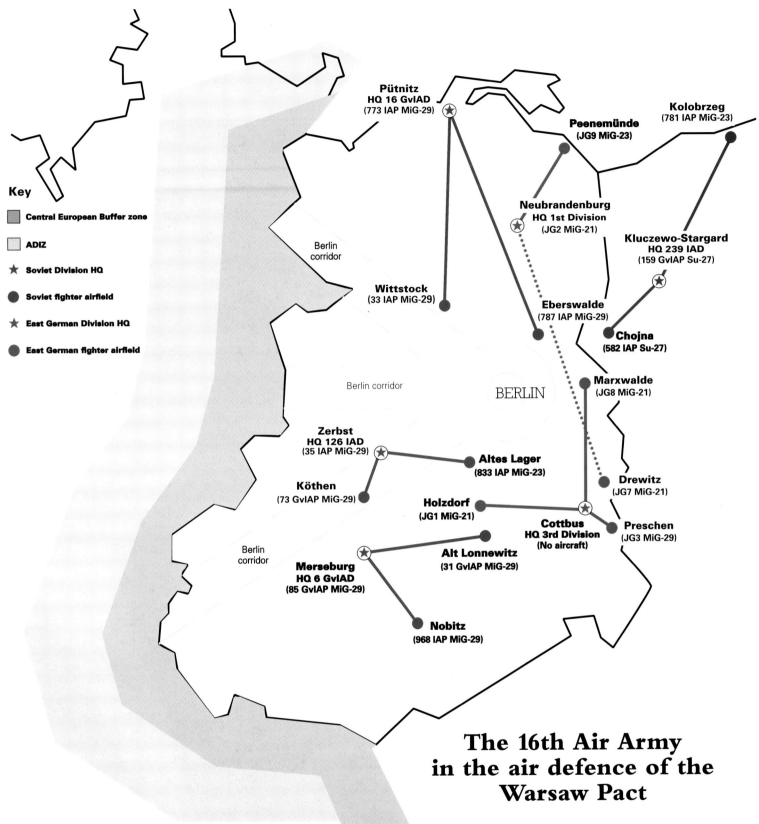

Key

■ Central European Buffer zone

□ ADIZ

★ Soviet Division HQ

● Soviet fighter airfield

★ East German Division HQ

● East German fighter airfield

Pütnitz
HQ 16 GvIAD
(773 IAP MiG-29)

Peenemünde
(JG9 MiG-23)

Kolobrzeg
(781 IAP MiG-23)

Neubrandenburg
HQ 1st Division
(JG2 MiG-21)

Kluczewo-Stargard
HQ 239 IAD
(159 GvIAP Su-27)

Berlin
corridor

Wittstock
(33 IAP MiG-29)

Eberswalde
(787 IAP MiG-29)

Chojna
(582 IAP Su-27)

Berlin corridor

BERLIN

Marxwalde
(JG8 MiG-21)

Zerbst
HQ 126 IAD
(35 IAP MiG-29)

Altes Lager
(833 IAP MiG-23)

Drewitz
(JG7 MiG-21)

Köthen
(73 GvIAP MiG-29)

Holzdorf
(JG1 MiG-21)

Cottbus
HQ 3rd Division
(No aircraft)

Preschen
(JG3 MiG-29)

Berlin
corridor

Merseburg
HQ 6 GvIAD
(85 GvIAP MiG-29)

Alt Lonnewitz
(31 GvIAP MiG-29)

Nobitz
(968 IAP MiG-29)

The 16th Air Army in the air defence of the Warsaw Pact

was strangled. When paid in ostmarks, Soviet military personnel had been something of an economic elite within East German society but, when paid in Deutschmarks, they rapidly became poor relations as East German wages started to catch up with those in the former Federal Republic.

The deteriorating economic situation in Russia itself also began to have an effect. There were frequent fuel shortages, and flying hours were progressively cut back. The gradual disintegration of the old USSR also led to bottlenecks in the logistics chain, with suppliers in newly independent states not always delivering necessary spares as eagerly as

they had done in Soviet days.

On the eve of reunification, the 16th Air Army controlled nine fighter regiments, six fighter-bomber regiments, two *Shturmovik* regiments, three reconnaissance regiments and two transport regiments, with a handful of miscellaneous squadrons. These 22 regiments controlled 625 combat aircraft, a figure that did not include the transports or the two-seat training versions of the MiG-23, MiG-25, MiG-29, Su-17 or Su-25. Each fast-jet fighter or fighter-bomber regiment generally comprised three squadrons of front-line aircraft, with a notional strength of 36 combat

This map shows how the three fighter divisions of the 16th Air Army were the Warsaw Pact's first line of air defence fighters, ahead of the fighters of the East German LSK/LV and Poland-based Soviet fighters. The Berlin air corridors, NATO buffer and Air Defence Identification zones are also shown.

Merseburg's MiG-29s wore blue regimental codes and prominent Guards badges. The regiment operated a mix of 'Fulcrum-As' and 'Fulcrum-Cs'. They were among the first tactical aircraft to leave Germany, and have not been illustrated before.

Two of the Pütnitz-based MiG-29s (one 'Fulcrum-A' and one 'Fulcrum-C') received this unusual disruptive-pattern two-tone green camouflage, perhaps as an experiment, and probably intended for the reduction of conspicuity in the ground attack role.

aircraft (plus two-seat trainers with each squadron and with An-2, Mi-8 and sometimes LET 410 liaison aircraft usually directly assigned to the regiment or division). A fourth squadron was home to the young, inexperienced Class 3 pilots, and lacked its own aircraft. In wartime, this fourth squadron would have been brought up to strength using aircraft held in reserve in the USSR, bringing regiments to a full wartime establishment of some 60 operational aircraft.

In fact, on the eve of German reunification, some regiments (particularly those that had only recently converted to a new type) were under-strength, and such deficiencies remained during the four-year rundown preceding final departure, although in isolated cases the withdrawal of MiG-29 regiments allowed some aircraft from departing units to be reallocated to squadrons that were staying. On the other hand, some of the regiments operating older aircraft types (e.g. the Su-17 and MiG-27) were larger, with up to 15 aircraft per squadron. It is possible that the MiG-29 units would have eventually built up to this kind of level.

Specialised aircraft types (including transports, reconnais-

sance aircraft and attack helicopters) were sometimes administered in smaller regiments, or in directly-reporting independent *eskadrilyas*. Regiments themselves had a staff flight with liaison aircraft and/or helicopters, and with a single example of the operational aircraft, bringing total strength to a notional 37 front-line aircraft. They were sub-divided into an aircraft wing (with the four flying squadrons, flight surgeon's and PT departments), a technical wing, a flight control battalion (with flight safety, radar and signals companies) and a support battalion (with administration, motor transport, airfield and guard companies).

Squadrons generally had between 12 and 20 operational pilots (all 'Sniper'-, first-, or second-class pilots), with four staff pilots. The latter consisted of the squadron commander, his deputy, the squadron navigation officer and the political officer. Their equivalents in the regiment staff would also usually be rated pilots. The squadron's aircraft were accommodated in a complex of hardened aircraft shelters (HASs), which were usually thickly covered by earth on which grass, scrub and bushes grew. In wartime, operations would have been conducted directly from the HASs

Although every MiG-29 regiment of the 16th Air Army maintained some MiG-29UB trainers on strength, each also operated a substantial number of MiG-23UB trainers. This red-coded MiG-29UB was operated by the 33rd IAP at Wittstock, who applied a lightning bolt to the LERXes of several of its MiG-29s, including this trainer. The codes of two-seat MiG-29s often did not fit into the overall sequence of regimental codes, sometimes indicating that these had been reassigned from other units. A MiG-29UB with blue-outlined yellow codes from Nobitz, for example, was among the aircraft on charge when the 33rd IAP returned to Russia.

but, in peacetime, aircraft were usually towed to the main airfield parking apron for operations. HAS (and indeed dispersed site) operations were practised for exercises, and alert aircraft, armed with live missiles, usually remained inside or outside their shelter. Runway-edge 'alert sheds' were not used.

The units based in Germany were among the best in the Soviet air forces, with long and distinguished histories and proud traditions. Several bore the 'Guards' honorific, a title awarded for distinguished service. The 'Guards' title can be awarded to entire divisions (whose component squadrons will retain their existing titles, and which may be Guards units in their own right), to regiments or even to component squadrons within a regiment. Guards units usually apply a distinctive badge, consisting of a garland of golden laurel leaves surrounding a red banner that bears the legend 'Gvardiya'. The Guards badge was not the only decorative marking to be worn by 16th Air Army aircraft. Some wore

a badge recognising their first-rate technical condition, this consisting of a dart-like 'aircraft' shape piercing a pentangle. Red stars painted below the canopy on other aircraft usually represented the destruction of a target drone. A handful of units even carried squadron or regiment badges.

The Soviet units were located mainly in a band running from north to south just east of the country's imaginary centreline, with the old East German air force located further east still, sandwiched between the Russians and the Polish border. Directly reporting to the 16th Air Army Headquarters at Zossen-Wunsdorf were the Northern Tactical Air Corps headquartered at Wittstock, and the Southern Tactical Air Corps headquartered at Wittenburg, together with the Reconnaissance Division headquartered at Allstedt, and the Theatre Transport Division headquartered at Sperenburg.

The Northern Tactical Air Corps controlled two Red Banner divisions. These were the 16th 'Swirskaya'

Apart from its bulged fuselage spine (shown to advantage in this unusual photograph of a 787th IAP aircraft), the 'Fulcrum-C' differed from earlier MiG-29 sub-variants in having reshaped wingtip ECM fairings, perhaps associated with a new active jammer. The new spine accommodated increased internal fuel as well as new avionics items.

Red Stars over Germany

When the Berlin Wall came crashing down, the MiG-29 fighter regiments in Germany were in the process of converting to the fat-backed 'Fulcrum-C', nicknamed 'Gorbatov' (hunchback). 'Fulcrum-As' released by this process would have been passed back to MiG-23 regiments in Russia, and may have been refurbished for export or converted for ground attack duties. This red-coded 'Fulcrum-C' was based at Alt Lonnewitz (otherwise known as Falkenburg) with the 31st GvIAP. The unit applied a Guards badge to the port side of the nose only, and operated a mix of MiG-29 sub-variants. The 31st GvIAP was one of three units which made up the 6th Guards Fighter Aviation Division (6 GvIAD), two of which (at Alt Lonnewitz and Merseburg) were Guards regiments.

Gvardeiskaya Istrebeitelnyi Aviatsionnaya Diviziya (Guards Fighter Aviation Division, GvIAD), headquartered at Püt-nitz, and the 125th Aviatsionnaya Diviziya Istrebeitelei-Bombardirovchikov (Fighter-Bomber Division, GvADIB) at Rechlin. Each of these divisions in turn controlled three regiments. Those attached to the 16th GvIAD were the 33rd Istrebeitelnyi Aviatsionnaya Polk (Fighter Aviation Regiment, IAP) at Wittstock (equipped with white-coded MiG-29s, including a single 'Fulcrum-C'), the 733rd (often reported as the 773rd) IAP at Pütnitz (with a mix of white-coded 'Fulcrum' sub-types) and the 787th IAP at Ebers-walde (with white-coded 'Fulcrum-Cs'). The 125th ADIB's lead unit was another MiG-27D/M 'Flogger-J' unit, the yellow-coded 19th GvAPIB at Mirow-Lärz. It was backed by the red-coded Su-17M4 'Fitter-Ks' of the Neuruppin-based 730th APIB, and by the yellow-coded 20th APIB, which was in the process of converting from the Su-17M3 'Fitter-H' to the Su-17M4 'Fitter-K'.

The Southern Tactical Air Corps had two divisions, both with a fighter role, and a single fighter-bomber division. These were the 6th 'Donezkaya and Segedskaya' GvIAD at Merseburg and the 126th IAD at Zerbst. The 6th IAD controlled three regiments, each equipped with a mix of 'Fulcrum-As' and 'Fulcrum-Cs'. These were the 31 Guards 'Nilopolskii' IAP at Falkenburg, whose aircraft wore red codes, the 85th Guards 'Sebastapolskii' IAP at Merseburg, with blue codes, and the 968th IAP at Nobitz, whose early ventral-finned 'Fulcrum-As' had blue-outlined orange codes, and whose 'Fulcrum-Cs' had red.

The 126th IAD also had three regiments, but while the

35th IAP and 73rd GvIAP at Zerbst and Köthen both operated a mix of red-coded 'Fulcrum-As' and 'Fulcrum-Cs', the 833rd IAP at Altes Lager had red-coded MiG-23MLDs. The 105th GvADIB at Grossenhain operated different versions of the MiG-27, with red-coded MiG-27D and MiG-27M 'Flogger-Js' attached to the 296th Aviatsion-naya Polk Istrebeitelei-Bombardirovchikov (Fighter-Bomber Regiment, APIB) at Grossenhain, and with blue-and red-coded MiG-27K 'Flogger-J2s' equipping the 559th APIB at Finsterwalde and the 911th (119th?) APIB at Brand, respectively.

The Theatre Reconnaissance Division controlled four reconnaissance units. The 11th 'Vitebski' Otdelnyi Razvedyvatelnyi Aviatsionnaya Polk (Independent Recon-naissance Aviation Regiment, ORAP) had white-coded Su-24MRs and MPs at Welzow, the 294th ORAP had Su-17M3 'Fitter-Hs' with three-digit black codes, and the 931st ORAP at Werneuchen flew a mixed bag of red-coded MiG-25s. The 390th Otdelnyi Razvedyvatelnyi Avi-atsionnaya Eskadrilya (Independent Reconnaissance Aviation Squadron, ORAE) flew a mix of EW, Elint and recce-configured An-12 'Cub-Bs', 'Cub-Cs' and 'Cub-Ds', An-26 'Curl-Bs', Il-20 'Coots' and Il-22 'Coot-Bs'. During 1991 these were joined by at least one Elint/EW-config-ured Il-76 'Candid-B'. Transport An-12s, An-24s and An-26s, plus the commander's Tu-134A3, were operated by the 226th OSAP at Sperenburg.

While no-one could deny the quantitative advantage enjoyed by the Soviet air forces in Germany, the sheer quality of the 16th Air Army was often underestimated in

This fat-backed 787th IAP 'Fulcrum-C' is seen departing from its base at Eberswalde on 11 May 1992, bound for Ros in Byelorussia. Clearly bearing the traces of a code reallocation (with 73 on the intake and 64 in small characters on the fin cap), the aircraft has five red stars painted below the canopy, each representing the destruction of a target drone. A large area around the gun bay has been repainted, although little care has been taken to ensure a precise colour match. Another unusual feature is the painted pattern on the hub of the nosewheel, whose significance is unknown. The aircraft carries underwing and centreline fuel tanks for the long ferry flight home. The pilot of this aircraft wears the old fashioned helmet with an external visor.

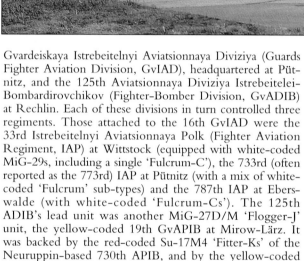

the West. Some NATO commanders and senior officers recognised the threat posed by the massive Warsaw Pact ground forces, but complacently assumed that the Russians would be unable to achieve air superiority. Comfortable hype and propaganda surrounded NATO's high profile, high-tech air forces, and to doubt them was simply not an option. One commonly repeated joke popular with NATO officers ran that two Russian officers were sitting in a cafe in Amsterdam (or Rotterdam, or Paris, or wherever) after a lightning advance across the North German plain. One said to the other, "Who won the air war then?" to which the other replied, "They did." The inference was clear, that while the five tank armies in East Germany might prove unstoppable, the Russian air forces were of little consequence. Such confidence in the superiority of NATO air power is praiseworthy – military men need to be confident. It may not have been wholly realistic, however.

Russian tactical aircraft in Germany were not tied to vulnerable fixed airfields in the same way as many NATO front-line fast jets. All Soviet aircraft can operate from semi-prepared strips and short stretches of taxiway or undamaged runway, while operations from highway strips were frequently practised. All of the airfields in East Germany were generously provided with well-camouflaged hardened aircraft shelters and had many potential emergency runways, some even having prepared runways on the grass areas,

with hard core packed down and covered in turf, while other airfields were directly linked by taxiways to straight stretches of autobahn, with pre-surveyed aircraft dispersals. In addition to these small, convenient highway strips, there were 11 longer, better-prepared autobahn strips, each with a runway in excess of 2500 m (8,200 ft) long and 22.5 m (74 ft) wide. These were located at Kavelstorf (south of Rostock), Netzeband (south of Wittstock), Oranienburg, Vehlefanz (north-west of Berlin), and Friedershorf-Skaby (north-east of Brand) in the Northern Tactical Air Corps area. In the south, such strips were located at Klein-Bademeusel (north-east of Finsterwalde), Ruhland (north of Grossenhain), Ottendorf-Okrilla (near Dresden), Leisnig (west of Leipzig), Osterfeld (south west of Leipzig) and Eichelborn (south west of Weimar). 16th Air Army and visiting aircraft could also use some abandoned former military airfields, including Haina (to which Werneuchen's MiG-25s sometimes deployed), the former helicopter base at Prenzlau, near Gross Dölln and the former transport helicopter base at Furstenwalde. Several of the Army Aviation helicopter bases could also accommodate fast-jet detachments.

NATO's Tornados and F-111s would not have had an easy task finding the 16th Air Army on the ground, let alone destroying it. Nor would things have been any easier in the air. Only one of the fighter regiments in East Ger-

A MiG-25RB of the 931st ORAP, originally based at Werneuchen, and (from May 1991) at Welzow. The 931st ORAP used four reconnaissance sub-variants of the MiG-25. The MiG-25RB was the basic reconnaissance bomber, with all-weather Peleng bombing system and five oblique and vertical ports for its three optical cameras.

The MiG-25RBK featured a large dielectric panel on the nose covering the antenna for the Kub SLAR, with additional panels below the nose. The similar MiG-25RBV had a smaller dielectric panel further forward for its SRS-9 Virazh SLAR.

An 11th ORAP Su-24MR lands at Welzow, trailing its two massive cruciform brake parachutes. The aircraft carries an Efir-1M pod under the starboard wing, and a Tangazh Elint pod on the centreline. The port underwing pylon is left empty but in operational use would carry a defensive AAM.

The store carried on the centreline of this Su-24MP 'Fencer-F' is unidentified, but may merely be an external fuel tank. The nose of the Su-24MP is covered in flush dielectric panels, and an unusual antenna fairing projects below the nose aft of the TFR radome.

many still operated the MiG-23 (and even this had the latest 'Flogger-K', which Israeli evaluation revealed to be a very capable aircraft, and a match for the F-16 in some limited circumstances), the rest all having re-equipped with the formidable MiG-29. Furthermore, reinforcements could have been expected in the shape of Sukhoi Su-27s, augmenting those that were already operational with Soviet forces in Poland.

There has been a great deal of controversy surrounding the relative merits of Russian fighters like the MiG-29 and the latest American teen-series superfighters. While it is true that the basic MiG-29 is handicapped by its limited endurance and poor maintainability, and by its inferior multi-role capability, the aircraft enjoys some performance advantages, and has better low-speed agility, acceleration and high-speed turn rate than, for example, the F-16. While the pilot has a higher workload cockpit, in some respects, this is partly balanced by the provision of an IRST and by the common use of helmet-mounted sights for off-boresight, emission-free, jam-proof target detection, acquisition and engagement. Furthermore, the MiG-29 probably has a better air-to-air weapons system than the F-16, with greater radar and missile range and with a heavier-calibre internal cannon. Moreover, Russian MiG-29s based in East

Germany were armed with the R-73 (AA-11 'Archer'), which is judged by many analysts to be a superior short-range missile to the latest versions of the AIM-9 Sidewinder, and with the R-27 (AA-10 'Alamo'), which has been favourably compared with the AIM-120 AMRAAM (which is only now coming into widespread service in the USAF and US Navy).

Until the withdrawal from Germany began, 16th Air Army pilots had ample opportunity for air-to-air and air-to-ground gunnery practice and for live missile shoots over the Baltic ranges. Dedicated target towing aircraft were frequently detached to Damgarten (including yellow-coded L-39Vs and Su-25BMs) for example. Realistic training was also achieved by the regular use of captive missile acquisition rounds. These were inert missile bodies, with neither motor nor warhead, but with a live seeker head. This allowed the pilot to practise 'locking-up' his missiles, and gave a true impression of when and how a missile would and would not lock-on to a target.

The various MiG-27 and Su-17 fighter-bombers would not have proved easy prey for allied fighters, while they could have used their impressive array of air-to-ground ordnance to wreak havoc on NATO targets. Often dismissed as being rather crude and old fashioned, the latest

The Antonov An-12 'Cub' served in transport, reconnaissance and jamming/chaff-laying roles. Although its regimental code places it in a group of standard transport aircraft operated by the Sperenburg-based 226th OSAP, twin underfuselage radomes would seem to identify this aircraft as a 'Cub-B' Elint aircraft, probably operated by the 390th ORAP at Sperenburg. Some analysts have suggested that its twin undernose radomes are too small to make it a 'Cub-B'. Supporting the theory that red 84 is a special duties aircraft is the fact that red 85 is an An-12BK 'Cub-C' (perhaps an airborne communications aircraft) with an ECM tailcone.

versions of the Mikoyan MiG-27 and Sukhoi Su-17 are in many respects extremely capable interdictor/strike aircraft. Hampered by a somewhat limited radius of action, the types are rugged and dependable, extremely resilient to battle damage and capable of operation from the most primitive semi-prepared airstrips. Both aircraft types are compatible with a wide range of air-to-surface weapons, and the units in East Germany were operational with passive radar-homing missiles like the Kh-25MP (AS-12 'Kegler') for the 'Wild Weasel' role. This was particularly important after the early withdrawal of dedicated defence suppression MiG-25BM 'Foxbat-Fs' from Werneuchen and Su-24MP 'Fencer-Fs' from Welzow.

As early as 1984, NATO analysts suggested that the SEAD (Suppression of Enemy Air Defence) role was taken especially seriously by the 16th Air Army, and that its war plans presupposed the establishment of three fronts in Europe, each of which would have three sanitised corridors, in which NATO SAMs and aircraft were to be rendered ineffective. Through these corridors, each of which would have been 25 miles (40 km) wide and 100 miles (160 km) deep, would have flowed the various tactical and strategic strike aircraft attacking NATO's comparatively vulnerable rear areas. Even as early as 1984, these analysts were concerned by the increasing inventory of AS-12 anti-radiation missiles being held by the 16th Air Army.

The later versions of the MiG-27 (the MiG-27M and MiG-27D) and the Su-17M-4 were equipped with enhanced weapons systems and could also use the laser-guided Kh-25ML (AS-10 'Karen'), the TV-guided Kh-29T

(AS-14 'Kedge') and the radio-command guided Kh-25MR. The Kaira system of the MiG-27K gave further improved night/adverse weather capability and allowed the aircraft to use laser-guided bombs like the KAB-500. This marked a much wider range of precision-guided weapons than was available to NATO fighter-bombers during the same period, and was in addition to a formidable built-in armament of heavy-calibre cannon and compatibility with the full range of 'dumb' freefall slick and retarded bombs, cluster bombs, gun pods and unguided rockets of every conceivable calibre, as well as napalm and fuel air explosive weapons.

Even those Western analysts who accepted that the 16th Air Army enjoyed numerical superiority, and that its equipment was of broadly comparable quality to that of its NATO counterparts, consistently underrated the operational capability of Soviet units. The Soviet pilot was widely assumed to be an unthinking, inflexible automaton, relying on strict ground control and unable to respond to changing tactical circumstances. While there may once have been grains of truth in such an assessment, it was hardly applicable during the late 1980s. There were undeniably shortcomings: Soviet pilots certainly flew less than their Western counterparts, and junior squadron pilots arrived on their squadrons with less useful experience than NATO first tourists, having gone straight from advanced flying training and academic weaponeering to type conversion, without any equivalent to, for example, the RAF's Tactical Weapons Units. This laid a heavy responsibility on front-line squadrons to teach tactics and type-specific weapons

Despite its unusual finish, this An-12BP 'Cub-A' is understood to be a standard transport aircraft, operated by the 226th OSAP at Sperenburg. An-12s played a major part in the withdrawal of 16th Air Army units from Germany, shuttling men and material back to Russia. Germany-based aircraft were augmented by An-12s from Rostov and from bases in Poland. The aircraft may also have been involved in some disreputable occurrences, since it has been reported that they were sometimes seen loading up with large numbers of new German cars (perhaps stolen to order) which were driven straight aboard after arriving at one of Sperenburg's many subsidiary entrances.

*The 390th **ORAP** at Sperenburg includes three Elint-configured An-26RTR 'Curl-Bs'. These are identifiable by the antenna array above and below their fuselages, but were painted in the same overall light grey as most of the 226th **OSAP**'s transport An-26 'Curl-As'. The aircraft were believed to have been used for Elint and Sigint duties.*

*Below right: Two An-24Vs (and a small number of the 10 An-26s) assigned to the 226th **OSAP** wear this blue, grey and white VIP colour scheme. The Russian flag has been added to the scheme on some of the aircraft.*

*Below: The An-26 was a mainstay of the Theatre Transport Division at Sperenburg, and the 226th **OSAP** had some 10 aircraft on charge, together with two examples of the similar An-24V 'Coke'. An-24s and An-26s from units outside Germany were frequent visitors to Sperenburg, including aircraft nominally owned and operated by Aeroflot.*

procedures, and meant that first-tour pilots took several months to become productive.

The one area in which *Perestroika* really had an effect was in the military, where past failings were rigorously addressed and qualities such as initiative were actively encouraged. From the late 1970s, the Russian air forces began to acknowledge past weaknesses in tactics, leadership and pilot initiative, and in the provision of sufficient realistic night flying and low-level flying training. That such an acknowledgement was made publicly meant that the problems were already being addressed and, by the early 1980s, Western preconceptions about Soviet pilots had become dangerously unrealistic stereotypes, and in some respects

(e.g. aircraft handling at low speeds and high alpha, and in 'edge of the envelope' situations), line Soviet pilots may have been better prepared than their Western equivalents. Combat experience in Afghanistan slowly filtered through to operational units in Europe, and allowed the development of new tactics and the adoption of some new, more effective equipment (e.g. improved defensive aids and chaff/flare dispensers). This improved aircrew morale, which was already better in the 16th Air Army than in other elements of the Soviet air forces. An elite force (itself a morale-winner), the 16th Air Army traditionally had had a 'tip-of-the-spear' type of role, and it was widely recognised that only the best personnel were posted to its units.

While Gorbachev's reforms in some respects made the military a less attractive career (pay declined relative to other professions, and wives were seldom able to earn a second wage), the job increasingly became one for the highly motivated, and the incidence of political appointees and time-servers was reduced. The old *Zampolit* political officers found a new role as *de facto* welfare officers, helping to improve conditions and cohesion. Housing and pay were generally better than in the rest of the air force, and the Western Group of Forces was in the forefront of social developments, such as the *Zhensoviets* (women's councils), which functioned like Western wives' clubs, organising an impressive list of leisure activities and helping to remove the monotony and drabness of garrison life.

Regardless of whether Soviet/Warsaw Pact-trained pilots would have proved as effective as their Western counterparts, it is quite likely that the Warsaw Pact's tactics would

have proved difficult to defeat. The superiority in aircraft numbers made it possible for the Warsaw Pact to accept heavy losses in establishing the corridors through the NATO front line (although the ready availability of fighters, defence suppression aircraft and massive jamming capability might have made losses lighter than some pessimistic Russian planners believed). Assuming 85 per cent readiness, the Warsaw Pact could have put 1,500 aircraft in the air simultaneously in the Northern Sector, with 1,100 more in the Central sector, and 1,100 more in the South. Once the corridors were established, massive packages of aircraft would have punched through, with a ratio of escort fighters approaching one fighter for every two attack aircraft. One wave, passing through the three corridors on one sector of the front, might easily have contained over 1,000 aircraft, with three or four regiments going through each corridor. The Warsaw Pact air forces expected to sustain three waves per day on each sector, after starting the war with up to eight waves in a single day, before attrition, battle damage and pilot fatigue took their toll.

The sanitised corridors would have been formed in stages, with *Spesnatz* teams, missiles and air strikes taking out the most important, high-priority targets, such as any airfields or Hawk SAM sites within range, and facilities like GCI radar stations. Massive jamming, using ground-based stations, helicopters and fixed-wing aircraft, would have been accompanied by further dedicated SEAD sorties. An-12 'Cub-Cs' would have performed stand-off-jamming behind the FEBA, disabling any remaining early warning or GCI radar stations. These would also have laid chaff corri-

A pair of Ilyushin Il-20 'Coot-As' formed the backbone of the 390th ORAP at Sperenburg. Believed to have entered service during 1978, the pair carried huge ventral SLAR pods and had numerous other antennas. The SLAR carried by the aircraft was believed to have been able to look vast distances into West Germany, and to produce a high-resolution radar map with moving target indication. Until 1991 the pair was augmented by an Il-22 'Coot-B' in Aeroflot markings. The two Il-20s were among the last Soviet aircraft to leave Germany.

This solitary Tupolev Tu-134A-3 'Crusty', operated by the 226th OSAP at Sperenburg, was used as the personal aircraft of the commander of the Western Group of Forces, but was also used for other VIP and high-priority transport flights. Aeroflot Tu-134s were regular visitors to Sperenburg, and there have been reports that air force Tu-134UBL and Tu-134BSh bomber crew trainers also visited the base. The prominent spikes on the fin leading-edge bullet and tailcone of this aircraft are understood to contain communications antennas.

*Above and right:
Aeroflot Antonov An-22
'Cocks', perhaps
manned by VTA crews,
were frequent visitors to
East Germany and
participated in the
withdrawal of air force
units. These massive
transports offered an
outsized load capability
matched only by the
An-124. The aircraft
often taxied with their
outboard engines shut
down. The aircraft above
was photographed at
Welzow, while the
aircraft to the right was
visiting Sperenburg.*

*Sperenburg received a
daily mail flight from
Russia. This service was
usually operated by an
Aeroflot Il-18, although
Tu-154s like the aircraft
pictured to the right
were often substituted
when passengers
needed to be carried as
well. The use of Aeroflot
aircraft to support
military operations was
routine in the former
Soviet Union, and
aircraft were frequently
used as a 'reserve' by the
military's own transport
force. Aeroflot aircrew
were all air force
reservists anyway, liable
to be called up if
required. This Tu-154
wears a Russian flag
and a Russian civil
registration.*

dors through which the SEAD aircraft would approach. The anti-radar strike aircraft would have been accompanied by Su-24MP 'Fencer-F' and Tu-16RM 'Badger-J' escort jammers, with Tu-16PP 'Badger-Hs' extending the chaff corridor forwards, followed by 'Cubs' once the corridor was secure. The first mass strike package would be heavily escorted by fighters, and preceded by an offensive fighter sweep, whose duties would include destruction of any NATO AEW aircraft. A typical three-corridor wave would include some 600 attack aircraft, with 400 fighter-bombers, 100 Su-24 'Fencers', and 100 'Badgers' and 'Backfires'. The

escort force might typically have included 200 MiG-21s and MiG-23s, and 200 MiG-29s, with a handful of Su-27s and MiG-31s.

Fortunately, the reunification of the two Germanies, and the peaceful accord reached by President Gorbachev and his German opposite numbers, meant that this mighty war machine could start the process of departure without ever having been called upon to fulfil its assigned role. Although a four-year timetable had been established, the sheer size of the Soviet forces meant that the retreat would be something of a race against time.

Czechoslovakia offered its assistance with Soviet troop withdrawals, offering to provide up to four trains daily, while Bonn offered to use its Transall C.160s to expedite the withdrawal of Soviet forces. By the end of 1990, 12,000 troops had left Germany, with two full divisions and 80 smaller formations. This was slower than the Soviets themselves had planned, the speed of withdrawal having been reduced because of Polish refusal to sign transit agreements until an agreement was reached for the pullout of the 50,000 Soviet troops in Poland. This, and the $2-3 billion transit fees demanded by the Poles, prompted the Western Group of Forces to ship arms and supplies home by sea, at much reduced cost, with personnel being airlifted home. Desertions from the Western Group of Forces during 1990 totalled 145, including 49 who defected to West Germany.

Left: Aeroflot Ilyushin Il-76MD 'Candids' are frequently operated by the Voyenno Transportnaya Aviatsiya (Military Transport Aviation) and are believed to be actually assigned to numbered VTA regiments, returning to Aeroflot for ad hoc charters and services, for which their tail guns have to be removed, along with any other military equipment. This Il-76MD carries prominent chaff/flare launchers in massive pods scabbed on to the sides of the rear fuselage. An Elint-configured Il-76 briefly operated from Sperenburg.

A curfew was imposed during November 1990 and the Western Group of Forces commander, General Boris Snetkov, was sacked, in order to halt desertions and arms sales, reports having arisen that Soviet soldiers were selling their personal weapons in exchange for hard currency. No air force units were withdrawn during 1990, although aircraft numbers were lowered across the board, with some squadrons reducing their establishments from 15 to 12 aircraft. Snetkov was replaced by General Matvei Prokopovich Burlakov, who had overseen the withdrawal of Soviet forces from Hungary.

Nuclear warheads were claimed to be among the first weapons to be withdrawn from Germany, but in April 1991 doubt was cast on Soviet claims that all had been removed when a guard at Altengrabow, home of the 'Scud'-equipped 36th Missile Brigade, shot at three German officers who were taking photographs of the installation. Another Russian at the same installation nearly caused even more trouble. Warheads removed from 'Scuds' and other nuclear SSMs from all over the Western Group of Forces were stored in overcrowded, undermanned bunkers at the base, although it had been announced officially that all had been shipped home. A 28-year-old special forces senior lieutenant assigned to guarding the missiles offered to sell a 1,500-lb (680-kg) warhead to Greenpeace for DM500,000 (with a guarantee of asylum in a third country for him and his two comrades). The plan was abandoned in August, when the weapons were suddenly withdrawn in the wake of the unsuccessful coup against Gorbachev.

While the rest of the Soviet armed forces were put on alert as a result of the 1991 coup, the Western Group of Forces was not affected. Indeed, on the morning that the

coup was announced, the air base at Eberswalde went ahead and threw open its doors for a planned press facility following its public open day and air show.

Although withdrawals continued on schedule, with 44,000 military personnel having left Germany by mid-1991, together with 848 tanks and 1,750 AFVs, the Russians were starting to complain that finance had not been provided for 19,000 much-needed apartments for returnees, in addition to the 36,000 apartments being financed by Germany, and reminded Germany that even with the agreed building work 190,000 military families would be homeless on their return to the USSR. Burlakov warned that without funding, the tempo of withdrawals would have to be reduced. Squabbling broke out between the German and Soviet governments, the Germans disputing the value of Soviet-funded infrastructure being left behind, and hinting that the USSR should pay for environmental

Yellow 08 leaves the rain-soaked Gross-Dölln ramp for the last time. The 20th APIB was the last fighter-bomber unit assigned to the 16th Air Army, leaving for Taganrog and an uncertain future on 5 April 1994. The aircraft carries four external fuel tanks for the long ferry flight home. In the wake of the CFE treaty, aircraft like the Su-17 are being phased out of service, although they are far from obsolete, to be replaced by more modern, more flexible fighters like the MiG-29.

damage its forces had caused. Withdrawals continued on schedule, however, and by the end of 1991 almost 100,000 troops, 1,000 tanks, and 50,000 civilians had departed. These withdrawals included the 27th Guards, the 35th, the 39th Guards, the 57th Guards and the 207th Motor Rifle Divisions, and the 12th Guards Motor Rifle Division completed its pullout, which had started in 1990.

Training ranges at Altengrabow, Eisenach, Heidehof, Juterbog, Lieberose, Magdeburg and Wittstock were vacated during the year. Army Aviation lost its first two full regiments: the 225th OVP departed from Allstedt early in 1991, and was followed by the 486th OVP from Altes Lager on 1 August. 1991 saw the pace of air force withdrawals increase dramatically, with the withdrawals of handfuls of aircraft from different bases giving way to full-

scale unit departures.

The first 16th Air Army unit to leave was the 294th ORAP, whose Su-17M3s departed during April. These were followed by the Su-17M4s of the 730th APIB at Neuruppin on 26 April, and the MiG-29s of the 85th Guards IAP at Köthen, which left in May. Werneuchen's 931st ORAP ostensibly departed, with long-range tanks fitted for what promised to be a long ferry flight, but reappeared at Welzow. The Su-24MPs of the 11th ORAP at Welzow departed for Chortkov in the Ukraine on 7 June, leaving behind the Su-24MRs. The last departure in 1991 was that of the 73rd GvIAP at Merseburg, during July. There are persistent reports that some Merseburg aircraft were reallocated to Wittstock and Pütnitz, and that Köthen MiG-29s reappeared at Nobitz and Alt Lonnewitz, but this

Wearing long greatcoats to stave off the March wind, three pilots of the 19th Guards Fighter-Bomber Aviation Regiment proudly bear the unit's ceremonial red banner as their colleagues taxi past in their MiG-27Ds for the last time. Many of the pilots from this unit returned to East Germany after converting to the MiG-29, most of them going to the 733rd IAP at Wittstock to gain experience. The 19th Guards will reform itself as a MiG-29 fighter unit.

Left and far left: By comparison with the fighter-bomber pilots of the 19th GvAPIB, the banner party of the 33rd IAP at Wittstock took a more casual approach, disdaining their best uniforms in favour of the 'fighter pilot chic' of leather jackets, camouflaged flying suits and high-laced flying boots. In view of the wide variety of flying clothing used by the 16th Air Army, it was perhaps a minor miracle that four pilots could be found who could dress identically. They saluted each departing aircraft at the runway threshold. This aircraft was unique in having a unit badge below the cockpit.

cannot be confirmed. It is believed that Kothen's aircraft departed via Zerbst, while Merseburg's colourful MiG-29s left via Alt Lonnewitz.

By the beginning of 1992, 725 German-funded homes had been handed over, but this still left 15,000 returned families without accommodation, while the German government continued to dispute Soviet estimates of the value of vacated property. Despite this, the withdrawal process continued according to schedule, for the Soviet government was desperate to save foreign currency by withdrawing as quickly as was possible.

Army withdrawals during 1992 included the 9th, the 11th Guards and the 79th Guards Tank Divisions. In an attempt to pull forward its withdrawal timetable, the Soviets proposed the scrapping of 3,000 armoured vehicles (including T-64 main battle tanks) at the Wunsdorf, Kirchmoser and Werder maintenance depots in Germany, and the destruction of 70,000 tonnes of ammunition. German concerns about pollution and adhering to the CFE treaty made this difficult.

It was a big year for helicopter departures. During 1992

Army Aviation lost the 296th OVE from Mahlwinkel and the 485th OVP from Brandis in May, the 292nd OERVE from Cochstedt in June, the 178th and 440th OVPs from Stendal in July, and the 6th OVE from Dresden-Hellerau, the 298th OVE from Hassleben and the 336th OVP from Nohra in August. October saw the loss of the 172nd and 439th OVPs from Parchim, and the detachment at Mirow-Lärz.

During 1992 the 16th Air Army lost additional regiments. The MiG-29s of the 968th IAP left Nobitz on 8 April, and were followed by the Su-25s of the 357th OShAP on 28 April (the L-39s having left in March). The MiG-23MLDs of the 833rd IAP left Altes Lager on 13 May 1992, for Orenburg (the major MiG-23/-27 MU). Zerbst's 35th IAP departed with its MiG-29s on 10 June, although some of its aircraft and pilots went only as far as Wittstock. The first MiG-27s left Germany on 1 July, when Brand was emptied of its resident unit (variously reported as the 911th or 119th APIB), which moved to Kanolovo in Byelorussia. The MiG-25s from Welzow (which had moved to Welzow from Werneuchen) finally left for Siberia on 6 July.

During 1993 the USSR withdrew the 16th GvTD, the 20th GvMD, the 90th GvTD and the 94th GvMD. Army Aviation emptied Werneuchen of its 487th OVP and 41st OVE. The 22 and 23 March saw the departure of all of the remaining MiG-27s in Germany, as the 559th APIB left Finsterwalde, the 296th left Grossenhain, and the 19th GvAPIB left Mirow-Lärz. The 559th ended up in Morozowsk, but the 296th disbanded at Orenburg. Here the 19th also disbanded, but many of its pilots returned to Germany for service with the Wittstock and Damgarten regiments prior to the 19th Guards reforming as a MiG-29 unit at Millerovo, near Rostov. The 'Fulcrum-Cs' of the 787th IAP at Eberswalde departed for Ros (in Byelorussia) on 11

The last Soviet tactical aircraft to actually leave East Germany was white 08 of the 33rd IAP, which was forced to abort its departure from Pütnitz on 11 April, instead leaving the next day. The Wittstock-based 31st IAP flew from their home base to Pütnitz on 7 April, ready for a joint departure with the Pütnitz-based 733rd IAP. Thus, the aircraft left after MiG-29UB '64', which made the official last departure, and which beat-up the airfield for the watching crowd and press photographers, and which was featured in the Military Aviation Review section of World Air Power Journal, Volume 19.

Red Stars over Germany

May 1993, while the similarly-equipped 31st GvIAP left Alt Lonnewitz for Zernograd on 8 June, which was also the departure day for the Su-24MRs of Welzow's 11th ORAP (which went to Marinovka) and the Su-25s of the Tutow-based 368th OShAP (which went to Budyennovsk). The latter unit's L-39s had departed, with those from Brandis, more than a year earlier.

The last year of withdrawals, 1994, was marked by an increasing tempo of unit departures, with a DM550 billion incentive offered for an early completion of the withdrawal (by 31 August instead of the originally agreed 31 December), following discussions between President Yeltsin and Chancellor Kohl. During early 1994, with only three operational fast-jet bases left, the 16th Air Army was disbanded, leaving what was referred to as a 'Prekommando' of independent regiments still under the command of Lieutenant General Anatoly Fyedorovich Tarassenko.

The first 16th Air Army unit to leave in 1994 was the 20th GvAPIB, which on 5 April flew its Su-17M4s to Taganrog, for scrapping or reallocation to a naval unit. On

7 April, Wittstock's 33rd IAP flew its MiG-29s to Pütnitz, where, on 11 April, it left with the MiG-29s of the based 733 IAP. Both MiG-29 regiments flew to Andreapol, where they disbanded. Some 15 MiG-29s from both regiments had left earlier, in March, but three were lost in a landing accident during the transit. Some of the aircraft and pilots from the two units went on to Zernograd, replacing a PVO MiG-23P regiment, but remaining part of Frontal Aviation. Others went to a MiG-29 regiment at Primorsko-Akhartsk. The remaining transport helicopters and fixed-wing transport aircraft at Oranienburg and Sperenburg left their bases in dribs and drabs, and all had left by 31 August, the new departure deadline.

The last army unit to leave was the 6th MD, Berlin's garrison, which followed Potsdam's 34th Artillery Division, and the last remaining division from the Third Shock Army.

The former Group of Soviet Forces in Germany completed its withdrawal without much ceremony. The Germans were little inclined to entertain the notion of massive and spectacular Russian parades in Berlin, preferring to see what they saw as an occupying power skulk away with as little celebration as possible. Thus, the army was not able to participate in the leaving parade in which the Western allies marched through the Brandenburg gate on 10 September 1994, instead being confined to a smaller, lower key ceremony of their own. Burlakov's contribution to what had been a frustrating process was recognised, at least by his countrymen, since he received promotion to Deputy Defence Minister. The largest military contingent outside the Soviet Union, with five armies and 17 divisions, had finally gone home, after 49 years.

The 16th Air Army had planned a massive air show at Sperenburg, with one aircraft from every surviving squadron that had served in Germany (including those which had departed years before, and even including aircraft from strategic bomber units which had sometimes made temporary detachments to German bases), but this was made impossible by the Germans, who limited the celebration to an appearance by one of Russia's aerobatic teams (all three had been invited to the original 'spectacular'). The air force units did do their best to depart with dignity and honour, however, staging parades on the morning of each unit departure, to which local dignitaries were invited. Initially, aviation enthusiasts were welcomed at such events, but the atrocious behaviour of a tiny handful of (predominantly Dutch) spotters who claimed press facilities to which they were not properly entitled soon ensured that the press was excluded from most of the last unit departures. Their behaviour included the theft of maps

from aircraft cockpits, the uprooting of runway edge lighting, and a general lack of respect for their Russian hosts. This was unfortunate, since legitimate aviation journalists from the same country had established excellent and productive links with the 16th Air Army, which were broken off as a result of their countrymen's actions.

A scandal-hungry and anti-Russian press in Germany ensured that the Russian departures were overshadowed by stories of alcohol and drug abuse, desertions, soldiers selling their weapons, and senior officers operating a black market trade using the transport aircraft plying in and out of Sperenburg. There have been reports that defectors included at least one MiG-29 pilot, who was eagerly received by the US government. Certainly there were such incidents, but not on any great scale, and the 16th Air Army deserves to be remembered in a better light. In spite of everything – with fuel rationed, with flying severely restricted to minimise disturbance to the local population, and with no real role left to perform – the men of the 16th Air Army continued to display enormous professionalism. With little to do except wait for a return to Russia, where many squadrons would have to live under canvas until accommodation could be built and where many would simply be disbanded, units maintained an astonishingly high level of morale. Their departure from the former East Germany is a welcome sign that the Cold War is at last over and should be celebrated as such, and it should be remembered that if circumstances had been slightly different they would have proved extremely tough opposition for NATO forces.

Glossary

AA	Armeskaya Aviatsiya (Army Aviation)
ADIB	Aviatsionnaya Diviziya Istrebeitelei-Bombardirovchikov (Aviation Division Fighter-Bomber)
APIB	Aviatsionnaya Polk Istrebeitelei-Bombardirovchikov) (Aviation Regiment Fighter-Bomber)
BAD	Bombardirovchnyi Aviatsionnaya Diviziya (Bomber Aviation Division)
BAP	Bombardirovchnyi Aviatsionnaya Polk (Bomber Aviation Regiment)
GvADIB	Gvardeiskaya Aviatsionnaya Istrebeitelei-Bombardirovchikov (Guards Aviation Division Fighter-Bomber)
GvAPIB	Gvardeiskaya Aviatsionnaya Polk Istrebeitelei-Bombardirovchikov (Guards Aviation Regiment Fighter-Bomber)
GvIAD	Gvardeiskaya Istrebeitelnyi Aviatsionnaya Diviziya (Guards Fighter Aviation Division)
GvIAP	Gvardeiskaya Istrebeitelnyi Aviatsionnaya Polk (Guards Fighter Aviation Regiment)
GvMD	Gvardeiskaya Motostrelkovaya Diviziya (Guards Motor Rifle Division)
GvOA	Gvardeiskaya Obchevoyskovaya Armiya (Guards Infantry Army)
GvTA	Gvardeiskaya Tankovaya Armiya (Guards Tank Army)
GvTD	Gvardeiskaya Tankovaya Diviziya (Guards Tank Division)
IAD	Istrebeitelnyi Aviatsionnaya Diviziya (Fighter Aviation Division)
IAP	Istrebeitelnyi Aviatsionnaya Polk (Fighter Aviation Regiment)
IBAD	Istrebeitelei-Bombardirovchikov Aviatsionnaya Diviziya (Fighter-Bomber Aviation Division) (unofficial designation)
IBAP	Istrebeitelei-Bombardirovchikov Aviatsionnaya Polk (Fighter-Bomber Aviation Regiment) (unofficial designation)
MD	Motostrelkovaya Diviziya (Motor Rifle Division)
OA	Obchevoyskovaya Armiya (Infantry Army)
OERVE	Otdelnyi Eletronika Radiorazvedka Vertoletnyi Eskadrilya (Independent Electronic (and) Radio Reconnaissance Squadron)
OGvVP	Otdelnyi Gvardeiskaya Vertoletnyi Polk (Independent Guards Helicopter Regiment)
ORAP	Otdelnyi Razvedyvatelnyi Aviatsionnaya Polk (Independent Reconnaissance Aviation Regiment)
OSAP	Otdelnyi Smechannyi Aviatsionnaya Polk (Independent Transport Aviation Regiment)
OShAP	Otdelnyi Shturmovoi Aviatsionnaya Polk (Independent *Shturmovik* Aviation Regiment)
OVE	Otdelnyi Vertoletnyi Eskadriliya (Independent Helicopter Sqn)
OVP	Otdelnyi Vertoletnyi Polk (Independent Helicopter Regiment)
TA	Tankovaya Armiya (Tank Army)
TD	Tankovaya Diviziya (Tank Division)
VA	Vozdushnaya Armiya (Air Army)
ZGV	Zapadnaya Gruppa Voysk (Western Group of Forces)

Our account of the Soviet (and latterly Russian) presence in Germany will be continued in *World Air Power Journal,* Volume 21, with a detailed survey of the bases used by all of the regiments and squadrons, together with their unit markings, etc.

Sunset, and an Su-24MR returns to Welzow. The departure of the 16th Air Army from Germany marked the end of the Cold War. What many West Europeans saw as an occupation force and a major threat to peace has finally disappeared. The officers and men of the 16th Air Army might see it rather differently. They have returned home after fulfilling their sacred duty of defending the Motherland and its socialist allies against the danger of Western capitalist aggression. Whatever one's opinion of such a point of view, it can be seen that in maintaining a terrible balance of terror the Russians helped keep Europe free from war, and did so with professionalism and competence.

Illustrating one of the many contradictions of the Russian mentality, three young boys demonstrate that a Soviet preoccupation with military security may not have been all it appeared by playing atop a hardened aircraft shelter, seemingly oblivious of the taxiing Su-17M4 behind them. Moments later they crossed the active runway (between departing fast jets) to play amid the complex of shelters on the other side of the airfield. The same alert guards who kept an eagle eye on the Western photographers, and who would undoubtedly have prevented any from straying anywhere near the runway, regarded the antics of their families with amused tolerance.

Sharp 'Swords'

Tracor Flight Systems' F-100Fs

Europe's last Super Sabres

The F-100 enjoyed a long service life in Europe, serving with USAF squadrons based in Germany, and with the French, Danish and Turkish air forces, flying with the last-named until the late 1980s. Today, a handful of F-100s continue to fly in the target facilities role from Wittmund and Decimomannu, towing targets for gunnery practice by Luftwaffe fighters.

Tracor Flight Systems, Inc. has been operating its North American F-100F Super Sabres in Europe since 1983, first on a NATO contract in support of USAFE fighter squadrons (for which the F-100s were based at Bournemouth's Hurn airport) and, more recently, under successive contracts to the German Luftwaffe. The first such contract ran from 1988 until 1991, while the company is presently rebidding for a five-year contract to run from January 1995. To meet a Luftwaffe requirement for target-towing services to provide air-to-air gunnery training for its Phantom (and more recently also for its MiG-29) squadrons, Tracor maintains four F-100Fs at Wittmund on the north German coast. This is home to Jagd-geschwader 71 'Richthofen', one of the major user units, and is conveniently close to training ranges over the North Sea. The four aircraft based at Wittmund are N416FS (56-3916), N417FS (56-3842), N418FS (56-3996) and N419FS (56-3971), N414FS having been withdrawn from use in July 1994. (A fifth F-100F, N415FS (56-3844) is based at Holloman AFB, New Mexico, and is operated under

Left: *A Tracor Flight Systems F-100F manoeuvres at high level, carrying a DATS-3 tow target system below its port wing, and with 166.5-Imp gal (757-litre) fuel tanks inboard. The DATS-3 consists of an RMU-10 target winch and a Do Sk10 dart, weighing a total of 677 lb (307 kg). Fuel can be seen venting from below the fin trailing edge fairing for the AN/APR-26(V) radar warning receiver.*

Opposite page, bottom left: *Do Sk10 target darts wait to be loaded aboard the RMU-10 winches carried by Tracor's F-100Fs, which were originally to have been designated TF-100C. The aircraft in the background wears Flight Systems, Inc. titles.*

Above: *The 16-ft (5-m) long, 195-lb (88-kg) Do Sk10 dart gunnery target is reeled out from the RMU-10 tow reel pod carried on the port outboard underwing station of the towing aircraft. The dart is recovered after use, and user pilots are scored by simply counting the holes in the target. Where more than one pilot is using the dart, dyed bullets are used, which leave different coloured holes.*

Below: *Wearing Tracor Flight Systems logos, an F-100F taxis out for a tow mission at 'Deci'. The white colour scheme is extremely conspicuous, and helps avoid the possibility of over-enthusiastic customers firing on the tow aircraft instead of the target.*

Right: A starboard side view of N419FS shows the asymmetric load carried, with a 279-Imp gal (1268-litre) tank to starboard balancing the 166.5-Imp gal (757-litre) and DATS-3 TTS to port.

Left: The front cockpit of a Tracor F-100F. An ergonomic nightmare by modern standards, the cockpit is nevertheless typical of 1950s fighters, with a panel full of analog instruments, no head-up display, and black side consoles covered in tiny black switches, buttons, dials and knobs. A pilot used to the Hawker Hunter would feel immediately at home. The miss distance measuring equipment display is mounted below the coaming.

Opposite page, below right: This line-up of Tracor F-100Fs is on deployment at Decimomannu, Sardinia. The nearest aircraft in the line-up, N414FS, has been withdrawn from use since July 1994. The three aircraft pictured each carry different company names, although all are operated by Tracor Flight Systems, Inc., which currently has four F-100Fs in Europe.

Left: Bill McCallum is fairly typical of Tracor's three Europe-based Super Sabre pilots. An ex-USAF fighter pilot, McCallum flew tours of duty in the F-100 and fought in the Vietnam War. McCallum left the US Air Force in 1975, after flying F-111s. The F-100Fs are two-seaters, but are usually operated by a single pilot who doubles as target operator and who also transmits hit and near-miss data to the attacking pilots. This keeps operating costs to a minimum.

a separate contract, which will be described in a future issue of *World Air Power Journal*.) Although based and maintained at Wittmund, the F-100Fs undertake regular deployments to Decimomannu (shortened to Deci, and pronounced 'Detchy') in Sardinia, supporting Luftwaffe fighter detachments to use the ACMI range. The F-100s usually deploy twice yearly, between January and March and between September and November, when weather conditions in North Germany are at their worst.

The company's TF-100F Super Sabres were originally procured from the Royal Danish air force in the 1980s, with three additional aircraft being picked up from Turkish stocks later in the decade, but these were subsequently sold on to a private owner. The aircraft have been flying in their familiar overall-white colour scheme with a distinctive blue cheatline for many years, although the logos painted on the aircraft have changed frequently. Originally owned by Flight Systems, which was purchased by Tracor Flight Systems in the mid-1980s, the aircraft have also sometimes operated under the banner of Tracor Flight Services – a nominally independent company with the same chairman – to which they have sometimes been leased.

The F-100Fs are equipped with a DATS-3 target system, similar to the old USAF Model 15 A/A37U-15 tow target system, but with a Dornier Do Sk10 target dart replacing the original TDU-10. The RMU-10 target winch and Do Sk10 dart weigh a total of 677 lb (307 kg). The 16-ft (5-m) long, 195-lb (88-kg) dart gunnery target is reeled out from the RMU-10 tow reel pod carried on the port outboard underwing station of the towing aircraft. This is accompanied by a 166.5-Imp gal (757-litre) tank, with a 279-Imp gal (1268-litre) tank to starboard balancing the smaller tank and DATS-3 pod to port.

The Dornier target differs from the original in being fitted with a device which allows it to record hits and near misses, and a transponder to allow it to change its radar signature. The F-100F pilot reads the number of hits from a panel-mounted display and transmits them to the attacking pilot after each pass. The target is cut loose after all firing passes are complete. Although the F-100F is a two-seater, the aircraft

are usually flown by a single pilot, three of whom are employed by Tracor in Europe.

The aircraft have each amassed between 6,000 and 6,500 flying hours, but all have received a wing box modification giving a total airframe life of 9,000 flying hours. With an annual average utilisation of only 100 hours per aircraft, fatigue life is not going to be a problem for many years. A switch to an aircraft type with lower operating costs remains a possibility, particularly as more modern types are retired from front-line air arms.

Tracor holds an impressive stock of all necessary spares, purchased from a variety of sources, and has acquired a great deal of F-100 operating and servicing experience, not least because the company also has been heavily involved in the programme to convert surplus single-seat F-100Ds and two-seat F-100Fs to, respectively, QF-100D and QF-100F unmanned target drone configuration (retaining the capability of manned operation). A total of 340 such airframes was set aside for conversion, and after 100 QF-100D drones had been produced by Sperry at Litchfield Park, Arizona, between 1980 and 1985, responsibility for further conversions passed to Tracor Flight Systems at Mojave. Tracor produced 210 QF-100Ds and 30 QF-100Fs, 20 being rejected by the USAF for technical reasons, inevitable when dealing with such old airframes. Many F-100s have

been expended in missile tests and air defence exercises, although the type has now been replaced by drone conversions of the F-106 Delta Dart and F-4 Phantom. The QF-100 remained in USAF service with the 82nd Tactical Aerial Targets Squadron of the 475th Weapons Evaluation Group at Tyndall AFB until 1993 for support of William Tell gunnery/missile competitions, and with the 6585th Test Group at Holloman for use at the Army's White Sands missile range in New Mexico.

Multiple NOLOs

Here the final three aircraft – two QF-100Fs and a single QF-100D – were retained for pilot training until August 1994, but will now be used as ground targets. The QF-100 was not meant to be a 'one-shot' target, the intention being that each drone should survive an average of seven NOLO (No Live Operator) missions before destruction. The aircraft was expected to survive most missile engagements, using wingtip propane burner pods to increase IR signature and decoy IR-homing missiles away from the engine exhaust plume, and using underwing chaff and flare dispensers to simulate an enemy aircraft more closely. A self-destruct mechanism was fitted for use if the drone was too badly damaged to be landed safely, or if contact with ground control was lost for six minutes or more. This was removed when the aircraft were being

flown in a manned configuration.

The low unit price of an F-100 means that amortisation is very low (these aircraft have already paid for themselves), even if fuel consumption and maintenance man-hour requirements may be heavy. This factor alone makes the F-100 an extremely viable aircraft for the target facilities role, while its agility and high performance are also highly prized.

To pilot these veteran aircraft, Tracor employs equally experienced flyers. One of these is Bill McCallum, a native of Kansas City, Missouri. He started his flying career in 1953, and his first posting was flying F-86s with the 388th Fighter-Bomber Wing in New Mexico. The wing moved first to Hahn AB, Germany, and then to Etain, France, where it converted to the F-100 Super Sabre. After four years in Europe, Bill returned to the US and was based in South Carolina. In 1965, at Da Nang, and in 1968, with the 3rd TFW at Bien Hoa, he completed two tours of duty in South-East Asia. He then returned to Europe, first at Wethersfield and then Wiesbaden (Germany), before moving to Nellis and converting to the F-111, and leaving the Air Force in July 1975. His flying career was far from over, though, and after a short spell flying Lear Jets in the Las Vegas area he went to Tracor and returned to Germany. Bill reconverted to the Super Sabre and has been flying the aircraft ever since.

Above: A Tracor F-100F leads two German F-4Fs of JG 71 'Richthofen' into a break. The Wittmund Tracor detachment is co-located beside JG 71, and serves Luftwaffe aircraft undertaking armament practice camps over the North Sea ranges. The four aircraft frequently deploy to Decimomannu in Sardinia.

Top right: Tracor's 400 annual missions are divided roughly equally between Decimomannu and Wittmund, with regular deployments to Sardinia from September to November and January to March. The F-100Fs serve only Luftwaffe fighters at 'Deci', other air forces making alternative arrangements.

Centre right: A pair of Wittmund-based F-100Fs prepares for a tow mission. The nearest aircraft has the legend 'Tracor Flight Services' on its nose, apparently applied for a Farnborough air show appearance. Tracor Flight Services is an independent company with the same chairman.

Right: The F-100 has served as a day fighter, fighter-bomber, tactical recce platform, nuclear-strike aircraft and an unmanned target drone, but will end its days as a civilian-operated target tug.

Grumman F-14

Variant Briefing: *Part 2*

The Operators

A section (pair) of F-14As from VF-102 'Diamondbacks', an Oceana-based squadron which has become the sole Tomcat unit within Air Wing One. The squadron's aircraft have worn a variety of toned-down markings, including dark and light grey unit insignia, and (on some aircraft) dull red. The USA inscription at the base of the rudder is noteworthy.

Since the F-14 Tomcat operators were listed in *World Air Power Journal*, Volume 7, there have been many changes to the Tomcat community, the most important of which has been the change to a single F-14 squadron standard air wing, with a larger number of F/A-18 units. Some F-14 squadrons have re-equipped with new variants of the aircraft or have changed their carrier air wing assignments as part of the rationalisation of variants between the Atlantic and Pacific Fleets, but others have simply disbanded. By the end of 1995, the F-14 Tomcat fleet will have been reduced to fewer than 15 squadrons, from a peak total of 31 squadrons.

United States Navy

Today the US Navy has two F-14 Tomcat forces, one supporting COMNAVAIRLANT and one supporting COMNAVAIRPAC. COMNAVAIRLANT is responsible for providing combat-ready forces to fleet commanders operating from the North Pole to the Antarctic and between the Eastern Seaboard and the Indian Ocean. The numbered fleets in COMNAVAIRLANT's area of responsibility are the Second in the Atlantic and the Sixth in the Mediterranean. Atlantic Fleet Tomcat squadrons are controlled by Fighter Wing Atlantic (Fighter Wing One) at NAS Oceana when shore-based, but deploy with numbered air wings (CVWs) aboard the carriers of the Atlantic Fleet. The Atlantic Fleet FRS (Fleet Replenishment Squadron) is VF-101, which does not deploy and thus is not listed in the order of battle below. Since September 1994, VF-101 has become the sole Tomcat training unit for both the Atlantic and the Pacific Fleets, following the disestablishment of VF-124. Similarly not included in the order of battle below are the various test and trials units. Several Atlantic Fleet F-14 operators have already disbanded, including VF-33 'Starfighters' and VF-74 'Bedevilers', and others are set to follow as detailed in the table below:

One of VF-103's F-14As launches from the USS Ranger. Ranger has since decommissioned, and the 'Sluggers' have transitioned to the re-engined F-14B with Air Wing 17 aboard the Eisenhower.

AIRLANT

Air Wing One (USS *America* – CV-66)

Squadron	Variant	Notes
VF-102 'Diamondbacks'	F-14A (AB-100)	Transitioning to F-14B

Air Wing Three (USS *Dwight D. Eisenhower* – CVN-69)

Squadron	Variant	Notes
VF-14 'Tophatters'	F-14A (AC-100)	May transfer to CVW-17
VF-32 'Swordsmen'	F-14A (AC-200)	

Air Wing Seven (USS *George Washington* – CVN-73)

Squadron	Variant	Notes
VF-142 'Ghostriders'	F-14B (AG-200)	To disestablish April 1995
VF-143 'Pukin' Dogs'	F-14B (AG-100)	

Air Wing Eight (USS *Theodore Roosevelt* – CVN-71)

Squadron	Variant	Notes
VF-41 'Black Aces'	F-14A (AJ-100)	
VF-84 'Jolly Rogers'	F-14A (AJ-200)	May transfer to CVW-7, replacing VF-143

Air Wing Seventeen (USS *Dwight D. Eisenhower* – CVN-69)

Squadron	Variant	Notes
VF-103 'Sluggers'	F-14B (AA-200)	

Air Wing Twenty (Atlantic Fleet Reserve air wing, NAS Dallas)

Squadron	Variant	Notes
VF-201 'Hunters'	F-14A (AF-100)	May move to Carswell late 1994
VF-202 'Superheats'	F-14A (AF-200)	Ceased flying June, disbanded 9 July 1994

COMNAVAIRPAC is responsible for providing combat-ready forces to fleet commanders operating from the North Pole to the Antarctic and between the Indian Ocean and the Pacific Coast of the USA. The numbered fleets in COMNAVAIRPAC's area of responsibility are the Third and the Seventh. Pacific Fleet Tomcat squadrons are controlled by Fighter/Airborne Early Warning Wing Pacific at NAS Miramar when

shore-based, but deploy with numbered air wings (CVWs) aboard Pacific Fleet carriers. The Pacific Fleet FRS was VF-124, but this unit disestablished in September 1994, passing the entire F-14 aircrew training task on to VF-101 on the East Coast. The reduction from 11 to 10 air wings and from two to one reserve air wings will affect the Pacific Fleet severely; it will lose CVW-15, and CVW-30 during 1994-95.

AIRPAC

Air Wing Two (USS *Constellation* – CV-64)		
VF-2 'Bounty Hunters'	F-14D (NE-200)	
Air Wing Five (USS *Independence* – CV-62)		
VF-154 'Black Knights'	F-14A (NF-100)	
VF-21 'Freelancers'	F-14A (NF-200)	To convert to F/A-18 as VFA-21
Air Wing Nine (USS *Nimitz* – CVN-68)		
VF-24 'Fighting Renegades'	F-14A (NG-100)	
VF-211 'Fighting Checkmates'	F-14A (NG-200)	
Air Wing Eleven (USS *Abraham Lincoln* – CVN-72)		
VF-213 'Black Knights'	F-14A (NH-100)	Single F-14 squadron in wing
Air Wing Fourteen (USS *Carl Vinson* – CVN-70)		
VF-11 'Red Rippers'	F-14D (NK-100)	
VF-31 'Tomcatters'	F-14D (NK-200)	
Air Wing Fifteen (USS *Kitty Hawk*) (Air Wing will be disestablished 1995)		
VF-51 'Screaming Eagles'	F-14A (NL-100)	To disestablish March 1995
VF-111 'Sundowners'	F-14A (NL-200)	To disestablish March 1995
Air Wing Thirty (Pacific Fleet Reserve air wing, NAS Miramar) to disestablish late 1994		
VF-301 'Devil's Disciples'	F-14A (ND-100)	Ceased flying June 1994, to disestablish
VF-302 'Stallions'	F-14A (ND-200)	Ceased flying June 1994, to disestablish

One of VF-1's F-14As escorts a prowling 'Bear-F Mod 2'. The Tomcat's ability to intercept its targets far out from the carrier is highly prized.

VF-1 'Wolfpack'

The first of the front-line Pacific Fleet F-14 squadrons to form, VF-1 was formally commissioned on 14 October 1972, receiving its first F-14As on 1 July 1973. The squadron's first deployment with Air Wing 14 was aboard the USS *Enterprise* and took place between 12 September 1974 and 19 May 1975, the first F-14 embarking for pre-cruise training on 18 March 1974. Together with the F-14As of sister squadron VF-2, VF-1's 12 Tomcats flew 20 operational combat air patrol missions in support of Operation Frequent Wind, the evacuation of Saigon. The aircraft were fired upon by 37-mm AAA, but were not hit, nor did they have the opportunity to use their weapons in anger. During the WestPac tour, VF-1 flew a total of 850 sorties, and clocked up 1,400 flying hours. Unfortunately, the squadron also lost two F-14As after engine failures, but in both accidents the crews were able to eject successfully. These accidents signalled the fan-blade containment problems which plagued early versions of the TF30 turbofan. Second and third WestPac cruises (between 30 July 1976 and 28 March 1977, and 4 April and 3 October 1978) were made aboard the USS *Enterprise*.

VF-1 transferred to CVW-2 and USS *Ranger* (CV-60) in September 1980, embarking for WestPac/Indian Ocean cruises between 10 September 1980 and 5 May 1981 (for the Iranian and Afghan crises) and 7 April and 18 October 1982. During 1982, VF-1 won the CNO safety award for five years and 17,000 flying hours without an accident, as well as the prestigious Admiral Joseph Clifton award for the Navy's top fighter squadron (this returned to VF-1 in 1990, along with a Battle E). The squadron remained with Air Wing Two during a subsequent 13 January to 1 August 1984 cruise aboard USS *Kitty Hawk* (CV-63), and then moved back to *Ranger* (albeit still with Air Wing Two) later that year, undertaking NorPac cruises (18 August to 20 October 1986, and 2 March to 29 April 1987), and WestPac/Indian Ocean cruises (14 July to 29 December 1987 and 24 February to 24 August 1989) with CVW-2. VF-1 was able to add to its reputation between cruises, most notably in 1988 when exercises against USAF F-15s went exceptionally well, three squadron crews graduated from Top Gun, and four AIM-54s and 10 AIM-7s were fired.

During the Gulf War, VF-1 embarked aboard *Ranger* with CVW-2 for an Indian Ocean/Persian Gulf cruise between 8 December 1990 and 8 June 1991, and was the only F-14 unit to gain an aerial victory. One of the squadron's aircraft (162603/NE-103), flown by Lt. Stuart Broce and with RIO (and squadron CO) Lt Cdr Ron

Another experimental camouflage scheme worn by VF-1 Tomcats was this three-tone grey camouflage. Unit insignia was applied in a paler grey.

Above: In 1978, VF-1's F-14As were almost as colourful as they had been when the squadron received its Tomcats, with red and white insignia over a glossy light gull grey finish. Only the white undersides and control surfaces were missing. By 1980 only a tiny wolf's head, with no tail stripes, was carried.

Right: In May 1977, VF-1's CAG-bird received a disruptive splinter camouflage invented by artist Keith Ferris, amended by a US Navy F-14 pilot named Heatley – colloquially known as the 'Heater-Ferris' scheme. The pattern incorporates a black 'false canopy' under the nose.

McElraft, scored the Tomcat's only air-to-air victory in Desert Storm by downing an Iraqi Mil Mi-8 'Hip' helicopter on 6 February 1991. The apparent lack of success of the Tomcat was mainly due to coalition policy of assigning target aircraft to F-15s; the F-14 was strictly constrained to an escort role.

A further CVW-2/*Ranger* cruise was undertaken in the Indian Ocean and Persian Gulf between 1 August 1992 and 31

January 1993, participating in Operations Southern Watch and Provide Relief, after relieving *Independence* in the Gulf on 15 September. This was, however, to be the squadron's final deployment. With the rundown in the Tomcat fleet, and with USS *Ranger* slated to be among the first of the US Navy's carriers to embark only a single F-14 squadron, VF-1's proposed conversion to the F-14D and planned transfer to the

USS *Constellation* was cancelled. VF-1 finally disestablished on 1 October 1993, having dropped out halfway through the conversion training cycle and transferring some personnel to sister unit VF-2, leaving CVW-2 with a single F-14 squadron. Other sources suggest that VF-1 disestablished one day earlier, on 30 September 1993 (the last day of the fiscal year). The 'Wolfpack' and its 'Wichita' callsign were no more.

VF-2 'Bounty Hunters'

First formed on 1 July 1922, VF-2 was the first naval fighter squadron to be deployed aboard an aircraft-carrier (the USS *Langley*, CV-1). The squadron's use of a red, white and blue diagonal stripe (the carrier's marking) dates from this period, although the stripe is now often applied now in three shades of grey. From 1927 until the beginning of World War II, the unit was known as the 'Fighting Chiefs' or the 'Chiefs' Squadron because – in an unusual and farsighted experiment – its pilots were all enlisted men. VF-2 was established as an F-14 unit on 14 October 1972, receiving its first aircraft in July 1973. The squadron's history closely followed that of its sister squadron VF-1, the 'Bounty Hunters' partnering the 'Wolfpack' with CVW-14 and CVW-2 for cruises aboard the *Enterprise*, *Ranger* and *Kitty Hawk* between 1974 and 1993. VF-2's aircraft suffered the same engine failures as those of VF-1, caused by the fan blade containment problem, but

Seen in August 1977, this 'Bullets' F-14A wears a variation of the original squadron colour scheme with the traditional squadron badge displacing the tailcodes onto the inner faces of the tailfins.

fortunately VF-2 escaped the aircraft losses which bedevilled VF-1's first cruise. During the second cruise, however, things did not go so smoothly, and VF-2 lost an aircraft in a landing accident off the Philippines.

By May 1981, VF-2 had returned to form, and won the COMNAVAIRPAC Battle E awarded to the best West Coast fighter unit, and the Mutha trophy awarded to the best Miramar-based F-14 squadron, also winning the 1981 ComFitAEWWingPAC fighter derby and clocking up its 10,000th accident-free flying hour. TARPS-configured Tomcats were taken on charge during 1981, with VF-2 aircrew returning to 'school' with

VF-2 to learn to use the new system, and the techniques involved in flying tactical reconnaissance missions. The seven-month 1982 cruise aboard the *Ranger* allowed the squadron (the second West Coast TARPS unit to deploy) to develop many of the procedures later adopted fleet-wide as SOPs by the TARPS squadrons.

Adoption of the tactical recce role did not bring with it any let-up in the primary fighter role and, as if to demonstrate this, on 2 June 1984 VF-2 became the first unit to make a carrier launch while towing an air-to-air gunnery target banner.

Between 8 December 1990 and 8 June

1991, VF-2 accompanied VF-1, its sister squadron, on a WestPac/Indian Ocean/Persian Gulf cruise aboard USS *Ranger* (CV-61) as part of Air Wing Two, flying BarCAP, MiGSweep and MiGCAP sorties in support of Operation Desert Storm. 1991 also saw the award of the Mutha trophy, and one of the unit's pilots clocked up a record number of F-14 traps (126 in a year), and a record West Coast, active-duty career total of 744 traps. 1991 also saw victory in the High Noon gunnery competition, and a full work-up in the Bombcat role, culminating in a historic 28 August mission in which an aircraft fired an AIM-7, strafed a ground target with its gun and dropped a pair of Mk 83 bombs.

On its return to Miramar after the August 1991 to January 1993 CVW-2 Persian Gulf cruise, VF-2 bade farewell to the *Ranger*, and began conversion to the F-14D.

With its unrivalled history and TARPS mission, VF-2 was bound to be the survivor when Air Wing Two was reduced to a single F-14 squadron. The unit survived to complete conversion to the F-14D when VF-1 was disestablished, taking a mixture of new-build and rebuilt aircraft..

The 'Bullets' (VF-2's tactical callsign) spent 1994 preparing for deployment aboard *Constellation* as part of CVW-2, and undertaking a Pacific cruise between 6 May and 30 June 1994.

Left: By 1986, the red, white and blue 'Langley stripe' had been reduced in size and moved to the fin, as a background to the skull-and-crossbones badge. The stars were in toned-down grey, and moved from the rudders.

Below: Old and new. CAG and squadron commander's aircraft have tended to retain high-visibility markings, with the full-colour nose stripe.

VF-11 'Red Rippers'

VF-11 'Red Rippers' (callsign 'Ripper') transitioned to the F-14 during 1980, making its final F-4 cruise in May of that year and opening a new era for the Navy's longest continuously serving fighter squadron (VF-14 is older, but has spent some time as a bomber unit). Pairing with sister squadron VF-31 (longtime sister squadron with F-4 Phantoms), VF-11 joined CVW-3 aboard USS *John F. Kennedy* (CV-67), making its first cruise with the new aircraft type between 4 January and 14 July 1982. A mini-cruise in the Atlantic followed during May and June of 1983, with the unit participating in NATO's Operation Ocean Safari. A full-scale Mediterranean cruise began on 27 September 1983, beginning with a rare visit to Latin America for joint exercises with the Força Aérea Brasiliera still as part of CVW-3 aboard the *Kennedy*. VF-11 flew combat air patrols during the 4 December 1983 US Navy air strikes on Syrian positions in the Lebanon, during which two aircraft from the 28-strong package were shot down.

The squadron next made a short Caribbean cruise in July 1984. That same year, the unit was honoured with the award of both a Safety S and a Battle E. VF-11 'Red Rippers' and its sister squadron VF-31 moved to CVW-6 aboard the *Forrestal* (longtime home to the squadron during the F-4J era, with CVW-17) on 1 April 1985. The squadron made cruises in the Mediterranean, North Atlantic and Gulf (2 June to 10 November 1986, 28 August to 9 October 1987, and 8 April to 20 April 1988), receiving the 1986 Clifton Award for safety. *Forrestal* took VF-11 into the Mediterranean and Indian Ocean from 25 April until 7 October 1988, the squadron receiving a Meritorious Unit Commendation in 1988.

On 4 November 1989, VF-11 and VF-31 together deployed with CVW-6 aboard the *Forrestal* for a winter cruise to the Mediterranean, returning home on 12 April 1990. During the winter of 1990, the squadron sent a detachment to Luke AFB, for air combat training with the F-15s and

F-16s of the USAF's 58th TFW.

The 'Red Rippers' deployed to the Caribbean aboard the *Forrestal* between 29 November and 23 December 1990, before visiting the Mediterranean again from 30 May 1991, still with Air Wing Six aboard the *Forrestal*. The cruise brought with it operational flying in support of Provide Comfort over northern Iraq, and the squadron dispatched a single aircraft to Le Bourget for static display during the Paris air show. Also during this cruise, 'Red Rippers' Tomcats exercised with IDF/AF aircraft, involving much low-level overland flying. When the *Forrestal* completed this, its 21st and final, cruise on 21 December 1991, it became the Navy's training carrier. Its air wing was disestablished, and its two Tomcat squadrons moved to the West Coast, where they re-equipped with F-14Ds. After completing a three-month transition syllabus at NAS Miramar, with VF-124, the 'Red Rippers' stood up in early July 1992 as the first fleet F-14D 'Super Tomcat' squadron.

Lt Dave Burnham and Lt Cdr Paul Pompier made the first fleet F-14D flight on 6 July. F-14Ds were deployed to Alaska to participate in Exercise Cope Thunder later in 1992. The squadron subsequently joined CVW-14 for service aboard USS *Carl Vinson*

(CVN-7). 'Gold Eagle' (*Vinson's* callsign) began a WestPac cruise on 18 February 1994, sailing from San Diego to Pearl Harbor, and then on to Yokosuka. Rough seas and a pitching deck provided a challenging background against which the squadron prepared for its first F-14D night traps, while flying MiG sweeps, TarCAP and TARPS missions, and attack missions during which the APG-71, JTIDS and IRST were

One of VF-11's new F-14Ds wears unit markings in a grey almost as light as the camouflage itself, for minimum conspicuity.

used to 'shoot down' orange force F-15 Eagles. *Vinson* went on to the Persian Gulf in support of Operation Southern Watch, and returned home on 15 August 1994.

Below: VF-11 received its F-14s in the overall gull grey colour scheme, as seen on these two aircraft patrolling near San Diego.

Right: Sharkmouths are a routine addition to fighters, and VF-111 even uses one officially. The significance of these warthog jaws is unknown.

VF-14 'Tophatters'

VF-14 is the oldest continuously active squadron in the Navy, with a history dating back to September 1919 (albeit with periods as bomber, patrol and training units). It transitioned to the F-14 under the auspices of VF-124, together with sister squadron VF-32. The squadron (callsign 'Camelots') moved to Miramar during Christmas 1973 for conversion and finally returned to Oceana on 1 September 1974. The first Tomcats had started to arrive at Oceana in July 1974. Conversion to the F-14A was especially appropriate, since the squadron's original insignia was a grinning Tomcat, in white tie and top hat!

VF-14 made the F-14's first Mediterranean cruise from 28 June 1975 to 27 January 1976, this marking the first time that the E-2C and F-14 had been deployed together. The two aircraft proved to be a winning combination, and one which has provided US Navy carrier battle groups with unequalled air defence capability ever since. For this first cruise the squadron deployed aboard USS *John F. Kennedy* (CV-67) as part of CVW-1. Engine-related problems reduced serviceability and availability, but the only

F-14A actually lost ran off the deck when an arrester wire failed.

VF-14 made North Atlantic, Mediterranean, Caribbean, Atlantic, Mediterranean and Mediterranean/Indian Ocean cruises aboard the *Kennedy* (respectively from 2 September to 9 November 1976, 15 January to 1 August 1977, 7 November to 13 December 1977, 20 January to 22 March 1978, 29 June 1978 to 8 February 1979 and 4 August 1980 to 28 March 1981) before being reassigned to CVW-6, with whom the squadron deployed aboard USS *Independence* for a Mediterranean cruise (7 June to 22 December 1982), Caribbean cruises (6 June to 21 July 1983 and 15 August to 16 September 1983) before a full-scale Caribbean/Mediterranean/North Atlantic cruise which lasted from 18 October 1983 and 11 April 1984, and which involved the squadron in combat operations in two separate areas. Beginning in the Eastern Caribbean, VF-14 flew 82 combat CAP and escort missions in support of Operation Urgent Fury (the US invasion of Grenada) between 23 October and 5 November.

The *Independence* then proceeded to the Eastern Mediterranean, where more trouble was brewing. Although VF-14 was not

actively involved in the 4 December air strikes against Syrian positions in the Lebanon, it did fly BarCAP missions in support of the operation, and flew escort for VF-32's TARPS birds. An Atlantic/Caribbean cruise followed between 20 August and 9 September 1984, with a final pre-SLEP (service life extension programme) Mediterranean/Indian Ocean cruise aboard USS *Independence* between 16 October 1984 and 19 February 1985.

Reassigned to CVW-3 on 1 April 1985, VF-14 undertook a Mediterranean cruise aboard the *Kennedy* between 18 August 1986 and 3 March 1987, before returning for a second full-scale cruise between 2 August 1988 and 1 February 1989. Between these two cruises, the squadron visited the Caribbean (aboard the *Kennedy* again) between 4 and 17 December 1987. During this deployment, VF-14 participated in Sea Wind '88 (a bilateral exercise with Egypt) and Display Determination '88, a NATO exercise in Italian airspace. These exercises were followed by African Eagle '88, flying against the F-5Es of the Moroccan air force, which reportedly proved to be somewhat tougher opposition than had at first been anticipated.

Between 4 January and 1 February, VF-

14 visited the Caribbean again, and then on 15 August 1990 VF-14 joined the other squadrons of CVW-3 for a short-notice deployment aboard the *Kennedy* in support of Desert Shield, sailing into the Red Sea. The carrier returned home on 28 March 1991. The squadron deployed as part of CVW-3 on the brief post-SLEP shakedown cruise of the *Kitty Hawk* between 26 August and 17 September 1991.

The 'Top Hatters' had transitioned to the 'Bombcat' role by the spring of 1992, and practised air-to-ground operations during its next carrier deployment to the Mediterranean (again as part of Air Wing Three aboard the *Kennedy*) which began on 7 October 1993 and ended on 7 April 1993. It became the first East Coast squadron to launch from a carrier while carrying Mk 80-series bombs. During the cruise the squadron also flew CAPs in support of the Provide Promise emergency relief aid drops in Bosnia-Herzegovina, and received BDU-45s for their 'Bombcat' role. *Eisenhower* hosted VF-14 and the squadrons of CVW-3 for a brief Caribbean cruise between 17 May and 1 July 1994.

Some rumours suggest that VF-14 may transfer to CVW-17 to replace VF-103, although this cannot yet be confirmed.

Above: After losing its original high-visibility markings – which were applied to aircraft in the original grey and white scheme and which consisted of a red chevron on the fins – VF-14 was left with a simple top hat badge in a small disc.

Left: The fin chevron was reintroduced in outline form during the late 1980s. This aircraft has a small top hat emblem on its underfuselage fuel tanks, a common location for Tomcat unit insignia to be repeated.

VF-21 'Freelancers'

VF-21 'Freelancers' converted to the F-14A under the auspices of VF-124, the West Coast RAG. It received its first Tomcat in November 1983 and was formally established as an F-14 unit on 15 March 1984. Paired throughout the Tomcat era with VF-154, its partner from F-4 Phantom days, the unit made an early hit in 1984 when it won that year's Boola Boola trophy (awarded for the best AAM readiness of a Pacific Fleet fighter squadron), having chalked up a 100 per cent success rate with its AIM-7s and 83 per cent with AIM-9s.

The squadron joined CVW-14 aboard USS *Constellation,* sailing with it from 18 August to 15 November 1984 and from 6 to 16 December 1984 in the Eastern Pacific. A full WestPac/Indian Ocean cruise followed, between 21 February and 24 August,1985, with a short NorPac (northern Pacific) cruise with Air Wing 14 aboard the 'Connie' between 4 September and 20 October 1986. The ship next sailed for a WestPac and Indian Ocean deployment between 11 April and 13 October 1987. A similar cruise was again undertaken by VF-21 between 1 December 1988 and 1 June 1989. CVW-14 next made a NorPac cruise between 16 September and 19 October.

In 1990, VF-21 transferred with Air Wing 14 to USS *Independence* and sailed on a WestPac, Indian Ocean and Persian Gulf deployment from 23 June to 20 December, supporting the opening phase of Operation Desert Shield. The carrier was the first on the scene in the Persian Gulf (passing through the Straits of Hormuz on 2 August 1990) for participation in any necessary operations, but left the area before hostilities broke out. During this time, the CAG aircraft from each CVW-14 squadron wore a black tail with multi-coloured bands.

VF-21 was awarded a Safety S by CNO for its excellent safety record up to 1989 (and later won another in 1992). In 1991 VF-21 was transferred, along with CVW-14 and the *Independence,* to Japan to replace *Midway* as the sole carrier home-ported outside the USA. The 'Indy' sailed from CONUS on 5 July 1991 for Pearl Harbor, subsequently departing Hawaii for Japan on 22 July. Six days later the ship arrived in Japan, where it remained on cruise until 11 September 1991. It undertook three brief WestPacs by 15 April 1992, when the ship began a full WestPac/Indian Ocean/Persian Gulf cruise.

VF-21 had transferred to Air Wing Five (still aboard the *Independence*) at Pearl Harbour on the way out to Japan. During this cruise, the *Independence* visited Australia to participate in the celebrations commemorating the 50th Anniversary of the Battle of the Coral Sea, before going on to help police the newly established 'No-Fly

Above: VF-21's original Tomcat colour scheme included a black anti-dazzle panel which extended back over the canopy rails, and swept forward over the radome, tucking back below the nose. This radome decoration was removed from about 1985.

Right: With tailcodes moved to the rudders, a VF-21 Tomcat launches from the Constellation, on which it served as part of CVW-14. The yellow tail chevron acts as a background for the unit's sword and lion rampant badge. The overall light grey colour scheme was soon replaced.

Zone' over southern Iraq (Operation Southern Watch) and finally returning home on 31 December 1992. Four more mini WestPac cruises followed before 'Indy' again carried VF-21 and Air Wing 5 on a full-scale WestPac and Indian Ocean cruise between 17 November 1993 and 17 March 1994, including participation in Operation

Southern Watch and the Somalia crisis.

The end is now in sight for VF-21, as it has been announced that the squadron will disestablish in FY 1996. Rumours suggest that it will then convert to the F/A-18 Hornet as VFA-21, retaining the 'Freelancers' name and traditions. This will leave VF-154 as the sole Japan-based F-14 Tomcat unit.

Below: This VF-21 F-14A wears a rare badge on its tailfin inner faces, with a cartoon dog superimposed on the stars and stripes, and the caption 'Oop Ack baby'. Reports suggest that VF-21 is to become an F/A-18 unit, as VFA-21.

Grumman F-14 Variants

VF-24 'Fighting Renegades'

Converting to the F-14A in November 1975 and discarding single-seat F-8J Crusaders, VF-24 (callsign 'Nickel') joined Air Wing Nine as partner to VF-211, on 1 March 1976. Once known as the 'Red Checkertails', the unit soon switched to the 'Fighting Renegades' nickname to avoid confusion with its sister squadron. The first F-14 unit to win the coveted Mutha award (for the best Pacific Fleet fighter squadron) in March 1977, VF-24 began its first carrier deployment with a WestPac cruise between 12 March and 21 November 1977, aboard USS *Constellation*. The squadron received the Clifton Award for flight safety in July 1978, having received a second successive Mutha in March.

Between 26 September 1978 and 17 May 1979, VF-24, again embarked with Air Wing 9 aboard the *Constellation*. The unit flew extensive 'blue water' (no diversion) operations on the WestPac/Indian Ocean cruise, during a period of tension caused by the Yemen crisis. The squadron entered the 1980s making a WestPac, Indian Ocean deployment with CVW-9 and the 'Connie' from 26 February until 15 October 1980.

During this cruise, CVW-9 provided support for Operation Eagle Claw, the abortive US attempt to rescue the hostages held in the US embassy in Teheran. *Constellation*'s aircraft were roughly painted with black and red recognition stripes on the wings as a protection against friendly fire. *Constellation* was replaced on 'Gonzo Station' by USS *Midway* on 27 June, but made a hasty return when *Midway* was damaged in a collision and had to head for port to effect repairs. The next year VF-24 left on another WestPac deployment, starting on 20 October 1981 and returning on 23 May 1982. The 'Renegades' next joined USS *Ranger*, with the rest of Air Wing 9, and undertook an Indian Ocean cruise between 15 June 1983 and 29 February 1984.

On 20 May 1985, one of VF-24's Tomcats (159593/201) became the first F-14 to clock up 3,000 flight hours, a notable achievement. Later that year, on 24 July, the squadron sailed on another WestPac/Indian Ocean cruise on the *Kitty Hawk*, returning on 21 December.

Still as part of CVW-9 aboard USS *Kitty Hawk*, VF-24 made a round-the-world cruise from 31 January 1987 to 29 July 1987, this marking the last cruise of the *Kitty Hawk* before its SLEP. The unit then transferred, still as part of Air Wing 9, to USS *Nimitz* and made a WestPac and Indian Ocean deployment between 2 September 1988 and 2 March 1989, operating in support of Operation Earnest Will, protecting tankers in the Persian Gulf. A NorPac cruise was next, lasting from 15 June 1989 until 9 July. The 'Renegades' transitioned to the F-14A+ during spring/summer 1989, undergoing refresher training aboard the *Nimitz* in June. That same year, the squadron won the Boola Boola award. In the summer of 1990, the squadron began to develop tactics and techniques for the air-to-ground mission, becoming the first front-line fleet squadron to drop bombs (four Mk 84s) from the Tomcat on 8 August 1990.

The squadron took its F-14A+s on a WestPac/Indian Ocean cruise aboard USS *Nimitz*, as part of CVW-9, between 25 February and 24 August 1991, just too late to participate in Operation Desert Storm. This cruise included exercises with Thailand and Malaysia, and also provided plenty of trade in the shape of Soviet 'Bears' and 'Fitters' for the wing's two Tomcat units to intercept.

Once back in the United States, on 30 September 1991 the unit's F-14A+s demonstrated their new-found 'Bombcat' role at NAS Fallon, where VF-24 developed the FRS training syllabus and trained its own crews in the air-to-ground role. VF-24 next became the first West Coast fighter squadron to complete the Advanced Attack Readiness Program (AARP), although by this time – June 1992– the unit had transitioned back to the F-14A, the F-14Bs being consolidated into the Atlantic Fleet.

The WestPac/Persian Gulf cruise by *Nimitz* which began on 4 February 1993 saw VF-24 deploy again as part of Air Wing Nine, subsequently flying missions in support of Operation Southern Watch over southern Iraq. Equipped with TARPS pods, VF-24 undertook reconnaissance missions over the contended territory. A year later, the unit was at Nellis flying Red Force missions during Red Flag.

VF-24 is likely to disestablish in FY 1996, although an exact date has not yet been released. The squadron identity may be retained by renumbering one of the Navy's existing F/A-18 units, or it may follow other historic units (such as VF-1 'Wolfpack', VF-111 'Sundowners' and VF-114 'Aardvarks') into oblivion.

Right: Carrying a pair of AIM-54 Phoenix missiles, an F-14A of VF-24 launches from NAS Miramar. The curving chevron on the fin was originally red, outlined in black, but had been toned down by 1978 (except on CAG- and boss-birds). Full-colour, large-size stars and bars were retained into the 1980s, when the tactical blue-grey colour scheme began to appear, and when VF-24's aircraft received a smaller, more angular tail chevron.

Left: VF-24's CAG aircraft taxis at NAS Fallon during June 1981, with black tailfins and a red tail chevron. The red nine, surrounded by stars, indicates assignment to CVW-9. A black S, with red shadow, indicates the award of a Safety S to the squadron. CAG aircraft traditionally wear the 00 ('Double Nuts') modex.

Below: This VF-24 F-14A+ wears water-based temporary camouflage for participation in a shore-based bombing exercise. The aircraft is named 'Camel Smoker' and carries a bomb tally in red. Such temporary colour schemes are by no means rare on the F-14, although they tend to be carried only for very short periods.

VF-31 'Tomcatters'

VF-31 is the US Navy's second oldest fighter squadron, and began F-14 conversion with VF-101 on 8 September 1980. It received its first F-14s on 22 January and its first TARPS-equipped aircraft soon afterwards. The squadron (callsign 'Bandwagon' or 'Felix') officially stood up with Tomcats on 4 June 1981, joining VF-11 as part of Air Wing Three.

Kennedy took CVW-3 to the Indian Ocean and Mediterranean from 4 January to 14 July 1982, and on exercises in the Atlantic and Mediterranean from 27 September 1983 to 2 May 1984. It found itself in an unexpectedly hostile situation when it was called to readiness at 'Bagel Station' off the coast of Lebanon, to support the US presence in Beirut. On 3 December two of the squadron's TARPS aircraft came under fire, this triggering a retaliatory Alpha Strike against the offending Syrian positions during which an A-6 and an A-7 were lost. The cruise also resulted in two F-14 losses for VF-31, with one crew killed. Transferring with VF-11 to CVW-6, the squadron deployed to the Mediterranean again between 2 June and 10 October 1986, sailing with USS *Forrestal*. Forced to sail within sight of the coast to boost morale, the ship remained in a super-heightened state of readiness for often-predicted suicide attacks by boat and even air.

From 28 July until 9 October 1987, the unit undertook a NorLant deployment, followed by a further NorLant/ Mediterranean/Indian Ocean cruise between 25 April and 7 October 1988. CVW-6 next made a Mediterranean cruise from 4 November 1989 until 12 April 1990, returning there for another deployment from 30 May to 21 December 1991, after a brief Caribbean cruise between 29 November and 23 December 1990.

The 'Tomcatters' remained with CVW-6 and undertook the same cruises as their sister squadron, VF-11, flying much the same sort of missions but with the added tactical recce commitment made possible by the unit's handful of TARPS-capable

Above: Felix the cat adorns the tailfins and fuel tank noses of this VF-31 'Tomcatters' F-14A. During 1981 the tail insignia was replaced by a simple tailcode.

Right: By 1991, most VF-31 Tomcats had low-visibility markings, with tailstripes in dark grey, although radomes remained black.

F-14As. The May-December 1991 Mediterranean cruise aboard the *Forrestal* provided particularly useful training opportunities, and saw the squadron undertake low-level exercises with the Israeli air force.

The squadron moved to the West Coast upon the retirement of the *Forrestal* and the consequent disestablishment of Air Wing Six, and began to transition to the F-14D in early 1992. VF-31 officially joined CVW-14 aboard USS *Carl Vinson* (CVN-70) in July,

and began training using the first five of its F-14Ds from 8 July. Introduction of the F-14D brought about a slight change in colour scheme for the squadron, since only the CAG-bird retained the unit's traditional black radome, most other aircraft being delivered with radomes in light grey. F-14Ds went on cruise aboard the *Vinson* between

18 February 1994 and 15 August 1994, making a WestPac/Indian Ocean/Persian Gulf cruise and participating in Operation Southern Watch.

VF-31 may transfer from CVW-14 to another carrier air wing, leaving VF-11 with the *Vinson*. One of the two squadrons is reportedly to disestablish during FY 1997.

VF-32 'Swordsmen'

VF-32 converted to the F-14 at Miramar during early 1974. The first deployment was with USS *John F. Kennedy* on a Mediterranean cruise which began on 29 June 1978, as part of CVW-1. The squadron then undertook the same cruises as its sister unit, VF-14. The squadron made Tomcat history by participating in Exercise Red Flag during 1979. Air Wing 1 sailed again with 'Big John' between July 1980 and 28 March 1981. VF-32 (callsign 'Gypsy') then joined CVW-6 and deployed aboard its new home, USS *Independence,* from 7 June 1982 to 22 December. This was 'Indy's' first extended deployment with F-14s.

Operation Urgent Fury, the US invasion of Grenada in October 1983, was supported by the *Independence* and CVW-6. F-14s from VF-32 undertook their normal roles of fleet air defence and air superiority. After Grenada, the *Independence* continued on to the Mediterranean for a cruise lasting from 18 October 1983 until 11 April 1984, during which VF-32 TARPS aircraft flew the first live BDA sorties since the Vietnam War, photographing the damage caused by the December 1983 strike against Syrian positions in the Lebanon. The *Independence* next took its air wing to the Mediterranean and Indian Ocean from 16 October 1984 until 19 February 1985.

On 1 January 1989 two of VF-32's crews added to the F-14A's laurels by downing a pair of Libyan MiG-23s in an incident which marked the F-14's third and fourth kills, but which remains controversial to this day. Some aver that the Libyan aircraft were 'Flogger-Es' incapable of carrying a BVR missile, and thus not presenting a threat when engaged. Between 7 October 1992 and 7 April 1993, the squadron embarked with CVW-3 aboard the *Kennedy* for another Mediterranean cruise. The squadron remains partnered with VF-14 with CVW-3, assigned to the *Eisenhower*.

Above: For years, VF-32 used as its badge a version of Grumman's 'Tomcat' insignia, in pirate's costume and leaning on a sword.

Above right: By 1989, VF-32 had reverted to a simple sword insignia on the fins of its F-14s. Such a sword was originally carried on the aircraft's rudders and then, from 1979, across the fin.

Right: VF-32 Tomcats in their original colour scheme had broad yellow fin bands and swords on the rudders.

Grumman F-14 Variants

VF-33 'Starfighters'

VF-33 accepted its first F-14s in December 1981 (when it was known as 'the Tarsiers'), having transitioned to the aircraft with VF-101. It was declared operational in January 1982, six months after the conclusion of its last F-4J cruise. The squadron mirrored VF-102, making a series of cruises as part of CVW-1 aboard USS *America*. Between 24 March and 18 April 1986, during a Mediterranean cruise with Air Wing 1 aboard the *America*, VF-33 flew operations off the coast of Libya, crossing Colonel Khadaffi's 'line of death' by entering the international waters of the Gulf of Sirte, which were claimed as territorial waters by Libya. These operations culminated in Operations Prairie Fire and El Dorado Canyon (airstrikes against Libyan targets).

Between 6 January and 19 February 1987, the squadron embarked on the *Theodore Roosevelt* for a brief shakedown cruise in the Caribbean, then continued to partner VF-102 aboard USS *America*. During late 1988 the squadron, officially redubbed the 'Starfighters' (although the 'Tarsiers' nickname lingered on unofficially), teamed up with the F/A-18C-equipped VFA-82 'Marauders' to act as threat aircraft against USAF F-15s, F-16s, F-111s and A-10s. The two squadrons later practised mixed-section tactics against VF-45 prior to another carrier deployment aboard USS *America*. As part of CVW-1, VF-33 made a NorLant and Caribbean cruise from 11 May to 10 November 1989. USS *America* next sailed with a composite CVW-9, transiting the Horn from west to east between 12 February and 7 April 1990. On this cruise VF-33 was the only F-14 squadron embarked.

Between 28 December 1990 and 18 April 1991, VF-33 again deployed with CVW-1 aboard USS *America* for a Mediterranean/Red Sea/Persian Gulf cruise, and flew operations in support of Operations Desert Shield and Desert Storm. The squadron initially flew strike escorts and MiGCAPs while the *America* was in the Red Sea, switching to the fleet air defence role when the carrier took up position in the Persian Gulf. Another cruise aboard USS *America* with CVW-1 began on 21 August 1991. This was a brief deployment into the Atlantic for Exercise North Star, and the carrier returned to port on 11 October.

A further cruise between 2 December 1991 and 6 June 1992 took the *America* and Air Wing One into the Mediterranean, where the two F-14 squadrons had the opportunity to practise dissimilar air combat against Tunisian F-5Es and Spanish navy AV-8Bs. For VF-33, however, the writing was on the wall, and the squadron disbanded on 1 October 1993, leaving VF-102 as CVW-1's sole Tomcat unit.

Top: VF-33's CAG-bird in 1988. Ordinary squadron aircraft were similarly marked from April 1984, before which the lightning bolt and star were in black outline form only. For a brief initial period, these markings were applied in yellow on a black fin panel, with a grey tip and leading edge.

Above: The VF-33 CAG-bird, 1992-style, wore markings similar to the original 1981-type squadron markings.

Left: The 'Starfighters' final colour scheme had a toned-down lightning bolt on the black fins and on the forward fuselage. The forward fuselage lightning bolt had not been seen since 1981, when it was yellow, outlined in black.

VF-41 'Black Aces'

Throughout the late 1970s and 1980s, VF-41 'Black Aces' (callsign 'Fast Eagle') sailed as part of CVW-8 aboard USS *Nimitz*. The squadron began conversion to the F-14A in April 1976, and was declared operational with the new type in December. A successful ORE cleared the way for an eight-month maiden cruise which began in December 1977 and ended on 20 July 1978. Further cruises aboard *Nimitz* followed, with a 10 September 1979 to 26 May 1980 Mediterranean/Indian Ocean cruise supporting Operation Evening Light in Iran and a work-up NorLant deployment beginning on 14 May 1981. Tragedy struck when a Marine EA-6B crashed onto the deck of the *Nimitz*, killing three crew from VF-41 and destroying three F-14s.

This was followed by a Mediterranean cruise beginning in August. The squadron soon found itself in action against the Libyan air force on 19 August 1981. Cdr Henry M. ('Hank') Kleeman and Lt David Venlet (in F-14 modex 102) along with Lt Larry 'Music' Musczynski and Lt (JG) Jim 'Amos' Anderson (in modex 107) claimed a pair of Libyan Su-22s with their AIM-9 Sidewinders. After days of the F-14s hassling with Libyan fighters attempting to close on the battle group, the two Su-22s went too far, firing a missile at the pair of Tomcats. The missile did not guide, and in retrospect some analysts believed the lead F-14 crew may have mistaken a tank being jettisoned for a missile launch. Whatever the truth, the action sealed the fate of the Libyan pilots. These represented the first kills by the F-14, and the first US Navy kills since the Vietnam War. They came at just the right time for the Tomcat squadrons, seemingly confirming the start of a new era for the aircraft, which at last seemed to be leaving many of its early troubles behind it. The engagement with the Libyan fighters marked the first air-to-air battle between variable-geometry fighters and provided a much-needed boost to morale and to recruiting.

1982 saw the squadron gain three major awards – a Battle E, a Safety S and the Clifton Trophy – while conducting another Mediterranean cruise between November 1982 and May 1983, and a one-month Caribbean shakedown for the new USS *Vinson* during May/June. The Joseph P. Clifton Trophy is probably the most prestigious and important prize that can be awarded to a Tomcat unit, being given annually to the US Navy's best fighter squadron. VF-41 stayed with Air Wing 8 aboard the *Nimitz* and undertook a Mediterranean cruise in 1985, from 8 March to 3 September, during which the squadron tested minor improvements made to the M61A1 cannon. *Nimitz* returned to the north Atlantic with VF-41 between 15 July and 16 October 1986.

For a round-the-world cruise, VF-41 transferred to USS *Roosevelt* along with the rest of CVW-8, departing on 30 December 1986 and returning on 26 July 1987. CVW-8 formally transferred to the *Theodore Roosevelt* in October 1987, and the squadron made a brief Caribbean deployment from 8 March to 8 April, before going on a full NorLant deployment aboard *Roosevelt* between 25 August and 11 October 1988. A second cruise, this time to the Mediterranean, began on 30 December 1988 and lasted until 30 June 1989. On both this and the previous NorLant cruise, *Roosevelt* carried an 'experimental' air wing comprising 20 F-14s, 20 F/A-18s and 20 A-6s, as opposed to the then-standard 24 F-14s, 24 A-7s and 10 A-6s. This maximised both the carrier's strike and air combat potential through the F/A-18's impressive 'swing' capability. Such an air wing (which soon became known as the 'Roosevelt Wing') became the US Navy's preferred composition until recently, when the realities of the post-Cold War world dictated an even more flexible structure with one enhanced F-14 squadron and three multi-role F/A-18 units.

At the end of 1988, CVW-8 sailed for the Mediterranean (on 30 December) and returned the following year on 28 June. 1989 was a good year for the 'Black Aces', the squadron gaining a Safety S from the CNO and a COMNAVAIRLANT Battle E. Between 19 January and 23 February 1990, CVW-8 conducted a Caribbean shakedown cruise for the new *Abraham Lincoln* (CVN-72).

Between 28 December 1990 and 28 June 1991, the squadron deployed aboard USS *Theodore Roosevelt* as part of CVW-8 for a Mediterranean/Red Sea/Persian Gulf cruise. Roosevelt sailed on 28 December 1990, and was joined by nine F-14s of VF-41 the following day. The carrier arrived in the Gulf on 19 January, and the two Tomcat squadrons flew MiGSweep, TarCAP, MiGCAP and HVACAP missions, eventually roaming widely over southern Iraq but still without finding any enemy aircraft to down.

VF-41 left the *Roosevelt* to join CVW-15 aboard USS *Kitty Hawk*, departing for a RimPac cruise on 22 June 1992. During this deployment, the squadron participated in exercise Tandem Thrust '92. This Pacific sailing was followed by another WestPac cruise from 3 November 1992 until 3 May 1993.

The squadron has since rejoined CVW-8, which is now reassigned to the *Roosevelt*, and made an Atlantic cruise between 19 May and 29 June 1994. VF-41 will take over the TARPS commitment upon the disbandment of VF-84.

Above: The first F-14As delivered to the US Navy were in glossy light grey, with white undersides and control surfaces. On these aircraft, squadron markings were extremely colourful, as exemplified by this red-striped VF-41 aircraft, which wore its tailcodes inside a massive black ace of spades.

Right: The late 1970s saw the introduction of an overall gloss light grey finish, on which squadron markings were reduced in size. This was replaced by a matt version of the same overall colour. The VF-84 aircraft in the background shows the next phase in Tomcat markings, wearing the overall matt blue-grey tactical camouflage on which all markings were toned down, applied in slightly different shades of grey with little contrast and no colour.

Below: This pair of VF-41 F-14As illustrate the standard and CAG/squadron commander colour schemes as applied during 1992. The far aircraft is painted in the original light grey paint, and has small patches of colour on its fintips, and on unit markings, warning stripes, etc., together with enlarged full-colour star and bar. Both aircraft have an attractive, tapering anti-dazzle panel with stripes, which extends back aft of the canopy.

Grumman F-14 Variants

VF-51 'Screaming Eagles'

VF-51 'Screaming Eagles' (callsign 'Eagles') took delivery of its first F-14A on 16 June 1978, converting under the guidance of VF-124. The squadron made its first cruise aboard the *Kitty Hawk* with CVW-15, departing for a WestPac deployment on 30 May 1979. The cruise was eventful, the carrier coming to action stations and holding off the Korean coast following the assassination of President Park, and then taking station off Iran in response to the kidnapping of 60 Americans by revolutionary Iran. A subsequent eight-month WestPac cruise lasting from 1 April until 23 November 1981 saw *Kitty Hawk*'s air wing notch up some notable achievements. CVW-15's aircraft logged 1,600 traps over the course of 3,400 flying hours. Every crew on board became centurions (logging 100 traps) and at peak sortie rate 785 hours were flown over just 22 days – much of it during monsoon conditions.

VF-51 gained a Boola Boola award in 1983, and that same year the squadron temporarily transferred, along with Air Wing 15, to the East Coast for embarkation aboard the new USS *Carl Vinson*, which was due to transfer to the Pacific Fleet. The

newly commissioned carrier's first deployment took it, and VF-51, on a round-the-world cruise from 1 March 1983 until 29 October 1983. This cruise involved the squadron in many exercises, including air-to-air combat missions against Moroccan F-5Es. The following year VF-51's F-14s made two short EastPac cruises aboard *Vinson* before embarking for a full WestPac cruise on 18 October 1984, to visit Australia and participate in Fleet Ex '85 in the new year. During that cruise, VF-51's Tomcats became the first US Navy aircraft to intercept a Soviet air force Tu-22 'Blinder' (on 2 December 1984), and subsequently its aircraft encountered curious Su-15s and MiG-23s, intercepting these with the aid of their powerful new Northrop TCS sets. This cruise also saw VF-51 make the first F-14 day and night automatic carrier landings.

During 1985, VF-51 was heavily involved in the filming of the Hollywood motion picture 'Top Gun'. This took place at NAS Miramar, from where the 'Eagles' also flew as aggressors in Red Flag 85-5.

Vinson took Air Wing 15 on another WestPac cruise from 12 August 1986 until 5 February 1987, returning for a second such

deployment between 15 June and 14 December 1988, which continued into the Indian Ocean. VF-51 made an unusual combined NorLant and WestPac cruise (albeit an extremely short one) between 5 September and 8 November 1989. This was followed by a WestPac/Indian Ocean deployment from 1 February to 31 July 1990.

In 1990 the 'Eagles' picked up the Mutha Trophy and a Battle E, as well as winning the West Coast fighter Derby and the ECCM trophy.

The planned transition of VF-51 and its long-term partner unit VF-111 to the F-14D (as the first F-14D squadron) was cancelled when defence cuts halted the F-14D conversion programme. This meant that only the more senior squadrons (VF-2 and the two units transferred from East to West Coast on the disestablishment of CVW-6, VF-11 and VF-31) received the new variant.

Instead, the 'Eagles' moved, along with CVW-15, to USS *Kitty Hawk* (CV-63). Together they sailed east-to-west around Cape Horn from 18 October 1991 until 11 December, during which time the Tomcats were able to fly DACT missions against Venezuelan, Chilean and Argentine fighters.

A far-reaching cruise from 3 November 1992 until 3 May 1993 took VF-51 to the

Indian Ocean and Persian Gulf, where Air Wing 15 flew in support of Operation Provide Relief and Southern Watch. Another cruise began on 24 June 1994.

Sister squadron VF-111 is scheduled to disestablish in March 1995, leaving VF-51 as the sole Tomcat unit within CVW-15. The unit will almost certainly take on the TARPS role from the 'Sundowners' when this happens.

Below: VF-51's first F-14As were delivered in the overall glossy grey scheme, and were decorated with red-striped black tailfins, with grey leading edges. CAG aircraft differed only in having multi-coloured stripes replacing the red ones.

Bottom: The adoption of toned-down markings has been accompanied by a variety of styles of unit insignia, including plain horizontal stripes in dull red or dark grey, and stripes with the unit's star and eagle superimposed, as seen here.

VF-74 'Bedevilers'

VF-74 'Bedevilers' (callsign 'Devil') began conversion to the Tomcat in February 1983, receiving its first aircraft in June and becoming fully operational in October 1983. The squadron embarked aboard *Saratoga* for a brief shakedown in the Caribbean between 26 January and 21 February 1984, then remained with CVW-17 (its parent unit during the Phantom era) and *Saratoga* for its maiden F-14 cruise, a 1984 Mediterranean deployment lasting until 20 October 1984. VF-74 was again aboard the *Saratoga* for its August 1985 Mediterranean cruise. The ship participated in Exercise Ocean Safari '85 on its way out, chopping to Sixth Fleet control on 7 September and then taking part in Exercise Display Determination '85. The squadron also played a minor part in the capture of the *Achille Lauro* hijackers.

Saratoga switched to Seventh Fleet control in November, after making the first night transit of the Suez Canal by a US carrier. The ship returned to the Mediterranean for operations off the Libyan coast during January, February and March, dropping out from the Sixth Fleet on 5 April and returning home. As part of its Mediterranean cruise in 1985/1986, this

time with CVW-17 on the *Saratoga*, VF-74 flew strike CAPs during HARM shoots against Libyan missile sites. Over this period VF-74 was at sea between 25 August 1985 and 16 April 1986, returning for another Mediterranean cruise from 5 June 1987 until 17 November 1987. A 12-day detachment to NAS Roosevelt Roads for

missile practice ended on 16 November 1988.

VF-74 sailed with the rest of Air Wing Seventeen aboard the USS *Saratoga* when it departed Mayport to join the *Independence* (with CVW-14) and the *Kennedy* (CVW-3) for participation in Operation Desert Storm. While still in the closing stages of conversion to the F-14A+, the squadron departed for this war cruise on 7 August 1990 and returned home on 28 March 1991.

VF-74 made a subsequent cruise (with its

aircraft now formally redesignated F-14Bs) aboard the *Saratoga* between 6 May and 6 November 1992. The squadron next deployed (with the rest of CVW-17) aboard USS *Constellation* for a post-SLEP shakedown cruise.

Between its last cruise and its disestablishment, VF-74 operated mainly in the adversary role, its aircraft adopting an unusual disruptive pattern, blue-grey camouflage scheme. The squadron disestablished on 28 April 1994.

Right: A VF-74 F-14A wears temporary desert camouflage, seen during June 1987. The last of the Atlantic Fleet F-14 units, VF-74 received toned-down F-14As.

Above: The Olympic rings on the nose of VF-74's CO's Tomcat, pictured in 1992, are of unknown significance. The squadron markings are usually applied in shades of grey, with only the lightning bolt itself in red. Unit commanders are traditionally assigned the 01 modex.

Right: For the last months of its career as an F-14 unit, VF-74 served in the adversary role, and its aircraft were painted in two-tone disruptive camouflage, with red modexes, in an approximation of the most common MiG-29 and Su-27 colour schemes.

VF-84 'Jolly Rogers'

VF-84 'Jolly Rogers' (callsign 'Victory') began conversion to the F-14 during October 1975, under the supervision of VF-101 at Oceana. The unit finally stood up with the Tomcat in mid-April 1977, when it was officially reassigned to Air Wing Eight, along with sister squadron VF-41, whose pattern of carrier deployments it mirrored. Decorated with a massive skull-and-crossbones on their fins, the squadron's F-14As were early achievers, chalking up an impressive 752.9 flying hours over only 23 days on an early (1978) cruise with CVW-8 aboard USS Forrestal. By 1980 VF-84 was aboard USS Nimitz making a NorLant, Mediterranean, Indian Ocean deployment with transits via the Cape of Good Hope and

Persian Gulf, returning home from 'Gonzo Station' on 26 May. Had Operation Eagle Claw not been abandoned as a result of the disaster at Desert One, when Nimitz-based RH-53Ds collided with a C-130 and had to be left in the desert, VF-84 would have undoubtedly had a role to play in the US hostage rescue.

The squadron assumed a TARPS reconnaissance commitment during 1981, flying TARPS missions over the Persian Gulf, and became the first Tomcat TARPS unit in either fleet to deploy the new pod operationally. Further cruises included an August 1981 to February 1982 Mediterranean deployment, a November 1982 to May 1983 deployment, and a 1985

Mediterranean cruise which saw the unit participating in Exercise Bright Star, and standing by in case required for action generated by the hijacking of a TWA Boeing 727 at Athens. Unfortunately, the 'Jolly Rogers' were unable to achieve the success of their sister unit, VF-41, during the 1981 cruise, none of their hassles with Libyan fighters giving an opportunity to open fire under the prevailing Rules of Engagement.

In 1982, the Nimitz spent some time on 'Bagel Station' off the Lebanese coast supporting the Marine garrison in Beirut. This involved constantly steaming within sight of the Lebanese coast, to provide maximum moral support for the US Marines in Beirut, and maintaining a 24-hour alert against suicide attacks and other terrorist threats. The squadron was not directly

involved in the 1985 operations to bring the hijackers of the Achille Lauro to book.

Later (but still as part of CVW-8) VF-84 made a NorLant cruise aboard USS Nimitz between 15 August and 16 November 1986, which included extensive air combat exercises with a number of opponents including the Royal Norwegian air force. The squadron next undertook a round-the-world cruise from 30 December 1986 to 26 July 1987, incorporating a stop for missile practice at NAS Roosevelt Roads. During 1988 the squadron and the rest of Air Wing Eight transferred to the Roosevelt. A NorLant cruise was next, between 25 August and 11 October 1988, followed by a Mediterranean deployment from 30 December 1988 to 30 June 1989. During 1989 a VF-84 Tomcat and crew made history by becoming the first fleet aircraft to make an arrested landing on the new carrier Abraham Lincoln (CVN-72). On board the USS Theodore Roosevelt, the 'Jolly Rogers' sailed to the Red Sea, Persian Gulf and Mediterranean from 28 December 1991 until 28 June 1992, missing out on participation in Operations Desert Storm and Desert Shield but nonetheless flying CAPS and sweeps over Iraq in support of UN operations in the area.

Between 11 March and 8 September 1993, VF-84 was the sole F-14 unit deployed during Roosevelt's Mediterranean cruise in support of the Special Marine Air-to-Ground Task Force.

Some reports suggest that VF-84 may disband in mid-1995, but other sources suggest that the unit will replace VF-143 with CVW-7.

Left: The 'Jolly Rogers' can trace their traditions back to the wartime VF-17, via a takeover of VF-61 in the 1950s. The original 'Jolly Rogers' were among the most successful users of the F4U Corsair, one of which is seen here in VF-17 colours, escorting a modern 'Jolly Roger' F-14A.

Right: VF-84's F-14As lost their black fins and black/yellow nose markings around 1982, when low-visibility markings and tactical camouflage were introduced. The markings crept back gradually during the mid-1980s, with restoration of the nose stripe (albeit in toned-down form). During the late 1980s, coloured fintips appeared on CAG-assigned aircraft, initially in yellow and later in red. Even on CAG aircraft, full-colour markings have not reappeared.

Left: The current VF-84 colour scheme is completely toned down, with all squadron insignia applied in dark grey over the tactical blue-grey camouflage. The squadron is the TARPS-equipped unit within Carrier Air Wing Eight, and continues to serve alongside the 'Black Aces' of VF-41. The 'Jolly Rogers' are one of the units scheduled to disband as part of the current drawdown of the F-14 force, which will end when all CVWs have been reduced to a single F-14 squadron.

VF-101 'Grim Reapers'

Until late 1994, VF-101 (callsign 'Gunfighter') was the East Coast fleet replenishment squadron for the Tomcat, responsible for training pilots and NFOs before they join Atlantic Fleet fighter squadrons. Permanently assigned to the training role from 1958, VF-101 successively acted as a training unit for the F4D Skyray, the F3D Skyknight and F3H Demon, and the F4H Phantom, operating from Key West and Oceana. A purely Phantom training operation for most of the 1960s and 1970s, VF-101 stood up as an F-14 component at NAS Oceana in 1975. The unit organised a replacement training programme for future F-14 pilots, backseaters and maintenance personnel, although VF-124 had already started training Tomcat crews (including those from the first Atlantic Fleet units) from 1973. By March 1977, such training was the sole responsibility of VF-101, which had finally discarded the last of its Phantoms by redesignating the F-4 element as VF-171, formally becoming the East Coast F-14 RTS during that summer.

VF-101's first intake of aircrew was for VF-41 and VF-84, these two units entering the conversion process in mid-1976 and standing up in February 1977. VF-101 did not train all the Atlantic Fleet squadrons, VF-14, VF-32, VF-142 and VF-143 converting under the auspices of VF-124 'Gunfighters' at Miramar. It did, however, oversee the conversion of VF-11, VF-31, VF-33, VF-74, VF-102, VF-103, VF-201 and VF-202, and today provides suitably trained replacement air and ground personnel for all Fleet F-14 squadrons. This involves the unit in converting aircrew to the new aircraft type (including carrier landing training), and giving rudimentary tactical and weapons training.

Above right: VF-101's initial marking consisted of a broad red tail band, bordered in blue, with 'AD' tailcodes edged in gold. The tailband had disappeared by 1978, leaving aircraft with an extremely plain finish.

Right: This F-14A carries the personal 'Moon-equipped' insignia of Commander Moon Vance, with a crescent moon on the tailfins and bloodshot eyes on the nose. The markings were painted on both sides of the aircraft.

Below: Before the present 'Grim Reapers' markings were adopted, VF-101's Tomcats seldom wore badges. This aircraft, with its winged anchor motif, was an exception.

As such, VF-101 makes numerous short deployments to sea, although its aircraft seldom stay on a carrier overnight. Known as the 'Gunfighters' for many years, VF-101 finally gave up that nickname in the winter of 1982 to avoid the clash with rival VF-124, instead using the 'Grim Reapers' identity. As the only Atlantic Fleet F-14 squadron not assigned to a carrier air wing, VF-101's aircraft have always worn the same 'AD' tailcode, although markings have changed frequently over the years.

F-14A+s (since redesignated F-14Bs) were taken on charge in 1988, these being used to train aircrew for F-14B squadrons from both Atlantic and Pacific Fleet units, until all F-14Bs were consolidated on the East Coast. VF-124 similarly took responsibility for all F-14D training.

On 12 September 1990, VF-101's CO dropped a pair of live Mk 84 bombs, demonstrating the squadron's new-found 'Bombcat' capability. VF-101 was tasked as model managers for the Tomcat Strike Fighter programme, undertaking to develop the air-to-surface training syllabus while also training fleet squadrons and replacement aircrew. This has since become a vital part of the Tomcat's role. VF-101 is the destination for RAF Tornado ADV aircrew flying the F-14 on exchange tours with the US Navy.

The dramatic post-Cold War drawdown of the Tomcat force has resulted in a much-diminished need for F-14 aircrew, and it was decided that to continue to maintain separate conversion training units for each fleet would be an unaffordable luxury. Accordingly, it was decided to disband one of the two units, VF-124 drawing the short straw. VF-101 is the surviving Tomcat training unit and now maintains a detachment at Miramar with F-14Ds, as VF-101 Det West, after the West Coast FRS, VF-124, disbanded in September 1994.

Grumman F-14 Variants

VF-102 'Diamondbacks'

The 'Diamondbacks' (callsign 'Diamondback') began transitioning to the F-14 during July 1981. Its first traps were made aboard the *America* during May 1982, by which time the squadron was virtually fully operational, having completed conversion smoothly despite the need for specialised training with the TARPS pod.

The squadron deployed with CVW-1 aboard the *America* in the Atlantic/ Caribbean (30 May 1982 to 8 July 1982) and North Atlantic/Mediterranean (23 August to 4 November 1982), before its first full Mediterranean/Indian Ocean cruise which included operations in support of the US peacekeepers between December 1982 and June 1983. Despite the squadron's relative inexperience, its performance on the cruise was enough to win it a handsome trophy from Grumman, in recognition that it was that year's top Atlantic Fleet TARPS squadron. Embarked on USS *America* as part of CVW-1 from November to December 1983, VF-102 provided a presence in the Caribbean following Operation Just Cause in October of that year. February 1984 saw a 20-day Caribbean exercise, again aboard *America*, before a full Central America/ Mediterranean/Indian Ocean cruise was undertaken between April and November 1984.

CV-66 and CVW-1 went to sea for Ocean Safari in the North Atlantic for a period which included the whole of September 1985. Between 10 March 1986 and 14 September 1986, VF-102 again saw action, this time in support of operations against Libya, during which VF-102 aircraft were fired upon by Libyan SA-5s and anti-aircraft artillery during Operation Prairie Fire. The squadron then flew top cover for the 15 April 1986 El Dorado Canyon airstrikes against Libyan targets. During February 1987, VF-102 participated in *Roosevelt*'s shakedown cruise in the Caribbean, then flew in Exercise Solid Shield '87, which gave the unit opportunities for practising DACT with USAF F-15 Eagles. 1988 saw a brief Atlantic deployment (from 21 March to 6 May 1988). Still as part of Air Wing 1, VF-102 sailed with the *America* on a Caribbean and NorLant cruise between 8 February 1989 and 3 April 1989, a Mediterranean and Indian Ocean cruise from 11 May 1989 until 10 November 1989, and a Red Sea to Persian Gulf deployment from 28 December 1990 to 18 May 1991 – the latter for combat in Operation Desert Storm.

In 1990 the 'Diamondbacks' earned the Grand Slam award. The following year they sailed on a NorLant cruise from 21 August until 11 October, participating in Exercise North Star. Later that year Air Wing 1 and the *America* sailed for a NorLant/ Mediterranean/Red Sea and Persian Gulf deployment between 2 December 1991 and 6 June 1992.

Between 11 August 1993 and 5 February 1994, VF-102 was the sole F-14 unit deployed with CVW-1 aboard USS *America* for a Mediterranean cruise, sister squadron VF-33 having disbanded on 1 October 1993. It is believed that VF-102 will eventually transition to the F-14B.

Above: VF-102's F-14As wear a band of red diamonds around the forward fuselage, and have traditionally used a diamond on the fin in which to display the appropriate CVW tailcode. Here a Phoenix- and Sidewinder-armed aircraft prepares to launch from USS America during September 1984. VF-102 is tasked with tactical recce duties, as well as fleet air defence. The aircraft depicted typifies VF-102's standard colour scheme, although aircraft did briefly have the squadron markings applied in shades of grey.

Left: Illustrating the CAG/squadron commander scheme used in 1984 is this F-14A, which has white diamonds on its red rudders, as well as the usual nose band and wing glove diamonds. A small number of aircraft in each squadron (usually those allocated to the CAG, CO and XO) retained colourful markings after the 1980s toning-down.

Right: The 1990s have seen a slight increase in the use of colourful squadron markings, still of limited extent and still tending to use dull shades. The overall light grey colour scheme has been reintroduced widely. This VF-102 F-14A has the full complement of diamonds, with the unit's rattlesnake marking applied in the fin diamond, and a small solid diamond replacing the hyphen in the VF-102 squadron designation on the ventral fin.

VF-103 'Sluggers'

VF-103 (callsign 'Clubleaf') transitioned to the F-14 during 1983, under the auspices of VF-101. The squadron spent the winter of 1983/1984 preparing to go to sea aboard the USS *Saratoga*, which had just emerged from a long SLEP, as part of Air Wing 3. The ensuing April-October 1984 shakedown cruise was spent with the Sixth Fleet, not least because of the continuing tension in the Lebanon. The cruise proved successful and the unit was awarded a Safety S. VF-103, again partnered by VF-74, undertook a Mediterranean and Indian Ocean cruise aboard the *Saratoga* between 25 August 1985 and 16 April 1986.

The *Saratoga* carried VF-103 to the Mediterranean again from 24 March 1986 to 15 April, operating in support of the US strikes against Libya. A 1987 cruise brought the opportunity for ACM flying with French Super Etendards, while the TARPS aircraft were able to photograph the Soviet helicopter cruiser *Kiev* from close quarters.

On 15 August 1988 the squadron began a temporary deployment aboard USS *Independence*, rounding the Horn and arriving at San Diego eight weeks after

departure. The squadron then rejoined the *Saratoga* for a further Mediterranean/Red Sea cruise, which was undertaken between 7 August 1990 and 28 March 1991, before which VF-103 had traded in its A model Tomcats for F-14A+s, taking these to war in Operation Desert Storm. One of the squadron's aircraft, flown by pilot Lt Devon Jones and RIO Lt Lawrence Randolph 'Rat' Slade, was shot down by an SA-2, the pilot being rescued by a force of USAF A-10s and MH-53s and the RIO being taken prisoner by the Iraqis.

Before its participation in Desert Storm, VF-103 adopted new-look markings, with a club and arrow insignia on the fins replacing the original arrowhead device. The unit began intensive training in the air-to-surface role. Equipped with F-14Bs, VF-103 flew in support of Operation Provide Promise along with the other squadrons of CVW-17 from USS *Saratoga* from 6 May 1992 until 6 November that same year. Sister squadron VF-74 disestablished on 28 April 1994, leaving VF-103 as CVW-17's only Tomcat unit. VF-103 had deployed alone for the final cruise of the 'Super Sara', which began on

12 January 1994 with a scheduled decommissioning date of 20 August.

VF-103 will reportedly leave the fleet for about two years, perhaps to convert to the advanced F-14D or, according to some reports, while its aircraft are further upgraded to some unspecified interim configuration.

Above: VF-103's traditional marking is a yellow arrow, but on the F-14 this has usually been presented in outline form only, except on CAG and CO aircraft. This F-14A also has full-colour, full-size national markings.

Above: A pair of VF-103 F-14Bs patrols shortly before Operation Desert Storm. The 1991 Gulf War marked the first US Navy combat loss of an F-14, one of VF-103's aircraft falling victim to an SA-2. Fortunately both crew ejected safely, one being rescued and the other being taken prisoner.

Right: When it transitioned to the F-14A+ (now known as the F-14B), VF-103 adopted a new squadron marking, with a curving arrow bisecting a clover leaf, superimposed on a baseball bat. The aircraft wears a small 's' on the lower part of the fin, signifying the award of a Safety S. VF-103 is the sole surviving Tomcat squadron within CVW-17, partner squadron VF-74 having disbanded.

VF-111 'Sundowners'

VF-111 (callsign 'Sundowner') was established as VA-156 on 4 June 1956. It was redesignated VF-111 on 20 January 1959. The squadron adopted the insignia of the old VF-111 (disestablished on 19 January 1959) but, while the new VF-111 can carry on the traditions of the old VF-111, which dates to World War II, it cannot claim that squadron's lineage.

The squadron began F-14A operations in 1978, replacing its F-4J Phantoms, and deployed aboard USS *Kitty Hawk* on 30 May 1979. This cruise with CVW-15 was extended until 15 February 1980 to enable *Kitty Hawk* to remain in the Arabian Sea off Iran and also to observe any Soviet activity in Afghanistan. Following a second WestPac and Indian Ocean cruise with the same carrier (between 1 April and 23 November 1981), the 'Sundowners' and the rest of CVW-15, including sister squadron VF-51, shifted to USS *Carl Vinson*, carrying out a world cruise (its first with TARPS F-14s) between 1 March and 29 October 1983. This took them from Norfolk to Alameda through the Caribbean, around the Cape of Good Hope via the Indian Ocean to Australia. En route the carrier spent time on 'Gonzo Station' off the coast of Iran and with the US Sixth Fleet off Lebanon.

During a brief EastPac cruise from 14 May to 28 June 1984, VF-111 participated in Exercise RimPac '84, and later that year a second such cruise (between 31 July and 22 August) took the squadron to Readex 4-84. At the end of 1984, VF-111 sailed for a WestPac and Indian Ocean deployment, departing on 18 October and returning on 24 May 1985.

Just prior to its 1986/87 WestPac and Indian Ocean deployment (from 12 August to 5 February) still with CVW-15 aboard the *Vinson*, one of the 'Sundowners' pilots had an embarrassing experience: on 5 May 1986 he landed on the wrong aircraft-carrier (USS *Constellation*) when meaning to land aboard the *Vinson* (then some 12 miles away) during daylight carquals.

VF-111's next deployment was another EastPac, WestPac and Indian Ocean cruise between 15 June and 14 December 1988, which included Operation Earnest Will. During this sailing, VF-111 flew more than 1,000 sorties and more than 2,000 flying hours, amassing 1,025 traps. The cruise also saw the first trials of the new KS-135A high-altitude camera and the 610-mm lens.

CVW-15 and VF-111 next travelled on a combined NorPac and WestPac sailing from 5 September 1989 until 8 November (participating in Exercise PacEx '89), followed by a WestPac and Indian Ocean deployment between 1 February 1990 and 31 July (participating in Exercise Team Spirit '90). In December 1991, the US Navy cancelled plans for VF-111 and VF-51 to be the first fleet squadrons to operate the F 14D Super Tomcat.

Returning to USS *Kitty Hawk* with CVW-15, VF-111 made an east-to-west sailing around the Cape of Good Hope between 18 October and 11 December 1991. From 3 November 1992 to 3 May 1993, VF-111 made an Indian Ocean and Persian Gulf cruise in support of Operations Restore Hope and Southern Watch. On 24 June 1994 VF-111 departed with the *Kitty Hawk* and CVW-15 on a WestPac, Indian Ocean and Persian Gulf deployment again involving Operation Southern Watch. This will be VF-111's last cruise, as the squadron will disestablish at Miramar in March 1995.

Left: Sharkmouths have been a common sight on 'Sundowner' Tomcats, particularly during the late 1970s and early 1980s.

Below: Throughout their lives (always spent with CVW-15), VF-111's aircraft have been assigned the modex code 200.

Above: During the mid-1980s, the 'Sundowners' went the way of all US Navy Fleet squadrons and were reduced to flying grey Tomcats with a 'colour scheme' that only hinted at their former glory.

Left: In 1989, VF-111's specially-painted CAG-bird sported a far more graphic 'sunburst' tail and 'Miss Molly' nose art. VF-111 was then part of CVW-15 aboard USS Carl Vinson.

VF-114 'Aardvarks'

The history of VF-114 (callsign 'Aardvark') includes its designations as VBF-19 on 20 January 1945, VF-20A on 15 November 1946, VF-192 on 24 August 1948, and VF-114 on 15 February 1950. The squadron's ant-eating mascot, named 'Zot', is a replica of the 'BC' comic strip aardvark. A 2-ft (0.6-m) replica carved out of wood was encased and prominently displayed in the squadron ready room.

After five cruises in Vietnam, the squadron began transitioning to the F-14A Tomcat on 15 December 1975 from the F-4J Phantom. Transition to the Tomcat was completed 1 January 1977, and the 'Aardvarks' made their first cruise with CVW-11 aboard USS *Kitty Hawk* (CV-63) in the western Pacific, departing on 25 October 1977 and returning home on 14 May 1978. Mediterranean cruises aboard USS *America* as part of CVW-11 followed in 1979 (13 March to 22 September) and 1981 (14 April to 12 November) – an unusual series of events for a West Coast squadron. The latter trip, which took CVW-11 to the Indian Ocean, saw USS *America* become the largest USN vessel to transit the Suez Canal. Before returning on 12 November 1981, VF-114 logged 3,100 flying hours and 1,500 traps. With the same air wing, the squadron subsequently joined USS *Enterprise*, fresh from its three-year overhaul, in 1982. Together they sailed on a NorPac, WestPac and Indian Ocean cruise from 1 September 1982 until 28 May 1983.

That year the squadron was awarded the Mutha trophy.

VF-111 stayed with Air Wing 11 aboard the *Enterprise*, deploying in 1986 for a WestPac, Indian Ocean and Mediterranean cruise between 15 January and 12 August. From this cruise, VF-114 adopted modex codes in the 100 series, replacing its previous 200-series codes.

1987 saw VF-114 depart for a short NorPac sailing (25 October to 24 November), followed by a WestPac and Indian Ocean sailing in 1988 (5 January to 3 July, for Operation Praying Mantis). In 1989 VF-111 embarked on a round-the-world cruise (including Operation Classic Resolve) from 17 September 1989 to 16 March 1990. The squadron retired its traditional orange flying suits in September 1990, but orange-coloured beer continued to be served at squadron functions, and the orange flying suits were reintroduced in early 1992.

The 'Aardvarks' next deployed with CVW-11 aboard USS *Abraham Lincoln* for its round-the-Horn cruise from Norfolk to its new home port of Alameda. Departing on 25 September 1991 and arriving on 20 November, *Lincoln* carried a composite air wing. The squadron next left for a full-scale WestPac, Indian Ocean and Persian Gulf cruise with CVW-11 aboard 'Honest Abe' on 28 May 1991, returning home on 25 November 1991. On this deployment, VF-114 flew in support of Operation Fiery Vigil, on what was to be VF-114's last cruise

In 1991 VF-111 gained a Safety S, and the Mutha Trophy in 1993. The 'Aardvarks' were disestablished on 30 April 1993.

Above: 'Bear' intercepts were once a common part of an F-14 squadron's life, as the Soviet aircraft kept an eye on US Navy activities or transitted en route to bases in Cuba, Africa and Vietnam. Here an 'Aardvarks' Tomcat escorts an AV-MF Tu-95RT 'Bear-D' near the Philippines in March 1983.

Right: By the mid-1980s, VF-114 had toned down (slightly) by deleting their orange fintips and ventral fins, while still flying orange-striped gloss grey Tomcats.

Grumman F-14 Variants

VF-124 'Gunfighters'

VF-124 (callsign 'Gunslinger') was established as VF-53 on 16 August 1948 and became VF-124 on 11 April 1958. In June 1961 the squadron moved from Moffet Field to NAS Miramar. As a fast-jet training unit, VF-124 operated virtually every version of the Vought F-8 and took delivery of the last example built in 1964. For many years the squadron was referred to as 'Crusader College', providing combat training for all F-8

fleet replacement pilots as well as basic, refresher and maintenance training. In addition, VF-124 had the supplementary task of providing fighter support for the USAF's Air Defense Command, a task which it carried into its F-14 days.

The 'Gunfighters' were the West Coast fleet replenishment squadron with the task of training Tomcat pilots and RIOs for the Pacific Fleet. In 1970, the former Crusader

training squadron became the first Tomcat FRS, although the first F-14A did not arrive until 8 October 1972 as the unit was busy establishing the infrastructure for future F-14 operations. In 1973 it was a VF-124 F-14 that appeared at the Paris Air Salon, where it was the star of the show. Crews from VF-1 and VF-2 had the honour of participating in the first Tomcat course, commencing that same year. The first carquals were undertaken aboard USS *Kitty Hawk* in 1974. These units were Atlantic-based squadrons, and California-based

VF-124 had the unusual; distinction of training two more Atlantic fighter squadrons (VF-142 and VF-143) before VF-101 assumed this responsibility. From then on VF-124 handled the conversion of eight regular Pacific Fleet squadrons. These were (in order) VF-24 and -211 (CVW-9), VF-114 and -213 (CVW-11), VF-51 and -111 (CVW-15), and VF-21 and -154 (CVW-14). TARPS training began in 1980. Between 1984 and 1985, two Reserve squadrons (VF-301 and -302) gave up their F-4S Phantoms, under VF-124's expert supervision.

In the years that followed VF-124 masterminded replacement crew training. On 18 January 1983, VF-124 passed 25,000 accident-free flying hours, a remarkable achievement for a unit so closely involved with the Tomcat's troublesome early years. Soon afterwards, in March, the 'Gunfighters' completed three years of flight operations without major mishap, despite the number of inexperienced 'nugget' air that passed through its hands. In that time, crews logged 18,150 sorties and over 2,700 traps.

The squadron accepted its first F-14D Super Tomcat on 16 November 1990 at Miramar, and was the sole F-14D FRS. The squadron sent four of the new F-14D Super Tomcats aboard the *Nimitz* on 2 October 1991 for the D model's first Fleet carrier qualifications.

In 1991, VF-124 acquired a small number of Beech T-34C Turbo Mentors for use as spotter aircraft on target ranges.

VF-124 was disestablished on 30 September 1994 (the last day of the fiscal year), passing over the entire training commitment to VF-101 on the East Coast, although the latter unit maintains a West Coast Detachment with F-14Ds. The squadron made its last cruise aboard USS *Ranger* on 11 March 1993.

Left: During the 1970s, typical VF-124 markings comprised the unit's twin 'swoosh' on the fins, echoed by the stripes on the top surface of the wings and elevators. Both the modex number and tailcode had white drop shadows.

Below: For the 1986 Reconnaissance Air Meet at Bergstrom AFB, several of VF-124's F-14s gained temporary camouflage applied with a broom.

Below: This Tomcat was a show aircraft during 1987. With VF-124's Distinguished Unit Citation below the canopy rail, a yellow Safety S was also carried on the port side. On the tail could be found the ubiquitous 'Tomcat' character and the legend 'Fightertown USA' – an allusion to NAS Miramar.

Below right: Smaller fin stripes were adopted during the 1980s, as worn by this black-tailed F-14 in 1989.

VF-142 'Ghostriders'

VF-142 was established as VF-193 on 24 August 1948, and was redesignated VF-142 on 15 October 1963. The 'Ghostriders' (callsign 'Dakota') transitioned to the F-14A Tomcat at Miramar, CA, in 1974. Prior to this, the unit had undertaken six combat cruises in South-East Asia, chalking up several North Vietnamese MiG kills with its F-4Bs and then F-4Js.

While becoming an F-14 user, the squadron shifted from the Pacific to Atlantic Fleet with Oceana, VA, as home base. Formerly, the squadron had flown the F-4J Phantom. As part of CVW-6, the 'Ghostriders' made their first carrier deployment aboard USS *America*, from 15 April until 25 October 1976. Air Wing Six and elements of the US Sixth Fleet were involved in the Fluid Drive evacuation of civilian personnel from Beirut's worsening civil war that year. VF-142 provided top cover for the operation.

Next came a south Atlantic cruise (10 June to 19 July 1977) and a Mediterranean cruise (29 September 1977 to 25 April

1978). The 'Ghostriders' then shifted in 1979 to CVW-7 aboard USS *Dwight D. Eisenhower*, making their first sailing between 16 January and 13 July. This was *Eisenhower*'s first deployment with the Mediterranean Sixth Fleet. The *Eisenhower*'s Indian Ocean and Arabian Sea cruise of the following year (15 April to 22 December 1980) was also a notable one. At a time of tension in Iran and Afghanistan, VF-142 embarked for 317 days including a continuous underway time of 251 days. Only a single port stop was made (five days in Singapore) and the ship spent two unbroken periods at sea, of 93 and 153 days, establishing a new record. During this time, VF-142 logged 3,673 flight hours and 1,813 arrested landings.

In 1981 VF-142 and CVW-7 participated in NATO's Exercise Ocean Venture on a cruise which lasted from 17 August to 7 October. This was followed by a Mediterranean deployment between 5 January and 13 July 1982, which coincided with Israel's invasion of Lebanon. VF-142 returned to the

Mediterranean from 27 April until 30 November 1983, supporting the US Marine peacekeeping contingent in Beirut, and its F-14s participated in Exercise Bright Star in Egypt that year also.

VF-111 made a Mediterranean cruise with CVW-7 and *Eisenhower* between 11 October 1984 and 8 May 1985, and the unit was awarded a Battle E in 1984. Later in 1985, the 'Ghostriders' sailed from the Caribbean to the north Atlantic for Exercise Ocean Safari '85, departing on 8 July and returning to port on 8 September. In 1987 the squadron made a brief Caribbean and South Atlantic deployment between 16 June and 28 July.

VF-142 made a Mediterranean cruise between 29 February and 29 August 1988, and later that year the 'Ghostriders' made detachments to NAS Key West and Roosevelt Roads for gunnery and EW training and for missile firing, respectively.

The squadron took its new F-14A+s aboard the *Eisenhower* with CVW-7 for a Mediterranean and Red Sea cruise which lasted from 8 March to 12 September 1990. This was the first carrier deployment of the F-14A+, which was redesignated F-14B on

1 May 1991. Paired with VF-143, the squadron remained with 'Ike' and CVW-7 during Desert Shield on a cruise which included a 7 August 1991 transit of the Suez Canal. The carrier, air wing and squadron withdrew from the Persian Gulf region before the start of the war with Iraq. Afterwards, between 26 September 1991 and 2 April 1992, VF-142 made a Mediterranean, Red Sea, Persian Gulf and NorLant cruise, during which it took part in NATO's Exercise Teamwork '92.

The squadron took its F-14Bs aboard the brand new USS *George Washington* (commissioned on 4 July 1992) for its shakedown cruise from 3 September to 23 October 1992. VF-142 then withdrew from the Fleet for two years to upgrade its aircraft. The 'Ghostriders' returned to active duty for the *Washington*'s first operational cruise (along with CVW-7), departing on 20 May 1994 to participate in the D-Day commemorations and, subsequently, in Operation Deny Flight.

This will, however, be the 'Ghostriders' final cruise. Owing to cutbacks in the US Navy's fighter squadrons, VF-142 is due to disestablish at Oceana in April 1995.

Above: During its 'colourful' years in the 1970s, VF-142's aircraft were bedecked with yellow and black stripes and yellow 'piano keys' on the rudders. On the reverse of the fins the F-14s carried a yellow lightning bolt and an array of coloured stars denoting the squadron colours within USS America's air group. Note the Safety S (in squadron colours) on the nose.

Right: The grey and white scheme gave way to overall grey in the late 1970s, and at the same time VF-142 adopted a whole new look. Gone were the garish markings, in favour of the graphic 'Grim Reaper' as depicted on the unit badge. The 'AG' tailcode reflects the new posting aboard USS Eisenhower.

VF-143 'Pukin' Dogs'

VF-143 (callsign 'Taproom') traces its history to VF-871, a Reserve squadron called to active duty for the Korean War on 20 July 1950. Its real history began as late as June 1962, with the redesignation of VF-53 and its conversion to the F4H-1 Phantom. VF-143 first went to sea aboard USS *Constellation* in February 1963, for a WestPac cruise. The following year, operating as part of CVW-14, the squadron became involved in the Gulf of Tonkin incident and flew in the Peace Arrow attacks on North Vietnamese naval facilities on 5 August that year. Having moved on to F-4Js in the years that followed, the 'Pukin' Dogs' finally gave up their Phantoms for the F-14A Tomcat at Miramar, CA, in 1974, while converting from the Pacific to Atlantic Fleet.

As part of CVW-6, VF-143 made its first F-14 carrier deployment aboard USS *America* (to the Mediterranean) from 15 April until 25 October 1976. During this time VF-143 provided top cover for the evacuation of US nationals from Lebanon. After a subsequent south Atlantic cruise (10 June to 19 July 1977) and Mediterranean cruise (29 September 1977 to 25 April 1978), VF-143 shifted in 1978 to CVW-7 aboard USS *Dwight D. Eisenhower*. Together with CVW-7, it made its first

deployment (a Caribbean sailing) between 18 September and 26 October 1978. At that time, *Eisenhower* was the US Navy's latest aircraft-carrier. VF-143 next travelled to the Persian Gulf for GulfEx '79, the last time any US unit could do so; the entire cruise lasted from 14 November to 4 December 1978.

Eisenhower, CVW-7 and VF-143 next made a Mediterranean deployment between 16 January and 13 July 1979. The 'Pukin' Dogs' then sailed from the Indian Ocean to 'Gonzo Station' during a 15 April to 22 December 1980 cruise when it replaced USS *Nimitz* after the ill-starred Operation Eagle Claw. Tension was running high in the area and VF-143 spent 152 days continuously at sea. The following year, VF-143 made a brief NorLant cruise, between 17 August and 7 October, to participate in NATO's Exercise Ocean Venture. This was followed by a Mediterranean cruise commencing on January 1982 – during which time Operation Peace for Galilee, Israel's invasion of Lebanon, was underway. The squadron exercised its new-found TARPS capability with three aircraft so equipped, and finally returned to port on 13 July.

VF-143 returned to the Mediterranean in 1983, from April to December, joining the

US Sixth Fleet off Lebanon and participating in Exercise Bright Star '83. VF-143's Tomcats provided air defence, 'intercepting' US F-4s, F-16s and B-52s at very long range from the carrier. At the same time, Tomcats flew simulated attack missions against Egyptian airfields while providing reconnaissance coverage courtesy of their TARPS pods. The 'Pukin' Dogs' next made two brief Caribbean and NorLant deployments – 7 May to 20 June and 9 July to 9 September (for ReadEx 2-84) – before returning to sea aboard the *Eisenhower* for a Mediterranean cruise commencing on 11 October 1984. During this time, VF-143 again found itself observing the worsening situation in Lebanon, although the US Marine ground presence there had finally been withdrawn in February, following terrorist bombings and retaliatory airstrikes. VF-143 returned home on 8 May 1985.

To take part in Ocean Safari '85, VF-143 embarked on a Caribbean and NorLant cruise between 8 July and 8 September 1985. After a lengthy break from sea-going operations, VF-143 returned to CVW-7 and 'Ike' for a 1988 Mediterranean cruise between 29 February and 29 August. While at sea, the squadron used its TARPS capability to photograph the Soviet warship *Baku*, a 'Kiev'-class carrier. On 26 May 1989, VF-143 began transitioning to the F-14A+ TARPS-equipped Tomcat with the delivery

of its first aircraft (BuNo. 161441), and soon thereafter became fully equipped with A+ models. Paired with VF-142, the squadron remained with the same carrier and air wing during Desert Shield, on a Mediterranean and Red Sea cruise which lasted from 8 March until 12 September 1990. All were withdrawn before the start of the war with Iraq in January 1991. 1990 was a good year for VF-143, which won the Arleigh Burke Award, the DoD Phoenix Award for maintenance excellence, the Tac Recce Trophy, and a Battle E.

In May 1991 the squadron became the first to drop live bombs from a (newly designated) F-14B. VF-143 then resumed Atlantic Fleet duties with a Mediterranean, Persian Gulf and NorLant cruise from 26 September 1991 to 2 April 1992, incorporated Exercise Teamwork '92.

Later that year VF-143, along with CVW-7, transferred to USS *George Washington* for its shakedown cruise in the Caribbean from 3 September to 23 October. The *Washington* returned to the Caribbean, briefly, with the 'Pukin' Dogs' from 19 January to 18 February 1994 before embarking on its maiden operational cruise on 20 May 1994. VF-143 was another of Air Wing 7's squadrons that participated in the D-Day commemorations of June 1994 before sailing for the Mediterranean and Operation Deny Flight.

Above: Wearing Eisenhower's/Air Wing 7's 'AG' tailcode, this F-14A from 'Pukin' Dogs' displays the blue fin flash and stripes long associated with the unit. While the stripes were generally carried on both sides of the fin, the winged 'Pukin' Dog' appeared on the outer surfaces only. Throughout the 1970s these were standard markings for VF-143, but this aircraft was specially painted in 1989 when the low-viz rules were relaxed slightly.

Left: As early as 1981, half of VF-143's Tomcat fleet had adopted this scheme. Squadron markings were applied in light grey over the blue-grey finish , but national insignia are almost invisible.

VF-154 'Black Knights'

VF-154 (callsign 'Blacknight') was established on 1 February 1951 when Reserve squadron VF-837 was called to active duty for the Korean War. The squadron was designated VF-154 on 4 February 1953. The unit flew FJ-3 Furies, F-8 Crusaders and finally F-4 Phantoms. The emblem of the 'Black Knights', showing an armoured knight at parade rest holding shield and sword, was designed by Lieutenant Junior Grade John Miottel in 1957 and drawn by cartoonist Milton Caniff of 'Steve Canyon' fame.

The 'Black Knights' transitioned to the Tomcat and, as the last US Navy squadron to adopt the F-14, made the fastest transition of any Phantom squadron. By 1984 VF-154 was operational with its full complement of 12 F-14s, including three TARPS-equipped aircraft.

VF-154 made its first cruise, an EastPac deployment, as part of CVW-14 aboard USS *Constellation*, between 18 October and 15 November 1984 for FleetEx 1-85. This was followed by an even shorter sailing lasting from 6 to 16 December 1984, for Exercise Kernel Usher '85.

The 'Black Knights' went to sea 'for real' with the *Constellation* from 21 February to 24 August 1985 on a WestPac and Indian Ocean cruise. In 1986 VF-154 participated in Exercise Marcot '86 during a NorPac deployment of 4 September to 20 October. A 1987 'Connie'/CVW-14 WestPac and Indian Ocean deployment from 11 April to 13 October took VF-154 to 'Gonzo Station' near the Gulf of Oman and included intercepts of Iranian P-3F Orions and flights in support of Operation Earnest Will.

VF-154 made another WestPac and Indian Ocean deployment from 1 December 1988 to 1 June 1989. On 16 September 1989 VF-154 sailed, still with CVW-14, on a NorPac deployment and returned on 19 October. Paired with VF-21, the squadron has operated aboard USS *Independence* (with CVW-14), the first carrier to arrive for Desert Shield in August 1990. This deployment lasted from 23 June to 20 December.

In August 1991, VF-21 joined VF-154 aboard the *Independence*, which relieved the *Midway* as the sole aircraft-carrier home-ported at Yokosuka, Japan. 'Indy' departed for Japan on 5 August, arriving in Pearl Harbor on 22 August. Six days later it set sail again, reaching its final destination on 11 September. VF-154 was then operating as part of CVW-5. It embarked on a WestPac sailing between 15 October and 24 November 1991, followed by a similar cruise between 9 and 21 December. The following year, the *Independence* became the last US Navy carrier to visit Subic Bay in the Philippines, carrying VF-154 on a WestPac cruise from 2 to 31 March.

VF-154 sailed, via Australia, for an Indian Ocean and Persian Gulf deployment and participated in Operation Southern Watch from 15 April to 13 October 1992. Several brief WestPac cruises followed in 1993 – 25 to 30 January, 15 February to 25 March (Exercise Team Spirit '93), 11 May to 1 July, and 21 September to 14 October.

Between 17 November 1993 and 17 March 1994, VF-154 was deployed aboard the *Independence* for a WestPac and Indian Ocean cruise supporting US operations in Somalia and Operation Southern Watch. On 28 May 1994, VF-154 departed for RimPac '94, with CVW-5 and the *Independence*, returning on 4 July.

VF-154 carried over its markings from the Phantom to the Tomcat, adopting black and red fin stripes. The shield is a more recent addition, compensating for the lack of colour on current aircraft. Extending the anti-glare panel from the nose to behind the cockpit has long been a VF-154 trademark, although this is now done in a 'toned-down' fashion.

VF-191 'Satan's Kittens'

VF-191 (callsign 'Hellcats') was founded in July 1942 as VF-19. The squadron's only wartime deployment was with USS *Lexington* (CV-16) in July 1944; equipped with the Grumman F6F Hellcat. After a four-month cruise, the squadron's tally reached 155 air-to-air kills and 25 ships sunk. The unit saw action again in Korea (with F8Fs) in 1950, when they were remarkably joined by aircraft from the 'Blue Angels' – the only time the US Navy's aerobatic display team has gone to war. Following this fighting,

VF-191 graduated from the FJ-3 Fury to the F11F Tiger and then to the F-8 Crusader, with which it flew the bulk of its missions on 'Yankee Station' over Vietnam. VF-191 made a single cruise with the F-4 before being disestablished on 1 March 1978.

'Satan's Kittens' were re-established on 4 December 1986 and trained with VF-124 to become one of two new F-14 squadrons (along with VF-194) intended to operate with the newly established CVW-10 aboard USS *Independence*, which moved from the East Coast to replace USS Kitty *Hawk*. The squadron actually undertook carquals in the eastern Pacific aboard USS *Enterprise* with F-14As from 24 July until 5 August 1987, but this was the only time that VF-191went to sea.

'USS *Independence*' titles appeared on some of the squadron's assigned Tomcats in 1987/88 but no cruise was ever made. Instead, VF-191 and its sister squadron VF-194 became the victim of US Navy cuts which saw the elimination of one carrier air wing (CVW-10). As a result, after a brief flirtation with the F-14, VF-191 itself was disestablished on 30 April 1988. Plans for

VF-191 to stand up to become the third F-14D squadron (along with VF-51 and VF-111) were cancelled.

The red fin markings carried by VF-191 'Satan's Kittens' Tomcats during 1987 and 1988 had a rather temporary appearance. Even more short-lived were the 'USS Independence' titles and 'NM' tailcode of Carrier Air Wing Ten, as seen on this aircraft at NAS Miramar in January 1988.

VF-194 'Red Lightnings'

Like its sister squadron VF-191, VF-195 (callsign 'RedFlash') has its origins in World War II as a Grumman F6F Hellcat squadron. Established in 1942 as VF-20, it was redesignated VF-9A after the war in 1947. In 1949 the unit was subjected to yet another change in identity, this time becoming VF-91. Embarked on USS *Philippine Sea* (CV-47) during the Korean War, VF-91 flew 1,938 combat missions with Grumman F9F-2 Panthers.

Over the years that followed, VF-91 flew the F9F-6, FJ-3 and finally the F-8. VF-91 was the first West Coast squadron to stand up with the Crusader, and also the first US Navy squadron to deploy with the new type.

On 1 August 1963 the squadron was renamed again, becoming VF-194 'Hellfires'.

The 'Hellfires' went to war in Vietnam with USS *Bon Homme Richard* as part of Air Wing 19, and later served aboard USS *Ticonderoga* (again) and USS *Oriskany*. Having seen action over South-East Asia, VF-194 became the last US Navy squadron to give up its F-8s, in favour of the F-4J Phantom.

The squadron's only Phantom cruise was made with Air Wing 15 aboard USS *Coral Sea*, commencing in February 1977. On returning from that deployment, VF-194 was finally disestablished on 1 March 1978.

The unit's brief association with the Tomcat began at NAS Miramar on 1 December 1986, when VF-194 was recommissioned as one of the new fighter squadrons for Air Wing 10. CVW-10's intended operational home was to be USS *Independence,* which began a major SLEP (service life extension programme) in 1985, emerging in 1988. VF-194 began working up at NAS Fallon and went to sea in summer 1987, flying from USS *Enterprise* with CVW-10.

Independence's name appeared on some of VF-194's Tomcats, as it did on some VF-191 aircraft but, along with VF-191, the 'Red Lightnings' were disestablished on 30 April 1988 due to US Navy budget cuts. Plans to re-establish the squadron as the fourth F-14D squadron were cancelled when the F-14D programme itself was cut short.

VF-194 was lucky to get to sea, but between 24 July and 5 August the short-lived squadron operated its Tomcats from the deck of USS Enterprise in the eastern Pacific. The unit's simple red lightning bolt markings are seen here on the VF-194 CAG-bird, as it takes the wire aboard 'Big E'. Other aircraft had a more involved decoration, with the lightning bolt intersecting the tailcode. The squadron badge showed an ace of spades pierced by a lightning bolt. The unit's motto was Dictum Factum – which roughly translates as 'No sooner said than done'.

VF-201 'Hunters'

VF-201 (callsign 'Hunter'), established 25 July 1970, is one of two Naval Air Reserve squadrons at NAS Dallas which operate the F-14A. The squadron's insignia is a sword against a Texas flag and a formation of four aircraft.

VF-201 and VF-202 are part of Reserve Air Wing 20 (CVWR-20). The squadron made the first of its two sea-going active-duty training deployments aboard USS *Forrestal* between 14 and 26 June 1987, with the F-14A. This was followed by a similar Atlantic sailing between 24 July and 3 August 1989, aboard USS *Dwight D. Eisenhower*.

One aircraft received by the 'Hunters' was the last F-14A built (BuNo. 162711) before production shifted to the F-14A+ (now F-14B) model. The US Navy Reserve fighter force has been in the forefront of recent cutbacks and, currently, VF-201 is the only surviving F-14 Reserve unit – clinging on with Reserve Air Wing 20. No such squadrons are left on the West Coast, as the dissolution of CVWR-30 in late 1994 means that only VFC-13 (now equipped with the F/A-18) remains in that part of the world.

Part of the unofficial 'Texas air force', VF-201's tail markings leave no doubt as to where the squadron's heart lies. On low-viz aircraft the tail flashes and map are black, with a white code. The recent dramatic reductions in the US Navy Reserve call into question how much longer these markings will be seen.

VF-202 'Superheats'

VF-202, established 1 July 1970, is one of two Reserve squadrons at Dallas which replaced the F-4S Phantom with the F-14A Tomcat. Squadron insignia is a horse's head chess piece against a tan star and yellow field, with the legend 'Fighting 202'.

The squadron accepted its first F-14A on 10 April 1987. In May 1988, the 'Superheats' concluded their transition to the Tomcat with carrier qualifications aboard USS *America* off the Virginia coast. The 'Superheats' are the TARPS squadron for Reserve Air Wing 20 (CVWR-20). The squadron participated in the USAF-sponsored 1988 Reconnaissance Air Meet (RAM '88) at Bergstrom AFB, TX.

The following year, VF-202 made its only active-duty training cruise. Embarked aboard USS *Dwight D. Eisenhower*, VF-202 deployed to the north Atlantic between 24 July and 3 August 1989, alongside its sister squadron VF-201. VF-202 was TARPS-equipped (with three F-14As) but cuts in the US Navy Reserve forces saw the unit disestablished in October 1994.

Above right: Wearing almost imperceptible 'low-viz' fin markings, this 1988-vintage VF-202 Tomcat still manages to display its 'Lone Star State' roots.

Right: Seen here in 1991, this more colourful gloss-grey aircraft carries a Distinguished Unit Citation, Battle E and Safety S, along with the Texas state flag on its fin.

VF-211 'Fighting Checkmates'

VF-211 (callsign 'Checkmate') traces its history to VB-74, established on 1 May 1945, and acquired its current designation on 9 March 1959. The 'Checkmates' stood up as an F-14A squadron at Miramar on 1 December 1975, following months of preparation and after operating the F-8J Crusader.

The squadron's maiden flight in a Tomcat was made on 23 December 1975. VF-211's first F-14A carrier landing was made aboard USS *Constellation* in June 1976. As part of Carrier Air Wing 9, and paired with VF-24, the squadron made its first cruise aboard *Constellation* between 12 April and 21 November 1977. A second WestPac and Indian Ocean cruise followed from 26 September 1978 to 17 May 1979. During this cruise, the Shah fled Iran in the face of the Islamic Revolution and in March the battle group took up station off Aden, in response to the fighting between North and South Yemen.

During its Indian Ocean cruise of 26 February to 15 October 1980, VF-211 spent 110 days on 'Gonzo Station' in response to the Teheran hostage crisis, and later participated in Exercise RimPac '80. On 15 October 1980, the squadron was selected for the TARPS mission, becoming the first West Coast squadron so equipped. VF-211 returned from a subsequent WestPac and Indian Ocean cruise (20 October 1981 to 23 May 1982) with 100,000 ft (30480 m) of TARPS film. For its combat readiness record over three cruises and shore deployments,

VF-211 was awarded a COMNAVAIRPAC Battle E. In July 1983, still with the same air wing (CVW-9), the squadron began a cruise aboard USS *Ranger*. For this WestPac and Indian Ocean deployment, VF-211 was at sea from 15 July 1983 to 29 February 1984. Unusually, this cruise began with the *Ranger* involved in surveillance missions off Central America, before staging via Hawaii three weeks later. A subsequent WestPac and Indian Ocean cruise was made with CVW-9

aboard the *Kitty Hawk*, from 24 July to 21 December 1985.

Embarked with the *Kitty Hawk*, VF-211 undertook a round-the-world cruise from 3 January until 29 June 1987 – *Kitty Hawk*'s last before its SLEP. The unit then moved to USS *Nimitz* (along with CVW-9) for a WestPac and Indian Ocean deployment, in support of Operation Earnest Will, from 2 September 1988 until 2 March 1989. VF-211 began transition to the F-14A+ (now designated F-14B) Tomcat in April 1989, but reverted to the F-14A due to a lack of F-14Bs. VF-211 remains TARPS capable.

A NorPac cruise for NorPacEx '89 (15 June to 9 July 1989) and a WestPac, Indian Ocean and Persian Gulf deployment (25 February to 24 August 1991) came next. In June 1992, VF-211 became the first West Coast Tomcat squadron to complete the Advanced Attack Readiness Program (AARP). During the WestPac, Persian Gulf cruise which began on 2 February 1993, the squadron flew recce missions in support of Operation Southern Watch and supported the presence in Somalia. VF-211 returned home on 1 August 1993. In February 1994, it operated from Nellis during Red Flag 94-2.

Right: A 'Checkertails' F-14A taxis 'off the wire' aboard USS Constellation during its 1980 cruise, when VF-211 was later on station off Iran.

Below: In 1986 several aircraft wore temporary brown and green camouflage for summer exercises at NAS Fallon.

Below right: Since 1989, VF-211 has flown the F-14B (F-14A+).

Grumman F-14 Variants

VF-213 'Black Lions'

VF-213 (callsign 'BlackLion'), established 22 June 1955, stood up with the F-14A Tomcat at Miramar in September 1976, replacing the F-4B Phantom. On 25 October 1977, the squadron embarked on its first cruise with Tomcats as part of CVW-11 aboard USS *Kitty Hawk*, followed by a WestPac sailing until 15 May 1978. During this period, VF-213 contributed significantly to the 16,000 hours flown by Air Wing 11 while embarked.

VF-213 was next temporarily detached to the Atlantic Fleet for Mediterranean cruises aboard USS *America* (again with CVW-11).

The first of these departed Norfolk on13 March 1979 and returned on 22 September 1979, followed by a 1981 cruise between 14 April and 12 November, taking in the Indian Ocean. In 1982, the squadron acquired the tactical reconnaissance role and took delivery of its first TARPS-equipped aircraft. With the same air wing, the squadron subsequently went on a NorPac, WestPac and Indian Ocean cruise with USS *Enterprise* (its first after three years overhaul) in 1982-83 (departing on 1 September and returning on 28 May). During this deployment, the 'Black Lions' used their new-found TARPS capability to photograph numerous Soviet Pacific Fleet

surface ships and submarines. In March 1983 the 'Black Lions' chalked up a remarkable 17,000 accident-free flying hours.

VF-213 was then back on the West Coast and its 1984 cruise with the *Enterprise* was another WestPac and Indian Ocean sailing. Changing its modex codes from 100 series to 200 series, VF-213 next departed for a WestPac and Indian Ocean cruise from 12 January to 13 August 1986, followed by a brief NorPac deployment between 25 October and 24 November 1987, all with CVW-11. The squadron then made a WestPac and Indian Ocean cruise between 5 January and 3 July 1988 (including

Operation Praying Mantis), during which time Commander Greg 'Mullet' Gerard became the first Tomcat pilot to log 2,000 flying hours on type.

VF-213 embarked on a round-the-world cruise from 17 September 1989 until 16 March 1990, its last deployment with USS *Enterprise* . While at sea VF-213 flew operations for Operation Classic Resolve.

VF-213 and the other squadrons of CVW-11 then transferred to USS *Abraham Lincoln's* round-the-Horn cruise between 24 September and 20 November 1990. This gave opportunities for DACT with Argentine and Chilean fighters, although the *Lincoln* had only a reduced 'split' air wing onboard for this transit to the West Coast.

CVW-11 was embarked in full strength for the maiden WestPac and Persian Gulf cruise of the *Abraham Lincoln*, which began on 28 May 1991 and lasted until 25 November. During this cruise VF-213 acted as adversaries for Omani Jaguar and Hawker Hunter squadrons, flew TARPS missions over Iraq and also provided support for Operation Fiery Vigil.

1992 saw the award of the Mutha Trophy, and the beginning of 'Bombcat' training in May. CVW-11 was the first single Tomcat squadron air wing, and a slightly expanded VF-213 partnered three F/A-18 units. A WestPac, Indian Ocean and Persian Gulf cruise aboard the *Lincoln* began on 15 June 1993, and ended on 15 December. During this deployment VF-213 flew missions for Operation Southern Watch and also in support of the US contingent in Somalia.

Left: This VF-213 F-14A, seen here circa 1978, is a classic example of a period US Navy colour scheme. The black lion of the squadron badge gained a golden mane and looked to one side rather than straight ahead It has also gained two tails in recognition of the Tomcat's twin fins.

Below: Between 1986 and 1987 several of VF-213's Tomcats received temporary disruptive grey or brown-green camouflages. This aircraft flew from El Centro in 1986.

VF-301 'Devil's Disciples'

VF-301 (callsign 'Devil'), which is also called the 'Fighting Infernos', was established 1 October 1970 as a Reserve squadron at Miramar and part of Reserve Air Wing 30. The squadron patch shows a red smiling satanic figure holding a pitchfork.

The unit was first commissioned on 3 January 1944 with the F4U-1 Corsair. VF-301's World War II history is brief – the squadron made a short deployment aboard USS *Steamer Bay* and a shore-basing at Luganville Airfield, Esperitu. VF-301 was disestablished on 1 August 1944. In October 1970 the squadron was resurrected as one of two Reserve units at NAS Miramar, CA, and equipped with the F-8 Crusader. Then, as later, they were part of CVWR-30. In 1974 transition to the F-4B began, followed by the F-4N in February 1975 and the F-4S in November 1980.

The squadron began the transition to the F-14A in 1985, although its first aircraft had arrived in October the previous year. The change-over from Phantom to Tomcat was a lengthy one and the F-4 remained in service with the 'Devil's Disciples' well into 1985. VF-301 received early production F-14s drawn from aircraft delivered to the USN as far back as 1973 and 1974. In total, the unit was allocated 12 Tomcats.

On 21 April 1985, VF-301 made the first Reserve deployment of the Tomcat, taking five aircraft to Yuma, AZ, for air-to-air training. The first deployment at full squadron strength was made for training at NAS Fallon, NV, beginning 4 August 1985.

US Navy Reserve fighter squadrons made two week active-duty training (AcDuTra) cruises to keep up their carrier skills. VF-301 made its first such deployment between 15 and 26 January 1986, in the eastern Pacific aboard USS *Ranger*, as part of CVWR-30. Subsequent cruises were held at two-year intervals and all in the same area. Between 10 and 22 August 1988, the 'Devil's Disciples' went to sea with USS *Enterprise*. Its next sea-going deployment was aboard USS *Nimitz* from 6 August to 16 August 1990, and the *Nimitz* was again VF-301's host for its last AcDuTra cruise between 15 and 24 August 1992. CVWR-30 was done away with by budget cuts in 1994 (leaving almost no West Coast Reserve fighter units). VF-301 was disestablished in October 1994.

Above: This VF-301 three-ship displays the current blue-grey paint scheme and low-viz squadron markings. When the unit was making the transition to low-viz markings, the arrow head on the fin was originally all-black, but has now been reduced to a simple outline.

Left: VF-301's original tail markings comprised a black arrow outlined in red, as seen on this high-gloss Tomcat (in 1986) partnered by a VFA-195 Hornet.

VF-302 'Stallions'

VF-302 (callsign 'Stallion'), established 21 May 1971, is a Reserve squadron at Miramar. The squadron badge comprises a red and black shield on a yellow background bearing a black stallion's head and a red sword, with the legend 'Fighting 302'. Like its sister squadron VF-301, the 'Stallions' were commissioned at Miramar as a result of the major reorganisation of the US Navy Reserve in the early 1970s. The squadron was first equipped with the Vought F-8K, until November 1973. VF-302 then became the first US Navy Reserve squadron to operate the Phantom. By February 1974 it was active with 12 F-4Bs and undertook its first AcDuTra cruise with the type at the end of the month. The early F-4Bs were replaced from late 1975 by reworked F-4Ns, which remained in use until the advent of the F-4S in 1981. By 1984 VF-302 had been selected as the second US Navy Reserve squadron for the F-14.

The squadron began the transition to the F-14A Tomcat in 1985, with the first aircraft arriving in April. Like those allocated to VF-301, VF-302's Tomcats were rather vintage machines. By 1986 the full complement of 12 F-14As had been delivered. The 'Stallions' are paired with VF-301 as part of CVWR-30 but, unlike its sister squadron, Fighting Three Zero Two was assigned the TARPS reconnaissance mission. In line with similarly-equipped Fleet squadrons, VF-302 operates three TARPS F-14s. The F-14 is designed to operate in tandem with the E-2 Hawkeye and VF-301 and -302 were unable to exploit their full potential until the the latest model E-2Cs were released to the US Navy's Reserve early-warning squadrons (in Miramar's case, this was VAW-78, the 'Fighting Escargots').

The squadron participated in the USAF-sponsored 1988 Reconnaissance Air Meet (RAM '88) at Bergstom AFB, TX. Its active-duty training cruises mirrored those of VF-301, namely; 15 to 26 January 1986 (USS *Ranger*), 10 to 22 August 1988 (USS *Enterprise*), 6 to 16 August (USS *Nimitz*) and 15 to 24 August 1992 (USS *Nimitz*).

Like VF-301, the 'Stallions' have fallen victim to the drawdown in US Navy strength and the squadron was disestablished at Miramar in October 1994.

Below: In 1986 VF-302's CAG-bird appeared in these colourful markings. The aircraft wore an overall gloss-grey scheme, and the squadron's 'stallion' insignia appeared on the rudders.

Below: VF-302's standard F-14s were among the most non-descript in the fleet. In 1994 the squadron fell victim to the severe cuts in the US Navy Reserve, and was disestablished in October.

Navy Fighter Weapons School

The Navy Fighter Weapons School, better known as 'Top Gun', is based at NAS Miramar and provides air combat training for fleet fighter pilots, acting as the centre of the US Navy's once-extensive network of dedicated adversary units. It provides training and standardisation for the dwindling number of adversary units and runs the 'Top Gun' course which takes hand-picked crews from the fleet and runs them through an intensive air combat course. This course is balanced between practice (fighting the school's instructors in their A-4s, F-5Es, F-16Ns and (recently) F-14As) and theory, learning about enemy tactics and equipment. 'Top Gun' graduates then return to their squadrons, where it is hoped they will pass on their new-found knowledge and skills.

Top Gun was established in the wake of the influential Ault Report, which analysed US Navy losses and the poor kill ratio being achieved by fleet fighter squadrons in actual air-to-air combat over Vietnam. The imaginative response was to produce a 'hands-on' training course which would be as close to actual combat as was possible, with highly experienced instructor pilots flying representative adversary aircraft using real enemy tactics in realistic training scenarios.

The Navy Fighter Weapons School decorates its aircraft with an appropriate badge, showing a MiG-21 centred in a gunsight pipper. The aircraft are not flown in standard US Navy markings, and instead use a variety of colour schemes more-or-less loosely based on the colours worn by aircraft of potential real-world adversaries.

The introduction of the F-14 to the Navy Fighter Weapons School was made possible by the surplus of aircraft created by squadron disbandments, and at last gave the unit an aircraft capable of simulating the BVR threat posed by aircraft like the MiG-29, MiG-31 and Su-27, as well as by potentially hostile Iranian F-14s. For this reason, FWS F-14s wear a variety of colour schemes, some being painted to represent Su-27 'Flankers', others to represent MiG-29 'Fulcrums' and still others to represent other types, including one wearing full Iranian markings.

Adversary units have traditionally opted not to use aircraft types already in fleet use, since the value of fighting a dissimilar aircraft type is greatly appreciated. However, it has been realised that an F-14 being crewed by FWS instructors, versed in Soviet tactics and simulating a MiG-31 is a very different matter to going 'head-to-head' with one of your squadron mates. At the bottom line, the F-14 can be flown to be an accurate representation of a potential threat, and that makes it useful. The same rationale has allowed two Reserve adversary units to re-equip with F/A-18s, which make great MiG-29 simulators (except in the low-speed, high-Alpha regime).

The disestablishment of most of the adversary squadrons will reduce the amount of 'on the road' and pre-cruise adversary training available to fleet fighter pilots, and the 'Top Gun' course will become progressively more important and useful. The unit's F-14s have a major part to play in widening the scope of threats which can be accurately simulated.

Above: One of the Fighter Weapons School's F-14As wears a pseudo-Su-27 'Flanker' colour scheme, with the fintips painted to alter their shape, and with a black radome and fins to replicate an early production aircraft.

Below: Another variation on the 'Flanker' scheme, this time with the white panels worn by most service aircraft. Closely matching the Su-27 in size and shape, the F-14 can also replicate the BVR multi-sensor capability with ease, although is not as agile. The F-14/AIM-54 mix is also used to imitate the MiG-31/R-33.

Above: Wearing convincingly realistic Iranian camouflage and national markings, this unique F-14A is another of those which serves with the Fighter Weapons School. A genuine Iranian-standard F-14A serves (albeit in standard US Navy colours) with VX-4.

VX-4 'The Evaluators' (VX-9)

VX-4 (callsign 'Vandy') was established on 15 September 1952, to undertake testing of air-launched guided missiles, and became the Navy's chief operational test and evaluation unit. Throughout its life VX-4 was based at Point Mugu, CA. VX-4 was the first US Navy Tomcat operator and, over the years, between seven and 12 aircraft have been on strength for systems evaluation and tactics development. VX-4 was allocated its Tomcats after the type received a preliminary evaluation at the hands of the Naval Air Test Center, Patuxent River.

In the Tomcat's primary role of fleet defence, its missile (specifically its long-range missile armament) is of the utmost importance. VX-4 was instrumental in proving the F-14's AWG-9/AIM-54 Phoenix system, particularly the latest AIM-54C. VX-4 was closely involved with AIM-9L Sidewinder all-aspect, short-range AAM programme. Other missile work undertaken in the Tomcat's earlier days was the ACEVAL/AIMEVAL (Air Combat Evaluation/Air Intercept Missile Evaluation) programme. Six VX-4 F-14s were detached to Nellis AFB in the late 1970s. Flying in conjunction with USAF types, they were instrumental in formulating the AMRAAM

Like several other US Navy Tomcat units, VX-4 experimented with a variety of camouflage schemes during the 1980s. This unmarked F-14A (BuNo. 158978) was seen at NAS Fallon in June 1985.

Concealing its identity well, BuNo. 159831 was another of VX-4's 1985 camouflage experiments, again using water-soluble distemper. The only markings visible over its roughly applied reddish-brown and olive green stripes is the modex '45', which appears in black on the nose.

(Advanced Medium-Range Air-to-Air Missile) requirement finally fulfilled by the Hughes AIM-120. VX-4 was the first unit to operate the Tomcat's undernose TCS (Television Camera System), a passive electro-optical system which extends the 'eyeball' range of the F-14 pilot up to 100 miles (161 km).

VX-4 was an important part of the F-14D 'Bombcat' trials, and by the early 1990s the squadron had two F-14Ds in service alongside seven F-14A/Bs and a mix of F/A-18s. In a departure from its previous guided-weapons work, the F-14D programme took the 'Evaluators' into the realm of 'dumb' bombing as the squadron undertook Mk 80 series free-fall bomb separation tests. More recently, VX-4 passed the AN/ALR-67 radar warning receiver fit for use in time to see combat during Operation Desert Storm.

The squadron is relatively large, with 39 officers including three Marines and a USAF exchange officer, 281 enlisted men and five civilians. VX-4 is perhaps best known for its

use of the 'Playboy Bunny' as an aircraft marking. The 'Bunny' has appeared on its F-14s, and in pre-F-14 days VX-4 operated two Phantoms (an F-4J and an F-4S) permanently in an all-over gloss black scheme with white 'playboy markings' – the infamous 'Black Bunnies'. The first Tomcat (BuNo 158358) to appear in a similar (matt) black scheme was painted for a VX-4 change of command ceremony. With the bunny logo on the tail, the aircraft wore

VX-4's 'XF' tailcode on a red fintip band, flanked by white stars. No actual serial was carried. By all accounts the scheme was popular with everyone but an unimpressed admiral, and the (water-soluble) paint was removed after two days. Since then it has reappeared sporadically on various F-14s to mark a number of special occasions.

In 1994 VX-4 was to have been formally disestablished, on 29 April, but this was delayed until 30 September. As part of the

major changes sweeping through the US Navy, VX-4 was combined with sister unit VX-5 'Vampires' to form the aptly numbered VX-9 (formally established on 29 April), headquartered at NAWS (Naval Air Warfare Station) China Lake, where VX-5 was chiefly involved in fixed- and rotary-wing air-to-ground ordnance testing and tactics. VX-9 will now be based there, taking advantage of the base's extensive ranges in eastern California.

Right: As a Tomcat operator, an important part of VX-4's trials work has to be done at sea. The squadron has made several deployments aboard USS Enterprise, most recently as part of its F-14D evaluations. Here a very understated VX-4 F-14D 'Super Tomcat' is about to launch from 'Big E'.

Below: One of the least public US Navy units, VX-4 was responsible for some of the Navy's best known aircraft – the 'Black Bunnies'. BuNo. 161444 was one of VX-4's longest serving Tomcats and is seen here in high-gloss 'Black Bunny' guise (complete with AIM-54C Phoenix), at Point Mugu in October 1987.

Grumman F-14 Variants

Naval Air Warfare Center (Aircraft Division) – formerly NATC and NADC

The Naval Air Warfare Center is a part of the US Naval Air Systems Command (Navair). Since 1 January 1992 the operations of the former Naval Weapons Center (NWC) at China Lake and the Pacific Missile Test Center, at Point Mugu, have come under the aegis of the Naval Air Warfare Center, as the Naval Air Warfare Center (Weapons Division), while those of the former Naval Air Test Center at Patuxent River, the Naval Air Development Center at Warminster and the Naval Engineering Center at Lakehurst have become elements of the Naval Air Warfare Center (Aircraft Division). These five main components of the NAWC now undertake the wide range of aircraft, weapons, engineering and systems testing and development previously allocated to 32 different organisations.

The Naval Air Warfare Center at Patuxent River was established in January 1992 by redesignation of the Naval Air Test Center. Its primary task is to test all new aircraft entering naval service, or any new variants of aircraft, or any new equipment entering service on naval aircraft, to determine their suitability for operational use. The unit also develops systems, servicing procedures and even computers. This necessitates close liaison between NAWC and the relevant manufacturers. Divided into Strike Aircraft, Fixed-Wing Aircraft and Rotary-Wing Aircraft Test Directorates, the NAWC maintains a number of F-14s on charge, including some

NF-14s that have been permanently converted for test duties. Operational testing carried out at NAWC has included (in 1982) take-off trials using a 6° ski-ramp. The NAWC also parents the USN Test Pilot's School.

VX-4 'Evaluators' at Point Mugu were parented by the NATC, and served as a fast-jet operational test and evaluation squadron, taking on the evaluation process as new aircraft or systems neared service entry. One officer described VX-4's role in the following words: "We test it, rock it, roll it, slam it, jam it, beat it, drop it and then ram it aboard the boat." VX-4 evaluated the F-14's Northrop TCS, and the aircraft itself when it began to be used in the 'Bombcat' role.

The former Naval Air Development Center at Warminster, Pennsylvania, is tasked with enhancing technology, improving existing equipment by refining software and hardware. It develops avionics and instrumentation for US Navy aircraft, and has frequently had examples of the F-14 on strength. Its current fleet includes a single F-14A.

Wearing an interesting two-tone grey colour scheme, with high-conspicuity orange tailfins, this F-14 serves with the NAWC (Aircraft Division) at Patuxent River.

Naval Air Warfare Center (Weapons Division)

Of particular relevance to the Tomcat community are the Naval Air Warfare Center (Weapons Division), China Lake (formally the NWC) and the Naval Air Warfare Center (Weapons Division), Point Mugu (formally PMTC).

China Lake (six miles east of Inyokem, California) is a major research development and test centre for naval weapons. It includes fully instrumented range facilities, with a variety of targets and even nuclear range facilities (no longer in use). It has

seen a wide range of guided, powered and free-fall ordnance tested for the US Navy. VX-5 'Vampires' was an operational test and evaluation squadron responsible for the development of weapons and tactics, and was parented by the Naval Weapons Test

Center at China Lake. It is not believed that VX-5 ever operated the F-14. VX-5 disestablished on 29 April 1994 and its aircraft and personnel became a detachment of the newly formed VX-9. VX-4 disestablished on 30 September, becoming another VX-9 detachment. Now that VX-5 and VX-4 have been amalgamated, the unit's Tomcats are based at China Lake with VX-9.

The Pacific Missile Test Center at Point Mugu, now an element of the Naval Air Warfare Center (Weapons Division), has been a Tomcat operator since the early 1970s. A missile test facility has been at the California base since 1946, with firing ranges stretching out to sea and telemetry instrumentation located on nearby Laguna Peak. Before the PMTC came the Naval Missile Center (NMC), which was a Tomcat operator from the type's earliest days. In 1972 the first AIM-54 firings were undertaken by an NMC F-14 (BuNo. 157983). NMC aircraft wore a variety of colour schemes, including a tail badge with a swan clutching a missile. Later the NMC crest appeared on the fin,superimposed on a dark blue and red chevron with the legend 'NMC'.

In the mid-1970s the PMTC was established. Its aircraft wore a blue tailband with the unit's triangular dark blue and gold eagle and anchor badge. On the whole, PMTC Tomcats wore the same light grey

Left: A line-up of F-14As and YF-14As at Patuxent River during 1973. One of the aircraft wears the badge of the Naval Missile Center, shortly thereafter redesignated the Pacific Missile Test Center. The prototypes have red bands across their tailfins, with large numbers superimposed in black.

colour scheme with white undersides as Fleet F-14s of the period did. At least one F-14 appeared in an experimental grey 'splinter camouflage' with toned-down markings. Tomcats from VX-4 flew alongside the PMTC's own aircraft. The targets for both units were usually QF-86 and QF-4 drones launched from San Nicolas Island, near the coast.

Right: This NAWC F-14A illustrates the drab markings currently applied to F-14s of the former PMTC. The unit has a mix of Tomcat sub-variants on charge.

Below: This PMTC F-14A carries Phoenix missiles under wings and fuselage, in the Point Mugu circuit. PMTC markings are here carried on a mid-blue tail band, but were later toned down.

NASA (National Aeronautics and Space Administration)

Two different F-14As have been used by NASA in support of two quite separate research programmes at the Administration's Dryden Flight Research Facility at Edwards AFB. The first of these was an F-14A (157991, actually the last of the 13 pre-production aircraft) which wore its 'last three' in lieu of an officially allocated NASA serial, after arriving on 8 August 1979. The aircraft participated in a joint US Navy/Grumman/NASA investigation into low-altitude, high-Alpha flight with asymmetric thrust settings, which was of

NASA's 'first' Tomcat, serialled NASA 991, passes over the dry lake bed on approach to the Administration's Dryden flight facility, at Edwards AFB, in 1986.

obvious application to the then-troubled F-14 community, which was suffering more than its share of spinning accidents, many caused by single engine failures. The ARI (aileron-rudder interconnect) was enhanced to help prevent wing rock, and to help prevent departure or spinning. Different shaped wing gloves were trialled on the aircraft, and flip-up canards were added on the nose, with an anti-spin parachute in the beaver tail fairing and an undernose air data sensor projecting from the empty IRST housing. The aircraft completed its test

programme on 1 June 1984, after 23 flights and 254 high AoA manoeuvres, including 54 engine-out stalls. The aircraft returned to Patuxent River on 6 September 1984.

A second early F-14A arrived at NASA from Patuxent River on 8 April 1984. The aircraft (158613) lost its 7T-201 codes and was allocated the NASA serial 834. Operating in support of a joint research and development programme with NASA's Langley Flight Research Center, the aircraft was used for a variable sweep flight transition experiment, of little direct benefit

to the F-14 Tomcat. The aircraft finally returned to Patuxent River on 11 September 1987, after an extension to its two-year loan period. Some scientists apparently favoured using an F-14 as the basis of the MAW (mission adaptive wing) tested on an F-111, and it is likely that future experiments will see the return of the Tomcat to NASA's fleet, especially as squadron disbandments see large numbers of early F-14As becoming surplus to Navy requirements. At the moment, however, no F-14s are flying in NASA colours.

Iran

The Imperial Iranian air force took delivery of 79 F-14As before the revolution which toppled the Shah and halted delivery of the last aircraft. This example was stored at AMARC for some years, and was then issued to VX-4. Cut off from spares support, serviceability of Iran's F-14As was poor, although this steadily improved. A number of aircraft (with their Phoenix missiles) were almost certainly delivered to the Soviet Union in exchange for Soviet-built aircraft and weapons, and Soviet help in maintaining the F-14s themselves. After a period during which the lack of spares and a shortage of skilled manpower progressively reduced aircraft availability, and during which the handful of F-14As were used primarily as mini-AWACS platforms during the Iran/Iraq war (when at least one was lost, to a Mirage F1), the number of F-14As active with the Islamic Republic of Iran air force have apparently risen dramatically. The type may now be operational in the long-range intercept role, and may even equip or partially equip more than the original two squadrons based at Isfahan and Shiraz before the revolution.

A Farewell To Arms

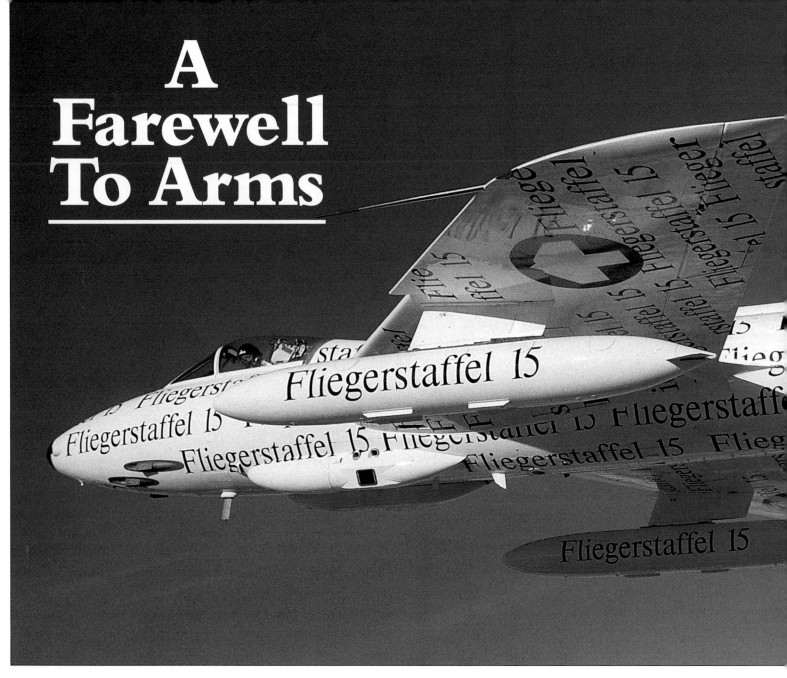

If the Hunter had not existed, the Swiss would have had to invent it. The strong airframe coped extraordinarily well with the turbulence encountered during low-altitude flights among the mountains, while the low purchase price and running costs allowed Switzerland to maintain a huge fleet of these versatile fighter-bombers. Finally, in 1994, the Hunter is nearing final retirement in Switzerland, its numbers no longer needed in the post-Cold War world.

Swiss interest in the Hawker Hunter began in 1953, when the Armstrong Siddeley Sapphire used in the Mk 2 and Mk 5 was viewed as a potential powerplant for the indigenous P-16. A Swiss test pilot evaluated the aircraft in England.

Powerfully supported by the air force, the Hunter competed with the P-16 as a potential de Havilland Vampire replacement. The indigenous aircraft predictably gained the support of the Swiss parliament due to its impact on jobs, the local aircraft industry and the nation's balance of payments. The cabinet initially recommended a purchase of 100 Hunters (J-4001 to J-4100) on 15 November 1957, this being accepted in January 1958. A SFr 312 million contract for the supply of 100 single-seat Hunter F.Mk 58s (the first 12, serialled J-4001 to J-4012, were RAF F.Mk 6s used to provide an immediate pool of aircraft for training) was finalised in early 1958. The first 12 aircraft were later returned to the UK to be brought up to full F.Mk 58 standard. Changes from the standard RAF F.Mk 6 were minimal and included the installation of a brake chute, Swiss standard

Left: The unit badge of Fliegerstaffel 15 is a paper aeroplane made from a folded newspaper. This full-size aircraft was appropriately decorated in November 1993 by 10 of Fliegerkompanie 18's reservists. Fliegerkompanie 18 is the unit responsible for the maintenance of Fliegerstaffel 15's Hunters. The aircraft is known as the 'paperplane' and has a specially modified version of the national insignia below the port wing, representing a paper aircraft.

Opposite page, bottom left: The last pilots of Fliegerstaffel 15 pose in front of the specially painted J-4015. From left to right they are Flying Officer Thomas Storrer, Captain Max Kugler, Captain Hans Peter Reusser, Captain Thomas Podmer, Captain Jürg Hoffer and Captain Daniel Moser. The disbandments of Fliegerstaffeln 3 and 4 in 1992 and of 2 and 21 in 1993 left only Fliegerstaffeln 5, 7, 15, 20 and 24 operational in 1994. All will disband by the end of December.

Below: The 'paperplane' flies over the Berner Oberland Alps near Saanen, an aerodrome formerly used by the Pilatus Turbo Porters of Lufttransportstaffel 7. The aircraft is carrying a pair of underwing fuel tanks, known locally as 'Flunts'. The Hunter F.Mk 58 is powered by the large-bore Avon 203/207, as is the RAF F.Mk 6. The Swiss aircraft have a brake chute fairing above the jetpipe, like RAF F.Mk 6As.

radios and reconfiguration of the outboard underwing pylons to carry a payload of up to 400 kg (880 lb). This first batch of aircraft equipped Fliegerstaffeln 1, 5, 8, 11 and 21, and were used in the fighter role, albeit with a heavy ground attack commitment.

Two repeat purchases were made in 1971 and 1974, totalling SFr 3.55 million for 60 aircraft (52 refurbished single-seat F.Mk 58As serialled J-4101 to J-4152 and eight two-seat T.Mk 68 trainers, serialled J-4201 to J-4208). This allowed the re-equipment of Fliegerstaffeln 4, 7 and 18, and the short-lived Fliegerstaffel 19. The two-seaters were fitted with more modern Martin-Baker ejection seats (as fitted to the Mirage III) and were used for conversion training and, by Fliegerstaffel 24, as ECM aircraft, with the right-hand seater operating the various ECM equipment fitted. The original F.Mk 58s had been modernised in service, receiving Saab BT-9 bombsights and provision for 1044-litre (230-Imp gal) underwing fuel tanks. The refurbished aircraft were similarly modified before delivery.

When the de Havilland Venom was with-

Top: Captain Ulrich 'Ueli' Leutert, commander of Fliegerstaffel 15, is seen in the cockpit of his Hunter, which is decorated with the squadron's 'paperplane' badge. Hunter F.Mk 58s were delivered with silver undersides and glossy polyurethane camouflage paint, while F.Mk 58As used lighter matt colours and grey undersides.

Above: J-4012 is dismantled at Interlaken prior to scrapping. The Air Force Logistics Command facility at Interlaken was the true home of the Swiss Hunters.

Left: This aircraft, used by Fliegerstaffel 15 during November 1993, wears the badges of two previous users, Fliegerstaffeln 7 (a fish) and 20 (a bison).

drawn in the early 1980s, the F-5E assumed the interceptor role. Full-time squadrons of the Uberwachungsgeschwader (Fliegerstaffeln 1, 11 and 18) were re-equipped, leaving only the surviving militia units (Fliegerstaffeln 4, 5, 7, 8 and 21) and re-equipped Venom units (Fliegerstaffeln 2, 3, 6, 15, 20 and 24) flying the Hunter, almost exclusively in the ground attack role.

In order to prepare the aircraft for their new role, a phased 'Hunter 80' modification package was funded. Under this, aircraft received a nose-mounted radar warning receiver, chaff/ flare dispensers in enlarged undernose ammunition link collectors (known as 'Sabrinas' after a well-endowed film star), and compatibility with a new range of air-to-ground weapons. Initially the Hunter squadrons received the Hunting BL 755 CBU (known locally as the 'low release bomb') and the number of underwing rocket rails was increased to 10, while from 1982 40 aircraft were modified to use the Hughes AGM-65 Maverick ASM. At the same time, the old ranging radar in the nose was deactivated in the recognition that air-to-air combat was, for the Hunter, very much a thing of the

Above: Seen in April 1993, one year before it was dismantled, J-4009 carries a sharkmouthed bomb under the starboard outer underwing pylon. J-4009 was one of the initial batch of ex-RAF F.Mk 6s, and was one of the aircraft used by Fliegerstaffel 2 for its last two-week period of training at Tourtemagne in April 1993. The staffel disbanded in December 1993.

Below: Hunter F.Mk 58 J-4080 waits to fly at St Stephan airfield. The placard on the ladder indicates that it is armed with live weapons, although Maverick live firings were undertaken only during detachments to ranges in Sweden. The aircraft was being used by Fliegerstaffel 15.

past. Some Swiss Hunters have been fitted with AIM-9 Sidewinder AAMs, but this has never been a standard modification. From 1963, J-4013 was used for compatibility and firing trials in connection with the Mirage IIIS programme, although it has since become an occasional Hunter weapon. Other rarely seen Hunter stores include a locally manufactured target drogue pod, usually carried on the starboard inboard underwing pylon, and used for air-to-air gunnery practice.

Since 1959, Swiss Hunters have been performing formation aerobatic displays. Officially recognised in 1964, a four-Hunter team displayed at the Lausanne Expo to commemorate the air arm's 50th anniversary. Initially allowed only 30 hours display training per annum, the team originally flew only 10 displays annually, with one overseas show from the mid-1970s. Since then, the team has gone from strength to strength, and won the Shell Trophy at the 1979 International Air Tattoo at Greenham Common. The team's aircraft were standard, except for the addition of a smoke generator, which worked by feeding dye and diesel oil into the jet efflux. In recent years the team's aircraft have also received a colourful red and white pattern which covers most of the underside of the wing, while retaining standard upper surface disruptive camouflage colours.

Other Hunters have occasionally worn

Above: J-4013 was the first new-build Hunter F.Mk 58, and since its delivery has served with the Gruppe für Rüstungsdienste, a civilian test organisation. The aircraft's belly carries a huge representation of a gentian violet, while a Mirage IIIC used by the unit featured an enormous sunflower.

Below: The badge of the Emmen-based Gruppe für Rüstungsdienste is worn on the nose of J-4013. The aircraft carries a number of black and white segmented circles as camera calibration aids, to help in the interpretation of films of weapons trials. Large patches of Dayglo have been applied to improve conspicuity.

squadron markings but, with the exception of the specialised EW aircraft of Fliegerstaffel 24, it should be realised that all Hunters are pooled and allocated to units on an as-required basis for periods of training. Squadron badges are applied unofficially, and may remain in place even after the aircraft has been used by other units. A handful of Hunters have received individual colours. The last example of an aircraft type traditionally receives nose art in the Swiss air force; thus, F.Mk 58A 4152 was named 'Robin Hood' and T.Mk 67 J-4208 was named 'Friar Tuck', each aircraft carrying appropriate Walt Disney characters along with their names.

In recent years, squadron anniversaries (and disbandments) have led to the temporary appli-

cation of special paint schemes. In 1973, one of Fliegerstaffel 11's Hunter F.Mk 58s (J-4053) carried an eye-catching tiger-striped scheme, in 1989 Fliegerstaffel 7's J-4007 was painted blue and yellow overall, and in 1993 J-4138 was painted in the colours of the Canton Valais (red to starboard and white), with the colour division down the centreline. Fliegerstaffel 15's J-4040 was painted white overall in 1993, with 'Fliegerstaffel 15' and 'Flkp 18' neatly lettered over every surface. J-4013, the first newly-built F.Mk 58, remained with the GRD after delivery and had camera calibration markings, with Dayglo trim on the nose and on the leading- and trailing-edges of the fin and wings, with a blue gentian painted under the belly.

Above and below: During its last two-week training period at Tourtemagne in April 1993, Fliegerstaffel 2 painted one of its aircraft red and white overall (white to port and red to starboard) with the colour demarcation running down the aircraft centreline. The paint job looked magnificent, but was unfortunately judged unfit to fly and too likely to be eroded by weather, with a danger of paint flaking off into the engine intakes. A torrential downpour removed the paint, partly revealing Fliegerstaffel 3 and Fliegerstaffel 20 badges below the white paint and the Fliegerstaffel 2 emblem.

Left and right: This Meiringen-based Hunter F.Mk 58A began life as an RAF F.Mk 6 (XG127), later being converted to FR.Mk 10 configuration before refurbishment and sale to Switzerland. It carries a target-towing pod under the port wing (inboard), with small drop tanks outboard.

Below: A Hunter F.Mk 58A lands at Sion during an annual training camp. The aircraft has practice bomb carriers on its outboard underwing pylons. Squadron markings are carried only on the pilot's helmet.

*Above and below: Fliegerstaffel 24 is a specialised **EW** training unit, and its **Hunter T.Mk** 7s can carry the **T-708** pod, which consists of a chaff/flare dispenser in the mid-section, with antennas for an **ECM** jammer forward. The task of **Fliegerstaffel** 24 will be taken over by **Fliegerstaffel** 12, which operates the **PC-9**.*

Switzerland's Hunters are being withdrawn one year earlier than had originally been planned, primarily for financial reasons. The ageing Hunters are becoming increasingly expensive to support, and the end of the Cold War has brought about a peace dividend even for neutral Switzerland. The rundown of the Hunter fleet began in 1990, when aircraft with fatigue cracks (primarily the refurbished F.Mk 58As) were withdrawn for spares recovery and scrapping at Dübendorf, Emmen, Interlaken and Meiringen. Attrition of the Hunter fleet during the 36 years in service has been light, with 26 losses claiming the lives of 15 aircrew. This equates to an accident rate of one per 12,000 flying hours.

Ironically, many of the earliest aircraft, including the first ex-RAF F.Mk 6 (and seven of the other initial 12) delivered in April 1958, remained in use in early 1994. The withdrawal of the Hunter will allow the disbandment of eight squadrons by 1994, and the dissolution of Fliegerregiment 3 and the closure of five emergency airfields (at Ambri, Raron, Saanen, St Stephan and Ulrichen) by 1999. Upon their final withdrawal, the surviving 80 or so Hunters will not be publically auctioned because they are still considered to be 'war material' and Switzerland has strict regulations controlling the export of military equipment. Instead, they will be scrapped, along with 3600 tonnes of ammunition, in a process which will cost the Swiss taxpayer some SFr 15 million. Twenty Hunters will be saved for museums or donation to foreign museums and air forces for preservation. Many Hunter pilots will be retrained, some younger pilots going on to the F-5 or Mirage, and others to the PC-7 or helicopters.

From 1995, European air show audiences who have thrilled to the sight and sound of the six Hunters of the 'Patrouille Suisse' will watch the same team perform with a similar number of Northrop F-5Es. While the F-5E Tiger II is indisputably a better, more viable combat aircraft than the Hunter, many will miss the graceful lines of the classic Hawker as an aerobatic display aircraft, and there are undoubtably many Swiss pilots who will miss the aircraft's impeccable handling, rugged dependability and useful firepower.

Air Combat Command

Initially created by an amalgamation of the giants of Tactical Air Command and Strategic Air Command, ACC has been considerably reorganised since its inception. It is now a far leaner organisation, having disposed of most of its non-offensive assets to other commands while at the same time suffering from the same cutbacks affecting the Air Force as a whole. Nevertheless, Air Combat Command forms the most potent air force organisation in the world, with a large CONUS-based strategic bomber and tactical fighter force at its behest, ready to deploy to any global trouble-spot at a moment's notice.

On 1 June 1992, Air Combat Command stood up to assume responsibility for all of the USAF's warfighting assets based on American soil. This amounted to an amalgamation of Tactical Air Command, which traditionally controlled the tactical fighter and fighter-bomber force, and Strategic Air Command, which controlled manned bombers, nuclear missiles and tankers. The resultant organisation was a vast and unwieldy collection of disparate units with widely varying missions, and immediately a rationalisation began to bring the new command into shape, a process which is still ongoing in mid-1994, although the basic, slimmer shape of the new beast has emerged.

In creating Air Combat Command, the Department of Defense had finally acceded to the 'fighter faction', for the new command was largely based on Tactical Air Command concepts. Today there is little of Strategic Air Command left in the overall flavour of the organisation – strategic bombers wear two-letter tailcodes and TAC-style serials – and even the command badge is similar to the winged sword used previously by TAC. The 'fighter faction' did not succeed in raising the new command to unified/specified status, which had been enjoyed by SAC.

Within the US defence structure, there are unified/specified commands which control the fighting in time of war. Unified commands are assigned to theatres (Central Command, Southern Command, Pacific Command, Atlantic Command and European Command) with specified commands assigned to specific mission areas (Strategic Command, NORAD, Special Operations Command, Space Command and Transportation Command). Unified/specified commands draw from peacetime organisations known as major commands, across all four services. Air Combat Command is designated a major command, and its assets are assigned as air components of four unified/specified commands. In addition to these direct assignments, other unified/specified commands can draw on ACC assets as and when required, although the unified commands also control tactical aircraft directly assigned. The rapid ability of ACC to supply air-

craft is of particular significance given the truly global nature of the US defence policy and is regularly practised with Exercises Brighter Star (CENTCOM), Cobra Gold and Team Spirit (PACOM), Crested Cap (EUCOM) and Ocean Venture (LANTCOM).

ACC's stated roles are to operate USAF bombers and CONUS-based combat-coded fighter and attack aircraft, to organise, train, equip and maintain combat-ready forces and to provide nuclear-capable forces for Strategic Command. Corollary missions are to assist in the interception of illegal drug traffic, and to test new combat equipment. Additional responsibilities, and in practice the most important given roles, are to provide aircraft for the five geographic unified commands, to provide air defence forces for NORAD and to supply certain air mobility forces to Transportation Command.

Since 1 June 1992, Air Combat Command has lost many of the assets previously assigned to it. Control of the ICBM force of the 20th Air Force has passed to Space Command, while the huge Strategic Air Command KC-135/KC-10 tanker fleet has now been transferred to Air Mobility Command units, the only tankers remaining in ACC control being the handful assigned to the 366th Wing power projection unit at Mountain Home. Much of the operational conversion mission has been passed to Air Education and Training Command, although ACC retains the training role for a number of specialised types.

In the reverse direction, ACC has regained control of the C-130 transport force, which TAC lost to Military Airlift Command in 1974, as it was deemed that its operations are sufficiently tactical in nature to warrant its integration into the ACC organisation. The special forces support mission had already been transferred to Special Operations Command in 1990. Other recent acquisitions have included some minor units (rescue, liaison and companion trainers) which are based at Air Combat Command facilities. The USAF is pursuing a 'one base, one wing' policy, so previous tenants from other commands are now often assigned directly to the host wing.

In terms of numbers, ACC is a vast organisa-

tion. In May 1994 the personnel total stood at 253,831, of whom 124,519 were active-duty personnel, 75,637 were Air National Guardspersons, 27,687 were Air Force Reservists and 25,988 were civilians. The annual payroll is a staggering $4.7 billion, although this figure is dwarfed by the $9.3 billion operations and maintenance budget.

In terms of aircraft numbers, the USAF measures its aircraft in three ways: total aircraft in inventory, PAA (Primary Aircraft Authorized), which is the number of aircraft provided to perform the operational mission, including training, and upon which the O&M budget is based, and combat-coded aircraft, which is the number of aircraft considered ready for military operations. In May 1994 the PAA of Air Combat Command consisted of 166 B-52, B-1B and B-2 bombers, 348 F-15C and F-16C fighters, 258 A/OA-10, F-15E, F-111 and F-117 attack aircraft, 45 F-4G and EF-111A electronic warfare aircraft, 25 KC-10 and KC-135 tankers and 381 aircraft of other types, giving a total of 1,223 aircraft. These fly an average of over 50,000 hours per month.

In addition to the active-duty force, ACC is the gaining command for the vast majority of the Air Force Reserve and Air National Guard force, where large numbers of C-130s, A-10s and F-16s are concentrated. Other types such as the F-4G, F-15, B-52 and B-1B are also in the reservist organisation and readily available for ACC use. Together, the AFRes and ANG can provide over 1,500 aircraft for ACC with 110,000 personnel.

Air Combat Command

HQ, Langley AFB, VA

1st Air Force, Tyndall AFB, FL

8th Air Force, Barksdale AFB, LA

9th Air Force, Shaw AFB, SC

12th Air Force, Davis-Monthan AFB, AZ

USAF Weapons and Tactics Center, Nellis AFB, NV

USAF Air Warfare Center, Eglin AFB, FL

Intended as a partial replacement for the F-111 in the precision attack role, the F-15E serves with four ACC squadrons. The USAF has received 209.

Global firefighters: the 'Gunfighters' of the 366th Wing at Mountain Home are dedicated to the rapid application of air power in any part of the world. Shown here are examples of the wing's aircraft (minus the B-1B bomber), which include a few T-38s for co-pilot training.

Concentrated at Cannon AFB, the F-111 force provides an unrivalled precision strike capability (F-111F) and the USAF's principal ECM jamming force (EF-111A).

Under current plans 19 E-8C J-STARS aircraft are to be procured for ACC, providing a similar control and targeting function for the land battle as AWACS gives the air battle.

Rolling out on Whiteman's runway is the first B-2A Spirit for the 509th Bomb Wing, displaying the auxiliary air intakes deployed at low speed. By November 1994 the wing had two aircraft, and had undertaken the first conventional bombing training sorties.

The F-15C will remain the USAF's premier fighter until at least 2003, when the first F-22A is expected in service. This example carries an AGATS gunnery target.

From 1974 to 1992 the C-130 force was controlled by Military Airlift Command, but has now been absorbed into the tactical planning of ACC. The 314th AW at Little Rock is now part of the 8th AF structure.

Star of the Desert: the Lockheed F-117A is ACC's prime first-strike weapon in a conventional war, tasked with taking out key targets in the defensive command and control network. A current upgrade programme reduces pilot workload and alleviates some of the problems associated with pinpoint bombing in adverse weather.

1st Air Force

From its headquarters at Tyndall AFB, First Air Force oversees air defence forces, and also provides the US geographical component of the North American Aerospace Defense Command (NORAD). The organisation's predecessor was once a major command (Aerospace Defense Command), with a huge fleet of interceptors assigned to protect the United States from Soviet bomber attack. Now that the threat is gone, so have the interceptors. 1st Air Force lost its last assigned active-duty aircraft in the recent USAF reshuffle, the Iceland-based 57th Fighter Squadron being reassigned to Eighth Air Force.

First Air Force was activated on 6 December 1985, within Tactical Air Command, having previously been ADTAC (Air Defence Tactical Air Command). At its inception it had three CONUS-based squadrons of F-15A interceptors (5th Fighter Interceptor Squadron at Minot AFB, ND, 48th FIS at Langley AFB, VA, and 318th FIS at McChord AFB, WA). Aircraft from these units were transferred to the Air National Guard, which now mans the entire CONUS air defence force. This comprises two dedicated squadrons of F-15s in Massachusetts and Oregon, and squadrons equipped with the F-16A/B Block 15 Air Defense Fighter in California, Florida, Michigan, Minnesota, Montana, New Jersey, New York, North Dakota, Texas and Vermont. First Air Force actually controls these units, through four geographically-aligned Air Defense Sectors. One of these (NEADS) is to transfer to ANG control in late 1994, and it is likely that the others will follow.

Further losses for 1st Air Force comprise the F-15 training mission, undertaken by the 325th Fighter Wing, which has been handed to AETC, and the Air Defense Weapons Center, a unit based at Tyndall AFB for the testing of new weapons and tactics, doctrinal air defence training and the control of drone operations. ADWC activities have been combined with those of the Tactical Air Warfare Center into the direct-reporting USAF Air Warfare Center at Eglin AFB.

While 1st Air Force is a very 'thin' organisation, it has the infrastructure in place to rapidly absorb assets should an attack be made on the NORAD region. In addition to air defence-dedicated ANG aircraft it can call on tactically-assigned fighters from both the active-duty and reservist fleets. First Air Force also uses E-3 Sentries from the 12th AF's 552nd Air Control Wing from time to time on NORAD-dedicated missions.

1st Air Force

Northeast Air Defense Sector (NEADS), Griffiss AFB, NY

Southeast Air Defense Sector (SEADS), Tyndall AFB, FL

Northwest Air Defense Sector (NWADS), McChord AFB, WA

Southwest Air Defense Sector (SWADS), March AFB, CA

8th Air Force

In the Strategic Air Command organisation, the 'Mighty Eighth' controlled the strategic bomber force located in the eastern half of the United States, partnering the 15th Air Force in the west. In the 1992 realignment, 8th Air Force took control of most of the manned bomber fleet, while 15th Air Force took SAC's tanker fleet away and joined Air Mobility Command.

Most 8th Air Force bases are located in a central swathe across the United States, and the organisation provides the air component for the unified US Strategic Command, which also gains the US Navy's strategic submarine fleet in time of war or tension. With the accent switching from the nuclear mission to conventional bombing, 8th AF bombers are increasingly tasked by other unified commands for theatre missions, and are regular participants in theatre exercises.

As the B-52 fleet dwindles, and both B-52s and B-1Bs are transferred to Air National Guard and Air Force Reserve units, 8th Air Force's most important programme is the equipment of the 509th Bomb Wing at Whiteman AFB, MO, with the Northrop B-2A Spirit. Once a mighty fleet of 132 B-2s was planned, but this has been reduced to a 'silver bullet' complement of just 21 aircraft. Of these one is a permanent test vehicle, and four would be expected to be undergoing overhaul or modifications at any given time. An operational force would comprise just 16 aircraft, split between two eight-aircraft squadrons.

Other active-duty bomber forces are in the process of reducing to two wings of B-52s (at Barksdale and Minot) and two of B-1Bs (at Dyess and Ellsworth). Just how many B-52Hs are to be retained for the remainder of the decade is a matter of some debate in mid-1994, the number varying between 47 and 74. Even the latter is being seen has insufficient to meet the Air Force's equipment requirements for a two-MRC (major regional conflict) scenario, and funding is being supplied to keep 94 B-52Hs in the inventory through FY 1995. This funding is unlikely to be continued beyond that date, and ACC has ear-marked B-52Hs with wing-crack and fuel-leak histories for retirement. Air Combat Command is expected to be able to field 100 bombers of all types to deploy in the event of regional conflicts, acting primarily in the conventional role but also able to cross the nuclear threshold should the need arise. Manned bombers are still the weapon of choice in this scenario simply because they are manned, and the decision to go nuclear is reversible right up to the moment of weapon release.

However, with 100 bombers deployed away from the United States, Strategic Command still requires a number of aircraft either on nuclear alert or able to be placed on alert at short notice, raising the required number of bombers still further. In the worst case, ACC is looking at a force of 20 B-2s, 94 B-1Bs and 47 B-52Hs, for a combined total of 161. With maintenance, delivery and training considerations, and the transfer of B-52s to the Air Force Reserve and B-1Bs to the Air National Guard, the command is realistically looking at just 80 operational bombers in FY95. Twenty B-52Hs were placed in storage as an attrition reserve in April 1994, and in mid-1994 there were plans to 'buy back' these bombers into active duty to make up for the shortfall.

In line with the changing world and changing foreign policy, all three strategic bomber types are being equipped for full conventional capabilities in addition to their nuclear roles. In 1991 Desert Storm displayed the considerable advantages of the precision-guided munition, which far out-weighed the extra cost when compared to unguided weaponry. Until recently the B-52G shouldered the burden of conventional warfare, but this has now retired from service. B-52Hs took up the mantle, being able to carry huge loads of conventional freefall weaponry, including naval mines.

Principal weapons of the B-52H are the ALCM (Air-Launched Cruise Missile), either in AGM-86B nuclear form or AGM-86C with conventional warhead, and the AGM-129 ACM (Advanced Cruise Missile), a nuclear weapon which employs low-observables technology. Up to 20 missiles can be carried, 12 externally and eight on the CSRL (Common Strategic Rotary Launcher) in the weapons bay. Freefall nuclear weapons are theoretically possible, but unlikely. In the conventional role the B-52H is being equipped with a range of precision weapons, including the AGM-84 Harpoon anti-ship missile, AGM-142 Have Nap electro-optically guided stand-off attack missile, the AGM-137 TSSAM (Tri-Service Stand-off Attack Missile) from 1997 and the JDAM-1 (Joint Direct Attack Munition) from about 2001. The latter two weapons both employ highly accurate INS/GPS guidance. The TSSAM is a stealthy missile with a range of about 375 miles (600 km) and various infra-red-guided sub-munitions, while JDAM-1 is basically a highly-accurate 2,000-lb-class bomb with a variety of fusing and warhead options.

Like the B-52H, the Rockwell B-1B has also recently adopted conventional missions. Previously solely assigned the nuclear penetration role with freefall weapons, the B-1B now regularly practises with freefall conventional bombloads, and takes its place on theatre exercises. PGM capability is expected in the next 10 years with the provision of TSSAM, JDAM and JSOW (Joint Stand-Off Weapon). The latter again employs accurate INS/GPS navigation, and has pop-out wings to achieve long stand-off ranges. Power for the weapon is currently under evaluation. JSOW is being integrated with the BLU-108B SFW (Sensor-Fuzed Weapon – commonly referred to as 'Skeet') for area anti-armour attacks. There are currently no plans to equip the B-1B with cruise missiles, although this capability is catered for in the design. In FY95 the number of combat-coded (i.e. fully deployable) B-1Bs is reduced to 38, a further 10 aircraft serving with the reserves and 12 in the training role.

Conceived as the ultimate strategic weapon, the Northrop B-2A was originally envisaged as a highly survivable penetration bomber that would succeed the B-1B in this hazardous mission. While this mission is nowhere near as important now as it was a few years ago, it is still ultimately the primary function of the B-2. However, in a time when politicians have their minds firmly set on reducing the vast burden of defence costs in the post-Cold War era, the USAF is presenting the Spirit as a 'pivotal tool' in a conventional war,

The 2nd Bomb Wing at Barksdale is one of two B-52H wings.

Previously the 96th Bomb Wing, the Dyess B-1B unit is now the 7th Wing.

Initially developed to take on the dangerous nuclear penetration mission, the Northrop B-2 can also undertake conventional attacks in dense threat environments. Much has been made of the type's conventional capabilities in recent months to attempt to maintain funding for the envisaged 20-aircraft operational fleet.

Partnering the 2nd BW in maintaining the B-52H force is the 5th BW at Minot. Considerable debate rages over the future of the 'BUFF', with extensive cuts forecast. Emergency funding has been made available to maintain the 94-aircraft fleet through FY95, at least.

Another force under considerable scrutiny are the F-111Fs of the 27th FW. The Pave Tack acquisition/designation pod gives the type outstanding PGM capability.

The oft-maligned B-1B nevertheless provides enormous offensive muscle in the conventional arena, in addition to its nuclear mission. This aircraft flies with the 28th Bomb Wing at Ellsworth, one of ACC's two B-1B wings.

The USAF's jamming force of EF-111As is undergoing a two-phase SIP (Systems Improvement Program) aimed at improving jamming capability.

This 7th Wing B-1B is seen landing at RAF Fairford during a regular deployment to England. Such exercises allow the crews to familiarise themselves with operations in Europe, while allowing local planners to practise integrating the B-1B's talents with the disparate tactical forces based in the theatre.

By an accident of geography, Eighth Air Force operates a handful of 'true' fighters in the shape of the F-15Cs of the 35th Wing in Iceland. The wing also operates rescue HH-60Gs and maintains the strategic staging post at Keflavik.

taking the 'first night' concept of the F-117 one step further. In other words, heavily-armed B-2s would open the air campaign, safely penetrating the most heavily-defended airspace and destroying the highest-value targets with precision munitions, thereby allowing less-survivable aircraft to operate in greater safety.

In mid-1994 the 509th Bomb Wing at Whiteman AFB had received two operational B-2As, and the 393rd BS was expecting to achieve IOC (initial operating capability) in 1997, followed by the 715th BS in 2001. Initial deliveries are of Block 10 aircraft, which are compatible with the B83 nuclear freefall weapon and Mk 84 2,000-lb-class conventional bomb. Succeeding Block 20 aircraft will add the B61 freefall nuclear weapon, and a range of conventional cluster bombs (CBU-87, CBU-89 and CBU-97). From mid-1997 TSSAM will provide a PGM capability, and later the GPS Advanced Targeting System/JDAM. The final two aircraft will be Block 30s, these featuring JDAM-1 capability and compatibility with 500-lb and 750-lb class conventional weapons and mines. The aircraft will also be the first with fully-capable defensive and offensive avionics, and a set of radar cross-section reductions. The remainder of the fleet will be brought up to Block 30 standard in the next century.

After many years of being assigned to tactical forces, Air Combat Command has finally recognised the enormous destructive power of the F-111 force and placed it in 8th Air Force alongside the strategic bombers. All F-111s are concentrated at Cannon AFB to ease maintenance, but the combined fleet makes for a ripe fruit for cut-seeking politicians. Far and away the most destructive and cost-effective aircraft of Desert Storm, the F-111F's reputation is perhaps its biggest asset in the fight to avoid retirement. It also has many friends both in the Air Force and on Capitol Hill. However, development funding is on hold pending the outcome of an acrimonious debate brewing over its future, and the aircraft is seen by many as the embodiment of the 'old' Air Force. If the aircraft survives in service, its already-impressive PGM capability (with Paveway II/III laser-guided bombs and GBU-15 EO-guided bombs) will be enhanced by the use of JDAM and perhaps JSOW. Nuclear capability with B61 tactical freefall weapons is retained.

Serving alongside the F-111F squadrons (and single F-111E training unit) are the USAF's EF-111A Ravens, which are responsible for active jamming of enemy air defences. These valuable machines are vital for achieving air supremacy in any conflict, and are undergoing a systems improvement programme to counter current and projected threats into the next century. The small force is in much demand from theatre commands, and also to join composite wings as they deploy away from the US.

Other 8th AF aircraft types are assigned as a result of changing USAF doctrine and for geographical reasons. For many years the bomber bases had T-37B or T-38A trainers attached to provide extra flight time. Originally detachments from flying training wings, the aircraft were assigned under the ACE (Accelerated Co-pilot Enrichment) programme. Now the aircraft are permanently assigned to the wing under the CTP (Companion Trainer Program).

Due to the geographical remit of 8th Air Force, it also exercises control over the C-130 tactical transports at Little Rock and Dyess, aircraft at the latter base sharing wing command with two B-1B squadrons. Little Rock is in the process of upgrading from C-130E to C-130H.

Surprisingly, there are two overseas bases assigned to 8th Air Force – Lajes in the Azores and Keflavik in Iceland. These are of great strategic importance as they are the principal transatlantic staging posts for deploying aircraft. While Lajes has no aircraft based there, the reassignment of Keflavik has resulted in 8th Air Force adding the few F-15C/Ds of the 57th Fighter Squadron to its complement. The future of this squadron is in considerable doubt, as its main trade was the shadowing of Soviet maritime reconnaissance aircraft in the GIUK (Greenland-Iceland-UK) Gap region, an activity which has all but ceased. Also based on Iceland are the HH-60Gs of a rescue squadron, which receives tanker support from HC-130s based in England.

8th Air Force

UNIT	TYPE	TAIL
2nd Bomb Wing, Barksdale AFB, LA		
20th Bomb Squadron	B-52H	'LA'
62nd Bomb Squadron	B-52H	'LA'
Companion Trainer Program	T-37B	'LA'

One more squadron to form to absorb aircraft reassigned from disbanding units.

5th Bomb Wing, Minot AFB, ND		
23rd Bomb Squadron	B-52H	'MT'
Companion Trainer Program	T-37B	'MT'

Two further squadrons to form to absorb aircraft from reassigned disbanding units.

7th Wing, Dyess AFB, TX		
9th Bomb Squadron	B-1B	'DY'
39th Airlift Squadron	C-130H	'DY'
40th Airlift Squadron	C-130H	'DY'
337th Bomb Squadron	B-1B	'DY'
Companion Trainer Program	T-37B	'DY'

27th Fighter Wing, Cannon AFB, NM		
428th Fighter Squadron	F-111E	'CC' (light blue)
429th Electronic Combat Squadron	EF-111A	'CC'
522nd Fighter Squadron	F-111F	'CC' (red)
523rd Fighter Squadron	F-111F	'CC' (blue)
524th Fighter Squadron	F-111F	'CC' (yellow)

35th Wing, Naval Station Keflavik, Iceland		
56th Rescue Squadron	HH-60G	'IS'
57th Fighter Squadron	F-15C, F-15D	'IS'

The 35th Wing was previously a 1st Air Force asset, but now reports to 8th Air Force. It is the major flying component of Air Forces Iceland. The complement of the 57th FS has been considerably reduced in view of the lack of Russian patrol aircraft activity.

28th Bomb Wing, Ellsworth AFB, SD		
37th Bomb Squadron	B-1B, T-38A	'EL' (black/yellow)
77th Bomb Squadron	B-1B	'EL' (blue)

65th Air Base Wing, Lajes Field, Portugal		
		no aircraft assigned

314th Airlift Wing, Little Rock, AR		
50th Airlift Squadron	C-130E, C-130H	'LK'
53rd Airlift Squadron	C-130E, C-130H	'LK'
61st Airlift Squadron	C-130E, C-130H	'LK'
62nd Airlift Squadron	C-130E, C-130H	'LK'

410th Bomb Wing, K. I. Sawyer AFB, MI		
644th Bomb Squadron	B-52H	'KI'
Companion Trainer Program	T-37B	'KI'

509th Bomb Wing, Whiteman AFB, MO		
393rd Bomb Squadron	B-2A	'WM'
715th Bomb Squadron	B-2A (to form)	'WM'
Companion Trainer Program	T-38A	'WM'

8th Air Force casualties in 1994 were the 319th Bomb Group (B-1Bs and T-38As with the 46th Bomb Squadron/'GF') at Grand Forks, ND, and the 384th Bomb Group (B-1Bs and T-38As with the 28th Bomb Squadron/'OZ') at McConnell AFB, KS. The base at K. I. Sawyer is due to close in September 1995, the 410th BW transferring its aircraft to the 2nd and 5th Bomb Wings from mid-1994.

9th Air Force

The most tactically-orientated of the numbered air forces, 9th AF controls ACC forces in the eastern United States from its headquarters at Shaw AFB, and provides the air component for US Central Command.

Ninth Air Force's aircraft assets are assigned to six major wings, comprising two with F-16s as the primary mission type, two with F-15Cs for battlefield air superiority purposes, one with F-15Es for strike and interdiction, and a close air support composite wing.

At Langley and Eglin Eagles rule the roost. The USAF is down to just two active-duty CONUS-based dedicated fighter units, both equipped with F-15Cs and a handful of D models for continuation training purposes. Aircraft at Eglin are the most advanced fighter Eagles, being FY84 MSIP aircraft with the APG-63 radar upgraded to APG-70 standard and a revised Tactical Electronic Warfare System. The AIM-120 AMRAAM is now fully operational, the Eglin wing having first carried the weapon into combat during the latter phase of the Gulf War, although it was not fired in anger during the conflict.

The elderly Eagle is still a considerable force in the air-to-air arena, as aircraft from the Eglin wing demonstrated during Desert Storm, but the type is becoming overdue for replacement in the air superiority role. To this end the US Air Force is hoping to procure the Lockheed F-22A, the first production example of which is expected to fly in 1996, with initial operational deliveries expected to the 1st Fighter Wing in 2003. Whether this multi-million dollar fighter ever enters service is open to constant debate on Capitol Hill, but does have the full backing of the Air Force, which sees the aircraft has its main priority programme. Although the F-22 is primarily an air superiority weapon, it will be able to carry two JDAMs internally and two TSSAMs on the wing pylons to give it a precision ground attack capability. This extra multi-role capacity should help it on its difficult passage through the budgetary process. Further weapons under development for the F-22 and other air-to-air fighters include the AIM-9X new-generation short-range air-to-air missile to replace the current Sidewinders.

Work has begun on a Precision Direction Finder system to fit to F-15Cs as they become surplus to fighter requirement in the next decade. This highly automated and very sensitive system, combined with the carriage of HARM missiles, will turn the F-15C into an effective replacement

The 23rd Wing inherits the traditions of the 'Flying Tigers', hence the tailcode.

The 347th FW at Moody lost two F-16 squadrons in 1994, including the 308th FS.

Armed with live Mk 82s, an A-10A of the 75th FS, 23rd Wing, departs Nellis AFB for an Air Warrior exercise. This is a joint Air Force/Army exercise using both Nellis and Fort Irwin ranges. The aim is to practise the close air support mission, fully integrating air and land assets into one cohesive force. The A-10 is an integral part of this joint-service effort.

Shaw's wing has renumbered from the 363rd to the 20th FW to preserve historic traditions.

The 20th FW has recently re-equipped with latest Block 50 F-16s, including some aircraft fitted with ASQ-213 HTS for defence suppression purposes.

Partnering Shaw's F-16 force is the 21st FS with A-10As for CAS and OA-10As for FAC duties. For the latter, armament is restricted to the internal cannon and target marker rockets.

Moody's Block 40 F-16Cs are principally tasked with night CAS/BAI missions, for which the LANTIRN system is indispensable.

Adorned with sharkmouth markings in common with the other 23rd Wing aircraft, the C-130s of Pope's two airlift squadrons are equipped with AWADS to allow the accurate airdrop of paratroops in all weathers.

Marked for the commander of the 23rd Wing, and carrying the colours of the four constituent squadrons, this F-16D carries an AIS wingtip pod for range work. The LANTIRN system turns the F-16 into a fully-autonomous laser-bomber, this operation becoming more important to the F-16 force for pinpoint attacks against enemy vehicles.

for the F-4G in the 'Wild Weasel' defence suppression role, currently being augmented by F-16s with the less-capable HARM Targeting System. Neither aircraft is seen as a complete replacement for the F-4G, chiefly as they are single-seaters and the provision of a dedicated crew member manning the RHAWS is a valuable commodity. However, both F-16 HTS and F-15 PDF are seen as adequate replacements, given the current nature of the threat and the financial climate.

Heavyweight punch for the 9th AF is the role of the 4th Wing at Seymour Johnson, which operates three squadrons of the F-15E, and which is heavily involved in supporting USAF overseas deployments. The F-15E is currently undergoing a review of its flight control software to alleviate dangerous departure characteristics caused by the increase in weight. This unit until recently also operated the KC-10 tanker, but these assets have been reassigned to Air Mobility Command, leaving the 4th as a single-type wing. Indeed, the F-15E training function is being transferred from AETC's 58th FW at Luke to the 4th to centralise maintenance.

Two wings of the 9th AF major on the F-16C. The 347th FW at Moody operates the Block 40 variant with LANTIRN capability, and is in the process of becoming a composite wing with the addition of a C-130 squadron and an A-10 unit. At Shaw AFB the 20th FW (renumbered from the 363rd) operates newly-received Block 50 aircraft, including some Block 50D machines. The latter are fitted with the ASQ-213 HARM Targeting System, a pod-mounted radar detection antenna which allows the location and classification of hostile radar systems and attack by HARM missile in the defence suppression role. In 1994 tests were carried out whereby an F-16 successfully 'blind'-launched a HARM at a target with position details supplied by satellite. Around 100 Block 50/52D aircraft are being procured by the USAF to fulfil its immediate defence suppression requirements pending introduction of the F-15 PDF or a dedicated lethal SEAD (suppression of enemy air defences) type. The latter option is seen as unlikely in the current climate, and would likely be based on advanced versions of the F-15 or F-16 if it ever goes ahead.

Block 50/52 F-16s introduce the IPE (increased performance engines) in the shape of the F110-GE-129 (Block 50) and F100-PW-229 (Block 52) with significant thrust improvements, APG-68(V)5 radar, Have Quick IIA radio, Have Sync anti-jam VHF and ALR-56M RWR, in addition to the improvements made to aircraft from earlier blocks. More improvements are planned, including ring laser gyro INS, head-

steered FLIR with helmet-mounted sight and colour MFDs.

The Block 40/42 F-16s at Moody and Pope are in the process of being optimised for a night CAS/BAI role, which relies heavily on the LANTIRN system but also adds missile approach warning system, laser spot tracker, anti-jam radio and NVG-compatible cockpits. Highly important to the CAS role will be the provision of an ATHS (automatic target hand-off system).

Ninth Air Force's remaining combat type is the OA/A-10, which serves with squadrons at Shaw and Moody. The aircraft is used for both dedicated close air support (A-10) and for forward air control (OA-10) duties. As part of the USAF's drive to establishing an impressive close air support capability, the A-10s are receiving a low-cost package which includes NVG-compatible cockpits, allowing them a measure of night attack capability. The A-10 is envisaged for use in primarily a low-density conflict, the F-16 Block 40/42 being the system of choice for high-density conflicts.

Previously a dedicated A-10 wing, the 23rd Wing at Pope is now established as an army support composite wing, tailored for rapid deployment alongside the troops of the 82nd Airborne Division at nearby Fort Bragg to form a very powerful land force power projection unit, in much the same way as the 366th Wing provides air power. Troops would most likely deploy long distance by C-141 or C-17, but the Pope wing has two squadrons of C-130s to provide para-dropping and tactical transport in-theatre. Close air support is provided by a squadron of F-16C Block 40s and one of A/OA-10s.

Called off at the last minute following a peace mission led by ex-President Jimmy Carter, the planned airborne invasion of Haiti to restore democracy involved the 23rd Wing heavily, and highlighted the nature of their operations. Hercules equipped with AWADS (adverse weather aerial delivery system) led a force of 60 C-130s and 53 C-141s loaded with paratroops from the 82nd and were *en route* to Haiti when the mission was scrubbed. The lead C-130 was fitted with GPS. Covering the invasion force were A-10s from the 75th FS, armed only with the 30-mm cannon and non-explosive rounds to minimise the chance of collateral damage. A similar unit is being established at Moody by replacing two of the wing's F-16 units with C-130s and A-10s.

One 9th AF oddity is the combat rescue force based at Patrick AFB. Consisting of a squadron of HH-60s with another squadron operating HC-130s for long-range search and refuelling support, the force is headquartered by the 1st FW at Langley, over 600 miles (970 km) away to the north.

These aircraft wear the wing's 'FF' tailcode, as do two staff transport squadrons at Langley which operate C-21As and UH-1Ns.

9th Air Force

1st Fighter Wing, Langley AFB, VA

UNIT	TYPE	TAIL
27th Fighter Squadron	F-15C, F-15D	'FF' (yellow)
71st Fighter Squadron	F-15C, F-15D	'FF' (red)
94th Fighter Squadron	F-15C, F-15D	'FF' (blue)
12th Air Logistics Flight	C-21A	'FF'
41st Rescue Squadron	HH-60G/HH-3E	'FF'
71st Rescue Squadron	HC-130N/P	'FF'
72nd Helicopter Squadron	UH-1N	'FF'

The three F-15 squadrons are under the control of the 1st Operations Group. The 41st and 71st RQS operate from Patrick AFB, FL.

4th Wing, Seymour Johnson AFB, NC

334th Fighter Squadron	F-15E	'SJ' (blue)
335th Fighter Squadron	F-15E	'SJ' (green)
336th Fighter Squadron	F-15E	'SJ' (yellow)
Companion Trainer Program	T-38A	'SJ'

The 4th Wing lost two KC-10 Squadrons (344th and 911th Air Refueling Squadrons) which deactivated in 1994, the aircraft being reassigned to AMC. An F-15E combat training unit will activate in FY94, probably the 461st FS which currently undertakes the role at Luke AFB within AETC.

6th Air Base Wing, MacDill AFB, FL — no aircraft assigned

20th Fighter Wing, Shaw AFB, SC

55th Fighter Squadron	A-10A, OA-10A	'SW' (black/red)
77th Fighter Squadron	F-16C, F-16D	'SW' (white)
78th Fighter Squadron	F-16C, F-16D	'SW' (red)
79th Fighter Squadron	F-16C, F-16D	'SW' (yellow)

23rd Wing, Pope AFB, NC

2nd Airlift Squadron	C-130E	'FT' (red)
41st Airlift Squadron	C-130E	'FT'
74th Fighter Squadron	F-16C, F-16D	'FT' (blue)
75th Fighter Squadron	A-10A, OA-10A	'FT' (black)

33rd Fighter Wing, Eglin AFB, FL

58th Fighter Squadron	F-15C, F-15D	'EG' (blue)
59th Fighter Squadron	F-15C, F-15D	'EG' (yellow)
60th Fighter Squadron	F-15C, F-15D	'EG' (red)

347th Wing, Moody AFB, GA

52nd Airlift Squadron	C-130E	'MY'
68th Fighter Squadron	F-16C, F-16D	'MY' (red)
69th Fighter Squadron	F-16C, F-16D	'MY' (silver)
70th Fighter Squadron	A-10A, OA-10A	'MY'

The 347th was redesignated as a Wing (from FW) on 1 July 1994, and lost the 69th and 308th FS (F-16Cs) in FY 94, although the 307th will renumber as the 'new' 69th FS.

9th Air Force casualties in 1994 were the 42nd Bomb Wing (B-52G and T-37B with the 69th Bomb Squadron/'LZ') at Loring AFB, ME, which closed, and the 416th Bomb Wing (B-52H and T-37B with the 668th Bomb Squadron/'GR') at Griffiss AFB, NY.

12th Air Force

Tasked with overseeing Air Combat Command bases in the western United States, 12th AF at Davis-Monthan AFB also provides the air component for US Southern Command. Far less tactical in nature than 9th AF, it controls many of the USAF's C²W (command and control warfare) assets, such as the reconnaissance fleet, F-117 attack force, E-3 Sentry fleet, command posts and jamming platforms. Adding a theatre transport

wing and the Air Force's principal power projection 'super wing' gives 12th AF perhaps the most interesting make-up of any similarly-sized formation in the world.

Reconnaissance assets are vested in the 9th and 55th Wings. The former operates the Lockheed U-2R on global reconnaissance missions, utilising the type for long-endurance monitoring missions employing radar, electronic and optical sensors. Despite the age of the design it is still very valuable due to its operational altitude and considerable loiter time. The fleet is being re-engined with the F101-GE-F29 turbofan (derived from

the B-2's F118 engine), which restores operational performance eroded by ever-growing mission equipment weights, while greatly reducing maintenance requirements and operating costs. Home-based at Beale, where the training function is undertaken, the U-2Rs are deployed to four operating locations around the world on a regular basis, and other locations as and when required. The detachment at Taif in Saudi Arabia has been active since the first days of the Iraqi invasion of Kuwait, and has remained there since as one of the primary means by which Iraq's military is monitored. Similarly, the aircraft has been

Displaying the current 'Mod Eagle' scheme, this 33rd FW F-15C carries fin-bands for all three of the unit's squadrons. Eglin's aircraft are to the latest MSIP standard.

ACC's other main Eagle fighter unit is the 1st FW at Langley AFB. The yellow fin-stripe of this aircraft identifies the 27th Fighter Squadron.

Carrying a full load of inert Mk 82 free-fall bombs, a pair of 4th Wing F-15Es heads out to a Florida range. The LANTIRN system and excellent APG-70 radar allow the F-15E to launch most weapons in the USAF inventory with outstanding accuracy.

The 'FF' tailcode of the 1st FW stands for 'First Fighter'. The Maltese crosses come from the wing's emblem.

As Langley AFB is ACC headquarters, the resident 1st FW operates some staff transport aircraft for command support. The 12th ALF operates the C-21A in this role.

Rotary-wing staff transport is handled by the UH-1Ns of the 72nd HS. Other 1st FW helicopter assets are the HH-60Gs (with HC-130 support) which are detached to Patrick AFB.

Wearing ACC-style serial and 'BB' tailcodes, U-2Rs fly with two Beale-based squadrons, one for operations and one for training. The U-2R is a valuable Comint/Elint/radar reconnaissance platform, fulfilling both strategic and tactical requirements.

Many ACC bases have T-38 Talons assigned to act as companion trainers, painted in a similar scheme to the wing's principal operational aircraft. This is a 9th Wing aircraft.

The mixed Boeing wing at Offutt (55th Wing) uses various RC-135 variants for global reconnaissance. The RC-135S aircraft were previously used for missile test observation, but now have added a theatre missile reconnaissance role.

The 355th Wing is principally an A-10 unit, but the 'DM' tailcode is also worn by special mission EC-130s.

Davis-Monthan accommodates two squadrons of EC-130H communications jamming aircraft. They have recently been joined by the EC-130E ABCCC aircraft from Keesler, now assigned to the 42nd Airborne Control Squadron.

of great value over the troubled region of Bosnia.

From its base at Offutt, previously the head-quarters of Strategic Air Command, the 55th Wing undertakes a mixed bag of missions, mostly using special variants of the Boeing C-135. For global electronic reconnaissance the wing has a fleet of eight RC-135V and six RC-135W Rivet Joint aircraft, augmented by a pair of RC-135U Combat Sent. These are regularly deployed to operating locations in England, Crete, Okinawa and Saudi Arabia to monitor communications and maintain radar threat libraries on potentially hostile nations. Working alongside U-2s, their work over Bosnia and Iraq has been of great importance in keeping allied commands abreast of any developments.

Offutt's other reconnaissance assets include the two RC-135S Cobra Ball aircraft. These were modified to receive telemetry data from foreign missile tests and to photograph re-entry vehicles. Because of their sophisticated missile tracking systems, they have also picked up a theatre 'Scud'-hunting role, allowing the early detection of this class of weapon. Three WC-135B aircraft have been modified for the 55th Wing as OC-135Bs to fly Open Skies missions. The trio is fitted with surveillance cameras for flights over former Warsaw Pact territory to verify compliance with arms limitations treaties. Three 'bounce-bird' trainer aircraft support the C-135 special missions fleets, designated TC-135B (Open Skies), TC-135S (Cobra Ball) and TC-135W (Rivet Joint).

The 55th Wing operates examples of ACC's smallest and largest aircraft. C-21s and T-38s are assigned for staff transport and the companion trainer programme respectively, while at the other end of the size scale is the Boeing E-4B, which in 1994 was redesignated the National Airborne Operations Center. This communications-packed version of the 747 has a primary strategic mission of flying the President and his battle staff during a nuclear attack on the United States, preserving the chain of command by linking with other airborne command posts and hardened ground stations, and by being able to break into civilian communications networks to make direct broadcasts to the nation. In an era of much-reduced superpower tensions, the E-4B has also been assigned a conventional mission.

So too has the EC-135C fleet based at Offutt. These aircraft again have a primary strategic function of exercising airborne control over the USAF's strategic missile and bomber force in time of nuclear tension or war. With the retirement of all theatre-based command posts, the EC-135C also makes occasional deployments to Europe, the Gulf or Far East to train theatre commanders in airborne command operations, or to assist in local operations should the need arise.

Operating the USAF's E-3 Sentry fleet is also a 12th AF responsibility, the 552nd ACW deploying aircraft from its base at Tinker, where they are based alongside the E-6As of the US Navy's Sea Control Wing One. AWACS has two principal missions: airborne early warning in support of NORAD and tactical air control in support of ACC and theatre operations. The former mission is of decreasing importance in today's political climate, but the Sentry is increasingly tasked with drug enforcement missions. The E-3 is currently the subject of an upgrade programme which adds Quick Look ESM and the ability to use GPS, increases computer memory, raises the JTIDS sys-

tem to TADIL-J (Tactical Data Information Link-Joint) standard and improves small-target radar detection. In addition to the Sentries, the 552nd ACW also operates a pair of EC-135K aircraft which act as navigation and communications support platforms for deploying tactical fighters. This role is also of decreasing importance owing to the greater use of the KC-10 for 'trailing' fighters on long overwater deployments. The TC-18E is also flown, this being a 707 which introduces aircrew to the type for initial training without incurring the expenses and structural damages associated with training in a mission aircraft.

Further large aircraft are operated by the 355th Wing at Davis-Monthan, which has two squadrons of EC-130Hs for communications jamming purposes and one of EC-130Es for battlefield airborne command post duties. The latter unit has recently moved from Keesler AFB, MS, and has adopted the 42nd ACCS designation. When it becomes operational in 1997, the E-8C J-STARS is likely to become a 12th AF asset, although it will be based at Robins AFB in Georgia, outside of the 12th AF geographical region.

Other 12th AF units include the 24th Wing in Panama, which flies a mixed bag of transport types in support of Central American operations. A type unique to this unit is the Chrysler C-27 Spartan (Aeritalia G222) which can operate from the short, unprepared strips which abound in the region.

For offensive operations, the 12th AF has a wing of F-16C/Ds at Hill AFB, squadrons of A-10s with the 355th Wing at Davis-Monthan, the F-117 force at Holloman and the USAF's 'super wing' at Mountain Home. The latter is a rapid-reaction power-projection unit which encompasses the major offensive roles within one wing. F-16C/Ds and F-15Es provide tactical muscle, while heavy bombing is catered for by the B-1B. Tanker support is in place, as is a squadron of F-15Cs to provide fighter cover for the wing's operations. Additional aircraft, such as F-4Gs and EF-111As for defence suppression and E-3s for command and control, can be rapidly added to the mix from other units to form a complete air force within an air force. This core unit trains together on a daily basis, and is thus at maximum readiness for rapid deployment into a combat zone. In the near future the 366th is expected to switch its KC-135Rs for KC-10s, and the now-elderly F-16C Block 25s for later models with LANTIRN and HARM capability.

At Holloman the F-117 force comprises two operational squadrons (8th and 9th FS) and a single training unit (7th FS). The latter also operates T-38s as companion trainers, these aircraft having recently received an all-over black scheme. A major upgrade programme (OCIP III) is enhancing the F-117's ability to undertake all-weather strike missions, and includes new cockpit displays and new imaging infra-red systems. Carbon brakes have been fitted to the operational fleet, allowing the aircraft to dispense with the brake chute.

Further training efforts at Holloman are concerned with foreign students. The 20th FS uses the last F-4Es in USAF markings to train Phantom crews for the Luftwaffe, while the 435th FS employs grey-camouflaged T-38s to provide advanced training for Taiwanese pilots in anticipation of the ROCAF gaining the first of its 150

F-16Cs on order. Holloman is also used to support the adjacent White Sands Missile Test Range, a US Army facility which is used to test a wide variety of air-to-ground and air-to-air missiles. A detachment from the Tyndall-based 475th WEG (an ACC direct-reporting unit) flies QF-106 drones from Holloman, with QF-4Es expected in the near future as the Delta Darts are expended.

At Davis-Monthan the A-10 squadrons of the 355th Wing provide a considerable anti-armour force, but also train pilots on this type. The 388th Fighter Wing at Hill operates F-16Cs, the wing's 4th Fighter Squadron being the first unit to receive the latest Block 50 aircraft.

12th Air Force

UNIT	TYPE	TAIL
6th Reconnaissance Wing, Robins AFB, GA		
	activating with E-8C J-STARS aircraft	
9th Reconnaissance Wing, Beale AFB, CA		
1st Reconnaissance Squadron (T)	U-2R, U-2RT, T-38A	'BB'
99th Reconnaissance Squadron	U-2R	'BB'

For its global reconnaissance tasking the 9th RW maintains four detachments. These are det. 2 at Osan AB, Republic of Korea, det. 3 at RAF Akrotiri, Cyprus, OL-CH (Operating Location – Camel Hump) at Taif, Saudi Arabia, and OL-UK (Operating Location – United Kingdom) at RAF Alconbury, England.

UNIT	TYPE	TAIL
24th Wing, Howard AFB, Panama		
310th Air Logistics Squadron	C-21A, C-27A, C-130H, CT-43	'HW'
49th Fighter Wing, Holloman AFB, NM		
7th Fighter Squadron	F-117A, AT-38B	'HO'
8th Fighter Squadron	F-117A	'HO'
9th Fighter Squadron	F-117A	'HO'
20th Fighter Squadron	F-4E	'HO' (red)
48th Rescue Squadron	HH-60G	'HO'
435th Fighter Squadron	AT-38B	'HO'

The 20th FS trains Luftwaffe Phantom pilots, while the 435th trains Taiwanese aircrew destined for F-16s.

UNIT	TYPE	TAIL
55th Wing, Offutt AFB, NE		
1st Airborne Command and Control Squadron	E-4B	–
2nd Airborne Command and Control Squadron	EC-135C	'OF'
11th Airlift Flight	C-21A	'OF'
24th Reconnaissance Squadron	OC-135B RC-135S, TC-135B, TC-135S	'Open Skies'
38th Reconnaissance Squadron	TC-135W, T-38A	'OF'
82nd Reconnaissance Squadron	TDY RC-135	
343rd Reconnaissance Squadron	RC-135U, RC-135V RC-135W	'OF'
922nd Reconnaissance Squadron	TDY RC-135	
CSA det.	C-135A, C-135B NKC-135A, KC-135E	'OF'

The 38th RS provides flight crew for the RC-135U/V/W. Global detachments are maintained by Det. 1/55th Wing at Earackson AFB, AK (formerly Shemya AB), the 82nd RS at Kadena AB, Okinawa, the 922nd RS at RAF Mildenhall, England, and Det. 1/922nd RS at Soudha Bay, Crete. RC-135s are also operated regularly from Riyadh, Saudi Arabia, to monitor Iraq and support Operation Southern Watch.

UNIT	TYPE	TAIL
355th Wing, Davis-Monthan AFB, AZ		
41st Electronic Combat Squadron	EC-130H	'DM' (blue)
42nd Airborne Command and Control Squadron	EC-130E (ABCCC) C-130E	'DM'
43rd Electronic Combat Squadron	EC-130H	'DM' (red)
333rd Fighter Squadron	A-10A, OA-10A	'DM' (red)
357th Fighter Squadron	A-10A, OA-10A	'DM' (yellow)
358th Fighter Squadron	A-10A, OA-10A	'DM' (black)

The 388th Fighter Wing at Hill was the first recipient of the F-16 back in 1979. In October 1992 the unit's 4th FS led the way with service entry of the Block 50.

Offensive muscle for the 366th 'superwing' is provided by six B-1Bs (based at Ellsworth), the 389th FS with F-16Cs and the 391st FS with F-15Es. This example of the latter demonstrates a level attack with inert Mk 84 LDGPs.

The Mountain Home wing has its own tankers in the shape of the KC-135R. These aircraft are to be replaced with KC-10s to enhance 'deployability'.

Fighter cover for the 366th is provided by the 'Wild Boars' of the 390th FS with F-15Cs. This aircraft carries AIM-120 AMRAAMs in addition to AIM-7s.

The F-16Cs of the 389th FS are early Block 25 aircraft, soon to be replaced by LANTIRN- and HARM-capable Block 50s.

The last F-4E Phantoms to wear USAF markings are those assigned to the 20th FS at Holloman AFB for training Luftwaffe F-4F crews. Eight F-4Es were originally bought by the Luftwaffe, but the survivors have been augmented by ex-USAF examples.

Holloman is best known as the home of the F-117, but also supports a sizeable training unit (435th FS) for Taiwanese pilots, operating the T-38 Talon.

Supplying airborne command posts for both strategic and (from 1994) tactical purposes is one of the 55th Wing's tasks. This is an EC-135C, equipped with Milstars equipment.

The E-3 AWACS fleet of the 552nd ACW is being upgraded with new equipment, including Quick Look ESM. Initial operating capacity for the full E-3C MSIP aircraft is slated for 1999.

An A-10A from the 355th Wing's 357th FS practises refuelling over the Arizona desert. The aircraft carries BDU-33 'blue bombs' on the centreline pylons, and examples of the TV- and IR-guided Maverick on the wing pylons. In addition to providing combat forces, the Davis-Monthan A-10 wing is also the schoolhouse for the type.

The 354th FS was based at McChord AFB to support Army operations from nearby Fort Lewis. However this arrangement was not suitable and the aircraft returned to Davis-Monthan in 1994. One A-10 squadron is scheduled to move to Moody AFB to join the 347th Wing.

366th Wing, Mountain Home AFB, ID

22nd Air Refueling Squadron	KC-135R	'MO' (green)
34th Bomb Squadron	B-1B	'MO' (white)
389th Fighter Squadron	F-16C, F-16D	'MO' (red)

390th Fighter Squadron	F-15C, F-15D	'MO' (blue)
391st Fighter Squadron	F-15E	'MO' (tiger)

The B-1Bs of the 34th BS are based at Ellsworth AFB, SD.

388th Fighter Wing, Hill AFB, UT

4th Fighter Squadron	F-16C, F-16D	'HL' (yellow)
34th Fighter Squadron	F-16C, F-16D	'HL' (red)
421st Fighter Squadron	F-16C, F-16D	'HL' (black)

552nd Airborne Control Wing, Tinker AFB, OK

8th Aerial Deployment and Control Squadron	EC-135K	'OK'
962nd Airborne Control Squadron	E-3B, E-3C	'OK' (green)
963rd Airborne Control Squadron	E-3B, E-3C	'OK' (black)
964th Airborne Control Squadron	E-3B, E-3C	'OK' (red)
965th Airborne Control Squadron	E-3B, E-3C	'OK' (yellow)
965th Airborne Control Training Squadron	E-3B, E-3C, TC-18E	'OK' (blue)

Direct-reporting units

Two major organisations report directly to Air Combat Command, namely the Weapons and Tactics Center (WTC) and the Air Warfare Center (AWC).

Previously known as the Tactical Fighter Weapons Center, the WTC is headquartered at Nellis AFB, from where the majority of its flying activities take place with the 57th Wing. The primary function of the WTC is the ongoing operational test and evaluation (OT&E) mission, using current front-line types to continually refine mission profiles and tactics. This function is undertaken by the 57th Test Group, which has a flying squadron at Nellis (422nd TES) operating the A-10, F-4G, F-15, F-15E and F-16. The 57th TG also performs OT&E work with the F-111F at Cannon and the F-117 at Holloman, although these are carried out by detachments at the front-line bases to ease maintenance requirements.

Related work includes the Fighter Weapons School activities. The FWS is divided into four divisions to operate the A-10, F-15C, F-15E and F-16. Each unit acts as a schoolhouse for service aircrew where they learn the advanced tactics handed down from the OT&E work. Once through the FWS course they return to their own units and instruct other members of their unit.

Training forms a large part of the WTC's repertoire for, in addition to the FWS work, it is involved in adversary training, organising Green Flag, Red Flag and Air Warrior exercises, and in running the vast ranges to the north of the base. These ranges are highly instrumented for air combat, contain various realistic threats and generally offer the best combat training environment available in the Western world. One 57th Wing squadron is responsible for organising the Air Warrior joint Air Force/Army exercises, while another handles the Flag series. This unit, the 414th TS, also operates F-16C/Ds in the adversary role, primarily to support the Flag exercises and teach regular units about the capabilities of foreign aircraft, but also to provide realistic adversaries for test work. A ground threat squadron performs similar work with SAMs, AAA and radar. These may be augmented by unconfirmed units which are reported to operate within the security confines of the Nellis range, notably the 4477th TES 'Red Hats' which is believed to be a Groom Lake-based squadron operating captured fighters of Russian origin.

Two HH-60G helicopter units are at Nellis, the operational 66th RQS providing rescue coverage for the Nellis ranges and the newly-established Combat Rescue School using the ranges to train crews for the CSAR mission. The 'Thunderbirds' Aerial Demonstration Squadron also call Nellis home when it is not on the road, using the

nearby auxiliary field at Indian Springs as a practice runway for displays.

Quite apart from its testing and training purpose, the 57th Wing has one operational unit, the 561st Fighter Squadron flying F-4Gs. Despite attempts to completely retire the 'Wild Weasel' Phantom, its abilities are such that two squadrons have been retained to provide the best defence suppression capability currently available. In conjunction with the Idaho ANG, the 561st FS has been very busy since its inception, manning detachments in Turkey and Saudi Arabia.

WTC has one other unit, the 99th Wing, based at Ellsworth AFB. This is the bomber schoolhouse, evaluating new bomber tactics and teaching them to active crews. The wing has no aircraft assigned, attendees bringing their own aircraft with them for courses.

USAF Weapons and Tactics Center

UNIT	TYPE	TAIL
57th Wing, Nellis AFB, NV		
66th Rescue Squadron	HH-60G	'WA'
414th Training Squadron (Red Flag) Adversary Tactics Division	F-16C, F-16D	'WA'
422nd Test and Evaluation Squadron (57th Test Group)	A-10A, F-4G, F-15C, F-15D, F-15E, F-16C, F-16D	'WA' (yellow/ black)
Det. 1 (Holloman AFB, NM)	F-117A	'WA'
Det. 3 (Cannon AFB, NM)	F-111F	'WA'
561st Fighter Squadron (561st Operations Group)	F-4G	'WA'
Aerial Demonstration Squadron ('Thunderbirds')	F-16C, F-16D	–
Combat Rescue School	HH-60G	'WA'
WSE (F-15C Fighter Weapons School)	F-15C, F-15D	'WA'
WSF (F-16 Fighter Weapons School)	F-16C, F-16D	'WA'
WSN (F-15E Fighter Weapons School)	F-15E	'WA'
WST (A-10 Fighter Weapons School)	A-10A, OA-10A	'WA'

Further 57th Wing units without aircraft are the 547th ATS and the 549th JTS, the latter conducting the joint Army/Air Force Air Warrior exercise.

UNIT	TYPE	TAIL
99th Wing, Ellsworth AFB, SD		
25th Flying Training Squadron	no aircraft assigned	
346th Test and Evaluation Squadron	no aircraft assigned	

Formed by an amalgamation of the former Air Defense Weapons Center and the Tactical Air Warfare Center, the USAF AWC is primarily concerned with testing and the operational employment of aircraft weapons and systems, including weapon delivery profiles. The former

TAWC part of the organisation is the 79th TEG. Electronic warfare is an important part of the unit's work, and a detachment at Cannon operates the EF-111A. Other main tactical types are flown from Eglin, a major current programme being the operational evaluation of the ASQ-213 HARM Targeting System carried by F/16C/D Block 50/52D aircraft for the defence suppression role.

The ex-ADWC part of the AWC is the 475th WEG, which operates from the old ADWC headquarters at Tyndall AFB. This unit is concerned primarily with the testing and employment of air-to-air missiles, and it consequently operates the USAF's fleet of drones, ranging from the diminutive Ryan BQM-34 Firebee, through the supersonic Beech MQM-107 Streaker to Convair QF-106 FSATs (full-scale aerial targets). For testing missiles the unit can use either the Gulf Test Range near to Tyndall, or the White Sands Test Range in New Mexico. A drone detachment operates from Holloman AFB to support activities at the latter.

Training is also a part of AWC activities, the organisation running the Blue Flag exercise and various air defence exercises, including William Tell. Participating aircraft occasionally get the chance for a live missile shot against one of the 475th WEG's target drones. Supporting range activities are a pair of E-9As – converted DHC-8 airliners with telemetry-receiving antennas in large fuselage-side fairings for relaying missile data and a maritime surveillance radar to spot boats which may inadvertently enter the open sea range during missile tests.

USAF Air Warfare Center

UNIT	TYPE	TAIL
79th Test and Evaluation Group, Eglin AFB, FL		
85th Test Squadron	RF-4C, F-15A, F-15C, F-15E, F-16A, F-16C, F-16D	'OT' (black/ white)
85th Test Squadron Det. 3 (Cannon AFB, NM)	EF-111A	'OT'

Additional units within the 79th TEG which do not have aircraft assigned are the 84th TS and the 86th FWS at Tyndall AFB, FL.

UNIT	TYPE	TAIL
475th Weapons Evaluation Group, Tyndall AFB, FL		
82nd Aerial Target Squadron	E-9A, QF-106A, QF-106B, BQM-34A, BQM-34B, MQM-107D	–
82nd Aerial Target Squadron (Det. 1, Holloman AFB, NM)	QF-106A, QF-106B	–

Additional units within the 475th WEG which do not have aircraft assigned are the 81st RCS at Tyndall ADFB, FL, 83rd FWS at Holloman AFB, NM, and the 84th RES at Hill AFB, UT. Further AWC units, none of which operate aircraft, are the 31st Test and Evaluation Squadron at Edwards AFB, CA, the 41st Training Group at Hurlburt Field, FL, which handles the Blue Flag computer war-modelling exercise and the 49th Test and Evaluation Squadron at Barksdale AFB, LA.

Much of the 57th Wing's work is concerned with developing and evaluating new tactics. This is the task of the 422nd Test and Evaluation Squadron, which operates this F-15C.

F-15Es are assigned to both the 57th Wing's 422nd TES and the F-15E Fighter Weapons School. This aircraft wears the badge of the latter, known as WSN for short.

The 57th Wing's best-known aircraft are the F-16 Block 32s of the Aerial Demonstration Squadron, better known as the 'Thunderbirds'. This two-seat F-16D is assigned to allow orientation rides to be given, and is traditionally flown by the team's narrator.

Aggressor expertise for Red Flag exercises and test purposes is provided by the Adversary Tactics Division of the 414th Training Squadron, flying F-16C/D Block 32s.

This late Block 40 F-16C is assigned to the F-16 FWS, which teaches advanced tactics to operational pilots. The graduates return to their units to pass on their new-found knowledge.

Badge of the F-16 FWS, also known as the WSF.

A-10 tactics are taught by the WST (Weapons School, Thunderbolt), which has a handful of aircraft.

The only front-line unit at Nellis is the 561st Fighter Squadron which, along with the Idaho ANG, flies the remaining F-4Gs. This aircraft wears kill marks for work in northern Iraq.

Previously with the 35th TFW, the 561st FS is known as the 'Black Knights'.

HH-60Gs are assigned to the 66th RQS at Nellis chiefly to provide rescue services in the vast range area. Recently established is the Combat Rescue School, which also operates the type.

The main unit of the AWC is the Eglin-based 79th TEG, whose 85th TES flies F-15s, F-16s and EF-111As, the latter operating from Cannon. This Block 50D F-16D carries an ASQ-213 HARM Targeting System pod and an ALQ-184 ECM pod.

In addition to the skull badge of the 85th TES, AWC aircraft carry the 'OT' tailcode for 'Operational Test'.

INDEX

INDEX

Picture acknowledgments

Front cover: René van Woezik. **4:** Boeing. **5:** J.L. Gaynecoetche via Paul Jackson, J. Alche, Sikorsky. **6:** Simon Watson, Westland. **7:** Salvador Mafé Huertas, Austin J. Brown/APL, René van Woezik. **8:** Simon Watson (two). **9:** Paul Jackson, Rockwell, Simon Watson. **10:** Ryszard Jaxa Malachowski (two). **11:** Jon Lake, Austin J. Brown/APL. **12:** Craig P. Justo (two). **13:** Craig P. Justo (two). **14:** Sikorsky. **15:** Westland, Lockheed, Paul Van der Elsaker. **16:** Simon Watson, NASA. **17:** Ted Carlson/Fotodynamics, Gilles Auliard, Bede. **18:** via Simon Watson (all). **19:** J.B.E. Hale (all). **20:** J.B.E. Hale (three), Pilatus. **21:** Pilatus, Bell. **22:** Simon Watson, Ryszard Jaxa Malachowski, PZL. **23:** Ryszard Jaxa Malachowski, Robert Hewson, Mick Jennings (two), Kamov. **24-27:** Jon Lake. **28:** Steven D. Eisner, US DoD via Randy Jolly. **29:** Lockheed. **30:** Saab. **31:** Peter Liander. **32:** Ake Anderson/Saab via Peter Liander, Peter Liander. **33:** Saab (two). **34-35:** Peter Liander. **36:** Ericsson (two), Robert Hewson, Saab. **38-39:** Saab. **40:** Peter Liander (two), Saab. **41:** Saab via Peter Liander. **42:** Peter Liander (two). **43:** via Peter Liander, Robert Hewson. **44:** Robert Hewson (two), Martin Stroud. **46-47:** Peter Liander. **48:** Peter Liander, Saab. **49:** via Robert Hewson, Peter Liander (two). **50:** Saab. **51:** Peter Liander (two). **54:** via Eric Stijger, Lutz Freundt. **55:** Lutz Freundt, Jon Lake. **56:** Stefan Petersen, Jon Lake. **57:** René van Woezik, Stefan Petersen (two). **58:** Stefan Petersen (three). **59:** René van Woezik. **70:** Jon Lake, Tieme Festner. **71:** Frank Rozendaal. **72:** Jon Lake. **73:** Jon Lake, M.J. Gerards, René van Woezik. **74:** René van Woezik, Jan Jørgensen. **75:** Marcus Fulber, Lutz Freundt. **76:** W. Greppmeier, Frank Rozendaal. **77:** Lutz Freundt, Tieme Festner, Frank Rozendaal. **78:** Jan Jørgensen, Frank Rozendaal. **79:** Marcus Fulber, Jon Lake, Hans Nijhuis. **80:** Jon Lake, Gert Kromhout, Hans Nijhuis. **81:** René van Woezik, Chris Lofting. **82:** René van Woezik (two). **83:** René van Woezik. **84:** Jan Jørgensen. **85:** René van Woezik, Martin Baumann. **86:** Jon Lake, Frank Rozendaal. **88:** H.A. Gravemaker, Jan Jørgensen. **89:** Chris Lofting, Hendrik J. van Broekhuizen. **90:** Chris Lofting, Richard Stone. **91:** René van Woezik, Frank Rozendaal. **93:** Chris Lofting, René van Woezik (two). **94:** Chris Lofting (two), Jon Lake. **95:** Chris Lofting, René van Woezik. **96:** René van Woezik, Lutz Freundt, Chris Lofting. **97:** René van Woezik, Chris Lofting. **98:** Gert Kromhout, Jan Jørgensen. **99:** Gert Kromhout (two), Bob Fischer. **100:** Chris Ryan, Chris Lofting (two). **101:** Chris Lofting, Jon Lake. **102:** Stefan Petersen, Marc Brouyere. **103:** Stefan Petersen, Marc Brouyere. **104:** Stefan Petersen, Marc Brouyere. **105:** Stefan Petersen, Marc Brouyere. **106-107:** Stefan Petersen. **108:** Rick Llinares/Flightline, Lt Don Slavin via Robert L. Lawson (RLL). **109:** Lt John Martin via RLL, RLL (two), Michael Grove via RLL. **110:** Doug Olson via RLL, LCdr Dave Baranek via RLL (two). **111:** Joe Cupido, via RLL, LCdr Dave Baranek via RLL. **112:** via RLL, Doug Olson via RLL. **113:** Michael Grove via RLL, LCdr Rick Morgan via RLL, via RLL. **114:** RLL, Michael Grove via RLL, Doug Olson via RLL. **115:** RLL (two), RLL, LCdr Dave Parsons via RLL, Grumman via RLL. **116:** RLL, Joe Cupido, Ted Carlson/Fotodynamics. **117:** RLL, LCdr Rick Morgan via RLL, Joe Cupido. **118:** Robert F. Dorr, Doug Olson via RLL. **119:** Bruce Trombecky via RLL, RLL, Geoff Pearce/Avia Graphics. **120:** via RLL, Doug Olson via RLL, Dave Baranek via RLL. **121:** RLL (two), Dave Ostrowski via RLL. **122:** Cdr Pete Clayton via RLL, LCdr Dave Parsons via RLL, Joe Cupido. **123:** Tom Kaminski, Grumman, Michael Grove via RLL, Dr J.G. Handelmann via RLL. **124:** RLL (two), Michael Grove via RLL. **125:** Lt John Martin via RLL, Michael Grove via RLL. **126:** Michael Grove via RLL, Bruce Trombecky via RLL. **127:** RLL, Michael Grove via RLL. **128:** Ted Carlson/Fotodynamics, Steven H. Miller via RLL. **129:** RLL (two). **130:** RLL (two). **131:** Keith Snyder via RLL, Cdr Pete Clayton via RLL, Michael Grove via RLL, Joe Cupido. **132:** US Navy via RLL, Lt Dave Swoboda via RLL. **133:** Jan C. Jacobs via RLL (two), Bruce Trombecky via RLL, Joe Cupido. **134:** RLL (two), Ted Carlson/Fotodynamics, Michael Grove via RLL. **135:** Michael Grove via RLL, Jan C. Jacobs via RLL, Bruce Trombecky via RLL. **136:** Tom Kaminski, US Navy via RLL. **137:** Ted Carlson/Fotodynamics, Bruce Trombecky via RLL, RLL. **138-145:** Christophe Donnet. **147:** Randy Jolly (four), Paul C. Ragusa. **148:** Ted Carlson/Fotodynamics (three), Peter Wilson, Northrop Grumman, Chris A. Neill, David Donald. **149:** Ted Carlson/Fotodynamics (three), Peter Wilson, Northrop Grumman, David Donald (two), Frank Gallego Serra, Stephen Hill. **151:** Don Logan, Frank Rankin-Lowe, David Donald (three), Renato E.F. Jones (two), Ted Carlson/Fotodynamics, Mark Munzel. **153:** Randy Jolly (two), David Donald (two), Régent Dansereau (two), Nathan Leong, Renato E.F. Jones (two), Don Logan, Renato E.F. Jones (two), Ted Carlson/Fotodynamics. **155:** Ted Carlson/Fotodynamics, McDonnell Douglas, Graham Robson, Steve Hill/EMCS (two), Ted Carlson/Fotodynamics (three), Randy Jolly, Don Logan. **157:** Ted Carlson/Fotodynamics (two), Jeff Rankin-Lowe, David Donald (nine).